CONFESSIONS OF A STORY-TELLER

Paul Gallico

CONFESSIONS

OF

A

STORY-

TELLER

London
MICHAEL JOSEPH

THIS BOOK IS DEDICATED TO MY SONS
William Taylor and Robert Leston Gallico

CONTENTS

CONFESSIONS OF A STORY-TELLER

Mainly Autobiographical

Some years ago I was flattered to receive an invitation to address the members of the Eton Literary Society upon some subject connected with writing which might be considered of interest to this young generation. The flattery contained in this, as far as I was concerned, was that I was the first American writer, and perhaps the only one, up to that time to be requested to give such an address.

It was, however, not my first connection with this famous school, for each year on St Andrews Day I am also invited to journey thither as a member of a fencing team to fence épée against the Etonian swordsmen. Thus I had learned to know Etonians and what they were like.

They were, it seemed to me, like any other boy who was quite likely to be bored stiff, even if he was a member of the Literary Society, through being compelled to sit still for an hour while some adult caracoled about on his literary hobby horse. I thought my young hosts might be grateful for a little unexpected entertainment.

Before delivering my lecture I was given dinner at Eton by the secretary of the Society, a most handsome young man clad in white tie and tails to which was added a coloured waistcoat of simply stunning magnificence denoting that he was a member, I gathered, of a most exclusive and exalted society. During the course of the dinner he asked me for the title of my address and when I suggested BELLES LETTRES VERSUS A PUNCH IN THE NOSE, OR HOW TO BEGIN A LITERARY CAREER FROM THE RECLINING POSITION, I could feel the shock waves extending back through three centuries of Literary Societies.

The young man tried hard not to show his disapproval and took the attitude that I was pleased to be facetious. I said that I had never been more serious, that the title was apt and relevant as would develop and would they take my word for it. The young secretary exchanged baffled and bewildered glances with

13

his acolytes and then gamely acquiesced. But I could see a number of mental reservations forming in young minds about inviting any more Americans.

The evening was notable in the annals of the Literary Society from the fact that to the great joy of its members the lecture avoided the subject of literature and was devoted to pugilism and the brief moment when my career and that of Jack Dempsey, the former heavyweight champion of the world, collided in a training ring at Saratoga Springs, New York. The year was 1922, when Dempsey was training to defend his title against the giant Argentinian, the late Luis Angel Firpo.

It did not take long to affirm the validity of the title I had suggested for I told them the story of an unknown sports reporter sent to cover the training camp of the champion. This reporter conceived the idea of entering the ring to spar with the latter in order to be able to write more convincingly what it was like to have the fist of the world champion connect with one's chin in battle.

The young sports writer found out and had plenty of time to reflect upon it while sojourning on the canvas, where he had been deposited by a Dempsey left hook, listening to the referee toll off a count which could have proceeded to 150 for all that I was concerned.

The point was that this brash stunt tickled the fancy of J. M. Patterson, publisher of the 'Daily News' for whom I was working, and led him to promote me not only to the Sports Editorship of his newspaper but to let me take on the writing of a sports column.

Perhaps it was something of an American exaggeration to hold that my career as a writer was based upon this stunt and this knock-out, but the sports column, a thousand words in length appeared thereafter for thirteen years, seven days a week. It was uncensored and uninhibited; it had to be in the hands of the composing room no later than six o'clock in the evening and the ideas transmitted to the cartoonist who illustrated it even earlier. It forced me to write every day, rain or shine, whether I felt like it or not, sick or well, happy or unhappy. It gave me that discipline without which no writer can hope to succeed. It formed working habits and thinking habits since a new idea had to be presented each day, or an old theme treated in a novel manner so that it seemed like a new idea. But above all it made me write, write, write. Roughly over that period, not counting other sports stories and coverages of sports events, I turned out some five million one hundred and ten thousand words. I must reiterate if one wants to be a writer there is no substitute for writing. Talking about it or just thinking beautiful thoughts isn't enough. Writing like everything else is a muscle and the more you use it the more flexible and useful it becomes.

I had wanted to be a writer for as long as I can remember. My infantile years were filled with fantasies and imaginings and castles sent soaring into the sky. I wrote my first short story at the age of ten, one evening in an hotel in Brussels back in 1907 when we visited the World's Fair being held there, my parents and I, on their annual summer holiday.

They left me alone in the hotel one night, to my distress, while they went out to do the town. There was pen and ink and hotel stationery available. The creative urge was overpowering. I had had this idea for a story for some time, ever since I had passed a construction site on Madison Avenue in the sixties where a new building was going up near where we lived.

I am going to insist upon telling you the plot because I was unable to get it published at the time and this has rankled.

Briefly a little boy wanders past the site and notices a pile of coloured pebbles on the sidewalk and a large Eyetalian – all construction workers in New York in those days seemed to be Eyetalians – is engaged in shovelling these stones into a wheelbarrow.

Small boy is fascinated with these pebbles and wishing to acquire some, for purposes never quite made clear in the story, begins to fill his pockets with them. The large Eyetalian either apparently outraged by this bald-faced larceny or simply failing sympathy with the needs of small boys, flies into a temper and cries, 'Hey you, beat it! Wotsamarra you? Gerrada here! Put-a dem stones-a back. Beat it.'

Terrified the little boy puts the stones back and beats it. The Eyetalian finishes his stint of shovelling the stones into the wheelbarrow and thereafter is summoned to other duties atop the steel skeleton of the building thirteen storeys above the ground.

There sudden disaster overtakes him! A mis-step, a slip! He falls, yet manages to seize a girder with his hands and there he is dangling in mid-air thirteen storeys above certain death.

Fellow workers shout to him to hang on until they can reach him. Help is almost at hand as they converge upon him. The Eyetalian holds on for dear life, but alas feels himself tiring, his strength rapidly waning, his grip beginning to weaken. Closer and closer comes the rescue party. Tireder and tireder grows the

Wop, as they were called in those days. *Will he be able to last? Can they reach him in time?*

Looking back over the years I am pleased to note that even at a tender age I had some feeling for the element of suspense. Had this been a serial, here would have been the place to have written 'Continued next week.' However, this was to be a complete short story with all the unities preserved.

Now for the twist! Willing hands are almost upon him, reaching forth to cheat the angel of death when the desperate clutch of the Eyetalian's fingers are loosed and as he plunges with a shriek to his death this awful retributive thought passes through his mind: (I was too young and inexperienced to know at that time that, of course, what would have flashed through his mind at that point was his past life).

'Oh,' thinks he, 'would that I had not been so cruel to that little boy who wished to fill his pockets with pebbles earlier this afternoon. Had I permitted him to do so there would have been one less shovelful of stones for me to shovel and I would have now had just that one little bit more energy and strength I needed to hang on until help arrived.'

Too late, too late! As the Eyetalian plunges past the 12th, 11th and 10th floors more Eyetalians working there hear him murmur regretfully as he passes, 'Just a li'l shovel of stones-a, just a li'l sh-shovel full-a stones-a!' And after that only the well known dull and sickening thud.

The title of this story was JUST A SHOVEL OF STONES and I was charmed with it. This was the days before psychiatry, psychoanalysis and the cult of the head shrinkers, and it has been suggested since that at the bottom of this juvenile grand Guignol *lay* the fact that I hated my Italian-born father and wished to kill him and so turned him into the big Eyetalian construction worker and neatly dropped him from the top of a building.

I doubt this. I may have been irritated with my dad that evening for parking me in the hotel while he and my mother went forth to revel, but not to the point of vicarious assassination. Consciously I adored my father, though I was sometimes terrified of him.

I am now too old a fox to bet either on or against the subconscious but I know that I had been carrying this short story around with me for many months in my mind, monkeying with it and polishing it up before I set it down on paper, a process in no wise changed in later life professionally. I have carried stories around inside me for over a year before they came right to the point where they warranted setting down on paper.

I can tell you better why I am publishing it now and why a version of it also appeared in an earlier edition of these stories when my father was still alive. Eight or nine years later when I was a young man and bombarding the magazines with short story attempts which, like homing pigeons, returned inevitably to the doorstep a day or so later with a printed rejection slip, I used to have Mozart thrown into my face.

Father, a composer

I am still amazed that Mozart remains my favourite composer and that I can never get enough of listening to his music, for in my youth he was held up to me as an example. Mozart, at the age of twelve, according to my father, himself a pianist and a composer, had already composed several symphonies, an opera or so, innumerable quartets and what is more had had them performed, while here I was a lolloping big looby all of eighteen to nineteen years and already a failure. I could not even get a short story accepted and printed. From which you will gather that I was no infant prodigy and that I was likewise born into a European household transplanted into America where the young were expected to produce.

I published this originally so I could say to dad, 'Who was this Mozart of twelve? An old man! Get me at ten Pop, here it is in a book.' Father roared with laughter. By that time he was reconciled to the fact that his son was irremediably a late starter. I reprint it herewith dedicated to his memory.

My father, Paolo Gallico, was an Italian of Spanish extraction, a concert pianist, composer and teacher, born in Mantua in Lombardy. My mother was Austrian. In 1895 they emigrated to New York whence my father went on a number of concert tours throughout the United States. I was born in New York City in July of 1897, just in time to avoid the twentieth century. In one generation I became more American than the sons and daughters of the American Revolution. I was educated in the free public schools of New York – Public School 6 at Madison Avenue and 85th Street, Public School 70 at 75th Street and 3rd Avenue and the De Witt Clinton High School at 10th Avenue and 59th Street.

In 1916 I entered Columbia University and graduated therefrom in 1921 with a Bachelor of Science Degree, having lost a year and a half due to World War 1. On my 21st birthday in 1918 I enlisted in the U.S. Naval Reserve Force where due to defective eyesight I was placed in the loathsome category of yeoman.

Once in the Service, however, I managed by means of High School football experience to effect a transfer into a combat branch and emerged after Armistice Day with the more respect-

able rating of gunner's mate. Discharged from the Navy I spent half a year working for a small newspaper syndicate and then returned to Columbia to take my degree.

The Science Degree is a part of the story, for I had intended to be a doctor.

This is no contradiction to what I said earlier that for as long as I could remember I wished to be a writer. I still wished to be a writer, or rather a story-teller, but I was not at all certain that A I could be a good one and B earn a living with it.

For some reason never quite clear to me writing was hooked up in my youthful mind with insecurity. Perhaps in some subtle fashion I was aware that writing was a kind of luxury profession, just as was music and piano teaching. I think there was a financial panic once during my childhood and I must have heard my parents refer to the fact that when money got tight the first thing that happened was that people stopped junior's piano lessons. But these same people never stopped calling for the doctor, no matter how tight money might be. At that age I didn't realise they just didn't pay him.

I shudder to think of the number of lives saved by my abandoning medicine. But when I was a boy around New York I did have a certain flair for it. I was the one who had the first-aid kit and when one of the gang hurt himself or acquired a cut or a bruise I knew how to wash it out with hydrogen peroxide, daub it with iodine and apply a fairly competent bandage.

I cannot remember any time from my earliest days when I was not aware that I should have to earn a living and that I must prepare myself for that day. We were not poor people, but neither were we well off and I think from an understanding of this and the precariousness of a professional life stemmed a curious kind of cowardice which at the age of fourteen or fifteen led me to rearrange my ambitions and organise my life along the following lines. 'Medicine,' I said to myself 'is a secure and certain profession. People will always need a doctor. Therefore I will become one and always have the means of earning a living and I will write on the side. Then it will make no difference if I fail to sell what I write.'

Accordingly when at the age of nineteen I entered Columbia University as a freshman, I registered for the pre-medical course which called for two years of ordinary college study with the emphasis on chemistry and biology, in other words the sciences, after which I would go into the College of Physicians and Surgeons, the medical school known as P. and S. Two close boyhood friends of mine were embarked upon the same course. During

*those two years I wrote stories constantly and with no more
success. Mozart, it was pointed out to me, at this age was a
European celebrity. I had yet to sell a single story.*

*At the end of my sophomore year, as the time drew near to
enter Medical School I took stock of myself and my ambitions,
the plans I had made, and arrived at the conclusion that they
were infantile and that I was just plain yellow. I knew in my own
heart that more than anything else I wanted to be a writer and
that the whole idea of embracing medicine and becoming a doctor
was cowardly and an evasion.*

*I can still look back and remember having one of those moments
of clarity which sometimes illuminate the dark pathway. And in
that moment I became aware that I would be a fool to dissipate
my energies and that success in anything called for the utmost
concentration in that field. If I genuinely and honestly loved
writing as I felt I did then I ought to concentrate upon becoming
a writer and let nothing else divert me or stand in my way.*

*This was a decision which not only had to be arrived at by
myself but also implemented by me. Without taking my elders
into my confidence I withdrew my application to enter Medical
School, threw over the pre-medical course, though I was committed to majoring in science, but I added as many subjects in
writing and literature as I could and put medicine out of my life.
The bridges were irretrievably burned.*

*During all my four years at the University I lived at home but
maintained my independence by working my way through, paying for my tuition and keep by means of a variety of jobs – tutor,
translator, longshoreman, usher at the Metropolitan Opera,
librarian, gymnasium attendant, labourer in a spark plug factory,
college correspondent for a downtown newspaper or whatever
odd jobs the employment agency at the University could dredge
up for me. I also took part in University activities, won my
numerals and letters rowing on the Freshman and Varsity crews
and functioned as captain in my senior year.*

*And what about writing at this period and the immediate results
of the great decision? Looking back the best I can say is that I
never gave up trying and success was meagre. I did proceed from
the horrid impersonality of the rejection slip to the personally
typewritten note from the editor, a few brief lines to the effect
that while the story submitted had not quite made the grade they
would like to see more of my work at some future date. And I
can tell you this come-on was enough to have me walking on air
for weeks. I had almost made it. Perhaps the next one would hit.*

When I was twenty-one I sold my first story to a pulp magazine. I think it was 'Blue Book.' I haven't the faintest recollection what it was about, but I got ninety dollars for it, which is probably more than Mozart got for his first opera.

A 'pulp magazine' incidentally is a cheap periodical published on a cheap grade of paper, hence the nickname 'pulp' as against the richer publications which were known as 'slicks.' The word slick had no connotation in connection with the contents of these magazines; it didn't refer to the stories being glib or clever. It related instead, as indicated, to the quality of the paper. The richer publications used a coated stock which made it slippery or slick to the touch. The reason for the coated stock was that it reproduced four-colour illustrations. In those days 'Blue Book,' 'Argosy,' and 'Adventure' were pulp magazines. 'Saturday Evening Post,' 'Cosmopolitan,' 'Red Book,' 'American Magazine' were slicks. The pulp might pay $125 for a short story, the slick would pay $1,000 and upwards. Naturally it was my ambition to sell to the slicks. Nor could success at cracking the pulp market be considered a step in that direction. It was a strange fact that pulp writers remained pulp writers and rarely did anyone who had made a name for himself writing for the pulps over a period manage to cross the line and break into the slicks. However, at that time I did not know this and if I had I should not have cared. The point was I had made a sale. I was probably saved from the fate of a pulp hack by my discovery of a new kind of market.

During my interim job as office boy for the Otis F. Wood syndicate between emerging from the Navy and returning to college I learned something about the syndicate business, chiefly that if one had a saleable literary property one could dispose of it a number of times to various newspapers in different cities of the United States. During my last two years at Columbia I devised short fiction sketches – what would be called short shorts today, and modelled after the late American story classicist O. Henry who was fashionable then and whose style and formulae were the basis of study in every short story class at that time. O. Henry was the master of the unexpected twist at the end, a twist which incidentally was carefully and unobtrusively planted in the narrative at the beginning of the story. Even today anyone wanting to write short stories would do well to read O. Henry.

These short stories I syndicated and sold myself, submitting them to Sunday papers in Boston, Philadelphia, Detroit, Chicago, etc. I regret to say New York remained unimpressed and absent from my list of customers. These newspapers paid me space rates *for these stories. Sometimes I got as high as $20 apiece for them.*

During my years at the University I went through the mill of short-story writing classes. I studied with John Erskine, Helen Hull, Dr Blanche Colton Williams, Walter Pitkin, Donald Lemon Clark and Thomas Uzzell. Some of these classes were given in the University extension school and others were private evening classes conducted by these teachers and into which I paid my way. I am compelled to report that I was an undistinguished pupil who sold none of the efforts or exercises written for those classes. There were others who did and received cheques from 'Harpers'' or 'Atlantic Monthly,' or even the big slicks. I remained unrewarded and consumed with jealousy.

I attended classes, wrote stories, had them reviewed and criticised, learned the jargon to which the art had been reduced by the pedagogues, and sold nary a line. But I have a dreadful recollection that not only did I not sell, but I became so saturated with the rules and regulations of storycraft, the mechanics and mathematics of construction, that I actually taught the stuff to small groups outside the university to eke out my college living. Why my students went for it and ever paid me money, or what good they got out of it, I shall never know.

When beginning writers ask me whether they should take a short-story course, I tell them yes, because I feel it cannot do them any harm and it might do them some good. If nothing else, it sets them to writing regularly.

Eighty-five per cent of the students of every writing or story course is made of frustrated and utterly talentless and feckless folk who are lured by the gold in them thar hills and the apparent ease with which successful writers appear to be able to tap the vein. They may be encountered in the extension courses year after year, hopefully but unsuccessfully pursuing the chimera. The simple truth is that they are neither writers nor story-tellers and never will be, if they go to school for a hundred years.

But where a man or woman has a natural talent for expressing himself with the written word, originality and a good recording ear for the reproduction of the speech of others, these classroom sessions unquestionably, to my mind, can help him. They frequently provide short cuts and save him time. If he must struggle and suffer and learn what to do and how to do it by himself, at least he can acquire there a foundation in what not to do.

I never heard of a writer coming to any harm in such a class and in 1948 when I was asked by Columbia whether I would teach an advanced short-story class in the extension school I accepted on condition that I be allowed to choose my students on

*the basis of some submitted work. I didn't want to waste time
on the hopeless ones.*

*I worked for a year with a bright, talented group and oddly
enough experienced here the thrill of success which had eluded
me when I was a student. Several members of my class sold
stories to magazines either during or immediately after the course.
I am sure they would have sold them anyway, but the pleasure of
having assisted at their incubation to development was inescapable. I gave up teaching because I couldn't bear to be tied down
to the academic year.*

*After graduating from Columbia in 1921, I married and took the
first job that was offered to me by my friends in the University
employment office. This was as a review secretary for the National
Board of Motion Picture Review, which was the voluntary censorship to which the motion picture producers agreed in the face
of the threat of State or Federal censorship. A half a year later
I became motion picture critic for the New York 'Daily News,'
the fledgling tabloid founded by Joseph Medill Patterson of the
'Chicago Tribune,' and there I lasted exactly four months and
twenty-nine days. On the thirtieth day I was removed from the
chair by Captain Patterson because my reviews were too Smart
Alecky. I was not fired from the 'News'; this was not the custom
of the publisher. He merely, in a fit of exasperation, told his
Managing Editor, Phil Payne, to get that man out of the movie
department. Payne hid me in the sports department as an anony-
mous and un-bylined sports reporter, odd jobs and re-write
man.*

*And here we return to the subject of my discourse at Eton,
namely how to begin a literary career from the prone or horizontal
position.*

*Assigned to write some 'colour' from the Dempsey training
camp at Uncle Tom Luther's at Saratoga, myself a heavyweight
still in good condition after four years as a galley slave but with
no experience of boxing, I asked Dempsey if he would let me into
the ring with him in order that I might find out at first hand what
it was like.*

*As I have indicated the results were drastic since I was un-
known and for all Dempsey and his camp were aware might be
a ringer sent to injure him or make him look bad. But any rate
after one minute and twenty-seven seconds I was flat on my
back with a cut lip and a prize headache. But I also had a story.
In an old-fashioned narrative one might say that in this manner
my fortune was made. Certainly it was the beginning. There were
other elements, but the fact was that the left hook that Dempsey*

*whistled to my unprotected chin changed the frown on the face
of Captain Patterson to a smile.*

*I wrote no more fiction for nearly eight years but applied myself
to my job as Sports Editor and columnist of the 'Daily News' and
the necessity of earning a living for my family and myself. But
while fiction was temporarily shelved I was writing, writing,
writing, day in and day out, Sundays included.*

*Every writer has a different story of his beginnings and of how
he obtained the needed practice and training for his craft, including those geniuses who need no training but do it right
the first time, but for me sports writing was a wonderful
incubator.*

*Reporting the American sports scene was story-telling, a rich
and inexhaustible lode of dramatic material. Daily I was in contact with those necessary elements of drama, good against evil,
suspense, frustration, climax and success. Every contest had its
villain as well as its hero. We wrote partisan sports in New York.
Our teams, our boys were heroes, the visiting firemen were
villains. I lived and worked in an era of great personalities in
sports, Dempsey, Babe Ruth, Helen Wills, Tilden, Ty Cobb,
Johnny Weissmuller, Man o'War, Paavo Nurmi, etc., all of them
highly colourful and dramatic men and women which sense of
drama was reflected in their contests and performances. Reporting
sports was a constant exercise in presenting dramatic material in
a dramatic fashion.*

*I became involved at the same time in sports promotion and
was led into curious by-paths which, oddly enough, likewise was
grist to the mill of the would-be writer, for it taught me showmanship, though I was aware of none of these things during those
years.*

*Shocked by the wretched and sordid manner in which amateur
boxing was conducted in New York in those days I persuaded
Captain Patterson to let me stage an amateur tournament and
invented the Golden Gloves and thereafter in addition to my
work as editor, reporter and columnist promoted such sports
extravaganzas as roller- and ice-skating races, water circuses, golf
driving contests, and a thoroughly mad canoe race around Manhattan Island.*

*It was a fast, gay, wonderful and completely thoughtless life.
Winter sports merged into summer sports, the season and years
flowed by.*

*To increase my understanding of the problems faced by the
men and women about whom I wrote and to be able better to
describe their skills I experimented with active participation with*

*some of these stars so as to be better able to describe the games
I was reporting.*

The speedboat king of that era was an American boat-builder
by the name of Gar Wood. He took me for a ride in one of his
'Miss America's' on the Detroit river at 125 miles an hour. I sat
in a racing car with one of America's leading race drivers for a
spin around the Indianapolis track. I familiarised myself with
major league baseball by going on to the field during the practice
sessions before a game to try to hit against the fireball pitcher
or catch his curves. In the same manner I learned the difficulties
and ruggedness of American football, a game I had played myself
in High School. I stood helpless on a tennis court while the drives
of Vincent Richards and Helen Wills whistled past my ears and,
of course, was equally feckless on a golf course against Bobby
Jones. But the close-up I received of the ability and timing of
these stars was of course invaluable. I also learned to fly, took
out a pilot's licence and logged some 500 solo hours and began
covering some sports events from the air.

Nobody censored my copy or told me what to write or what
not to write, or what to do or where to go or what to cover as
long as I remained within the laws of libel. My column became
known as the 'News' increased in circulation and stature, and
myself a minor celebrity recognised by taxi drivers as one of
the 'Young men of Manhattan' along with such well-known sports-
writers as Damon Runyon, Bill Corum, Dan Parker, Joe Williams,
etc. Our seats at the working press benches in Madison Square
Garden had our names emblazoned in bronze plaques.

Here was success from an unexpected quarter, financial, social,
etc., and the would-be fiction writer became submerged yet never
wholly forgotten, I still looked forward to the day when I would
'make' the 'Saturday Evening Post.' It took me twenty-five years
to achieve this ambition, that is to say from 1907 when I was ten,
the age at which I wrote my first story, to 1933 when I was
thirty-six years old.

I began gradually by breaking into the better magazines with
sports articles. This was the easy way for I had all of the material
at the tips of my fingers and the writing muscle was limbered.
It was just a matter of acquiring the more leisurely slant of the
monthly publication as against the immediacy of the daily journal.
And here I had another stroke of luck, I wrote and sold several
articles to 'Vanity Fair,' which in those days, in class and sophis-
tication, occupied the position the 'New Yorker' does now. Its
Editor was the late Frank Crowninshield, and the late Don
Freeman was Managing Editor. The Associate Editor was Clare

Boothe Brokaw, afterwards Congresswoman and then Ambassa-dress Clare Luce. I was invited to join their staff as an Associate Editor.

The publisher, the late Condé Nast, gave us all a free hand and the magazine was a wonderful and crackling proving ground for young writers. It printed anything I wrote and the editors egged me on to try all kinds of things including short pieces of fiction. In addition to my own byline I had five assorted pen names under which I wrote. Sometimes I had as many as three pieces in one issue under different names. The schooling and the encourage-ment I received were priceless.

In 1931 I acquired an agent, Harold Ober, and we have been together ever since and when he died in 1959 I felt that I had lost a second father.

Oddly enough it was not sports or a sports story which sparked my demolishing the barrier between the big time and myself and enabled me to break into the 'Saturday Evening Post' after so many years of endeavour and desk drawers filled with rejection slips, but the city side.

A news story broke one Christmas; a night editor performed a near miracle of getting it into the paper and thereby excited my imagination and capacity for hero worship. The story of this story and its subsequent landing me in the 'Saturday Evening Post' is told in the preamble to MCKABE, *the first short story in this book. Its sale and publication resulted in giving me the one thing I had lacked up to that moment, and without which I maintain no writer can function. That lack was self-confidence. From then on all my 'writing on the side' was concentrated upon fiction and my stories began to appear regularly in the 'Saturday Evening Post' and later in other magazines as well.*

This is not intended as a blueprint for anyone who wishes to become a professional writer, I am just telling you what happened to me.

In 1936 I took the decisive step of changing my entire way of life. I resigned my job as one of the then highest-paid sports-writers in the country, setting alight a perfect holocaust of bridges and went abroad to try in the future to earn my living as a free-lance writer of fiction, make or break. I was thirty-nine and run-ning scared.

What was I scared of? Of failing and having to go back to sports-writing! Previously I had become aware that I was in danger of letting the wrong kind of success go to my head and becoming that prize bore, the veteran sports-writer, of having years creep up on me with my boyhood and lifelong ambition fulfilled, of being a success in the eyes of the world and a failure to myself.

Once while I was sitting at the ringside in Madison Square Garden preparing to send a round-by-round account of the main event to my office, a colleague arrived late, climbed into his seat while the principals were being introduced, and, standing up, took his own sweet time over parking his typewriter, removing his overcoat, and counting the house. An irritated customer sitting in one of the ringside seats whose view was being blocked shouted: 'Siddown! You're nothing but a sports-writer!'

The words were not addressed to me, I was already sitting down, but they went through me like an arrow piercing the heart, for I too was nothing but a sports-writer. It was not the denigration that hurt for there was nothing dishonourable about being a sports-writer; it was a well-regarded and highly paid profession with its own pride. The searing truth held up before me was that this was not what I had set out to be.

I think, in fact I am certain, that my decision to go for broke dated from that evening which took place sometime in 1934. It was two years before I was able to implement it, but the decision had been made and I knew that I would go through with it. In 1936 one of my short stories sold to the movies for $5,000. It was a stake which would enable me to live for a while and write stories. If they sold, well and good. If they didn't . . .

I resigned from the 'Daily News,' went to England and rented a cottage in the little fishing village of Salcombe on the South Devonshire coast, 214 miles from London, and remained there a few months before going on to the Continent.

Ever since then I have earned my living as a writer. I never forgot my cottage in Devon or the charm of the little village town. The annual bass run off Salcombe in November is something to gladden the heart of any fisherman and I rarely miss it, for one of my hobbies is fishing.

Twice thereafter there was a kind of a half-way turning back but not because I had failed to sell my stories, but rather because I felt that through fourteen years of watching and writing about athletes I had become one-sided. I was still sufficiently naïve as to believe that I had to experience things properly to write about them. I had not yet wholly learned to trust my imagination and even more my instincts. In the winter I went back to the 'News' as a reporter on the City side to learn the business or to come in contact with that thing known as 'life.' The following winter I signed with INS as a feature writer to do special stories.

I soon found out that this nonsense was costing me money since *my assignments interfered with my writing and that furthermore working as a news reporter was not teaching me any more about things and people I didn't know already. I was simply wasting my time. Thereafter I did no more reporting except for a brief period during the war when I took an assignment as a war correspondent.*

In connection with the above I might say that life for a writer, at least for this one, is a constant series of alarums and excursions, of self-pamperings and self-delusions. There is always some distant place, a thatched cottage in England, a hacienda in Mexico, where, if you could only be, you would turn out the lyric prose and deeply significant stories that you find you cannot do wherever you happen to find yourself.

This is of course sheer nonsense, but it is a harmless kind of nonsense. It keeps one hoping and helps one to get around. I managed to achieve the house in England, the villa in Mexico, the chalet in Liechtenstein and many other places, and they were never the answer. One of the few stories that ever gave me any satisfaction was written in snatches on railroad trains and hotel rooms while I was batting around the country as a reporter. I have written in furnished rooms, on boats, in the city, in the country, and in aeroplanes. If I have something that I want to write, I know that I can do it anywhere and under any conditions. But I will not relinquish the cherished illusion of the need for far places. I don't even mind knowing it is a fake. It is delightful window-dressing. What one actually needs to write is an idea, a typewriter, a roof over one's head and three square meals a day, because writing is physical as well as mental work and therefore hungry-making. All one really gets out of the delusion that ideas will burn and words flow three or four thousand miles away from the place where one is at the moment, is a pleasant and diverting way of living and the broadening that comes with travel.

One is always seeking the touchstone that will dissolve one's deficiencies as a person and a craftsman. And one is always bumping up against the fact that there is none except hard work, concentration and continued application.

From 1938 on I have been a freelance professional writer, turning out short stories, serials, novels, film scripts, articles and essays. My market at first was limited to American magazines, the 'Saturday Evening Post,' 'Cosmopolitan,' 'Good Housekeeping,' 'American Magazine' and the defunct 'Collier's' and 'Liberty.' I have also written for 'Readers' Digest,' 'Esquire,' 'The New Yorker' and many others, and in later years my stories have appeared in publications abroad and in translation.

Some of my books have become best-sellers, others have appeared and vanished without so much as causing a ripple, and others still, to my greatest satisfaction, have maintained a quiet and steady circulation over a long period of years. I have had a few minor triumphs, some failures and down through the years an extraordinary amount of luck. If you were to ask me what so far in my thirty years career as a professional writer has given me the most satisfaction, I would tell you that it is the fact that in the Times Bookshop in Wigmore Street in London, as well as in Foyles, Hatchards and one or two other bookshops at Christmas time I have my own individual table where all of my books are displayed, from SNOW GOOSE, which was first published in 1941, to perhaps include this current volume.

All these things, with other evidences of popularity, a comfortable way of life, a house in the South of France, etc., are accounted in this world as solid success with every indication of security. I am still dissatisfied with things that I write and I am still insecure.

Since these are listed as confessions I will confess to you that from the time I resigned from the 'News' a quarter of a century ago up to and including this very moment I have never had a single moment of security. Mark this down as one of the occupational hazards of freelance writing for a living. Or if this is too gloomy a view ascribe it to my own personal neuroticism and perhaps infantilism, for even today when I have completed a manuscript and sent it to agent or publisher I await the verdict with the same anguish, fear and doubts, that I did when I was a boy and despatched a manuscript to a magazine with the usual stamped, addressed envelope enclosed for return.

The euphoria connected with an acceptance lasts for a week or ten days, after which the reaction sets in. Can I keep it up? Will I be able to do it again? What will the next one I write be like?

I should be more upset at these palpable evidences of neuroticism if most writers, male and female, with whom I have exchanged shop-talk had not confessed to some similar instances of disillusionment and insecurity which expressed themselves in one form or another. And we were all agreed that nothing was quite so shattering as a rejection or a sour notice or criticism from an editor, and the further along we went in our professions, the more damaging were the results of such a rejection. The first thought that arises to harass every writer when a piece is bounced, for whatever reason, is: 'I'm through. I'm all washed up. This is the end. I can never write again. I've lost the touch.' One feels as help-

less, dejected, and amateurish as the veriest tyro or beginner, as though one had to start learning over again.

Of course it is sheer nonsense; of course one writes again because one must, and if the subsequent piece is accepted with hosannahs, or merely accepted and paid for, all one's oozed confidence comes flooding back again and one rides atop the world – until the next fall.

I have always maintained that every successful writer is primarily a good editor, a premise that usually drives editors into tantrums when I tell it to them. But when the writer sits down to his typewriter to tell a story that he will offer for sale, he has already fulfilled most of the functions of editor. He has chosen his subject for timeliness, reader interest, the style of magazine at which it is aimed, the known likes and dislikes of the editor of that particular literary variety show, and the current state of mind of the public. He trims his material and sews his seam in a manner designed to be pleasing to all concerned. I maintain that's editing. The editor in the end merely confirms or denies one's judgment.

The hazards remain large, even after you have what the laymen likes to call a 'name,' and very often the greater the name, the stricter the standards set by the editor. The writer invests an idea, research, time, energy, and hard labour in the preparation of a story. At the end of three weeks or a month he has some fifteen to twenty pages of typescript. If the editor nods 'yes,' it is worth from one to five thousand dollars depending on who the writer is and how big the demand for him. And if he says 'No, thanks,' the income-tax people will let the writer deduct the market value of twenty sheets of used foolscap and depreciation on his typewriter, and the manuscript can then be used to light a fire. You can't afford to be wrong.

Short stories and novelettes that get into magazines in the class of mass circulation of the 'Saturday Evening Post,' 'Good House-keeping,' 'Cosmopolitan,' 'Woman,' 'Woman's Own,' 'Argosy,' or 'John Bull' are counted as successful since if nothing else they have had to meet certain standards which if not always highly literary are at least a guarantee that they can be published in a highly competitive field to divert ordinary people. They have passed editorial tests and hence are original, amusing, instructive, entertaining and readable. Working as a professional writer with a reasonable understanding of my medium I have long been aware that there are often more interesting and exciting things about a story than meets the eye, and among these is the story of the story, for there always is one connected with every effort.

Not that I hold with the frequently perpetrated theatrical cliché that the writer per se *is a romantic and fascinating fellow. His delineation on the stage, hacking away at a portable in the middle of an expensive indoor set somewhere on Long Island, or Chelsea, pausing for thinks, ruffling his fingers through his hair, making* moues *and lighting endless cigarettes, always makes me a little ill. Nothing is quite so static and unromantic as a chap sitting at a typewriter. And paradoxically nothing is to me quite as exciting and fabulous as the preparation of a story or the realisation of the hundreds of kaleidoscopic flashes of the human mind, both conscious and subconscious, not to mention bits and pieces of the liver and lights of the writer that go into it.*

For there is no creative product that so exposes the past life, the background, the adjustment or lack of adjustment to life, the fears and foibles, the failings and the strivings of the human being behind it as does writing. Music is an emotional abstract, painting and sculpture in themselves provide few clues to the personality of the artist. But everything a man ever thought or did, or was or hoped to be, will eventually find its way into his copy.

Why does a man write a story? For many reasons: an urge, a bite, a gripe, the need to get something off his chest, the desire to support his family, the hope of expressing something beautiful he feels inside him, the wish to entertain, to be admired, to be famous, to overcome a frustration, to experience vicariously an unfulfilled wish, or just for the pleasure of taking an idea and sending it flashing through the air like a juggler with many silver balls, or the dark satisfaction of pinioning that same idea or thought or human experience and dissecting it to its roots.

'To write beautifully of beautiful things' is enough for any man's ambition, but the ingredients that go into this writing are myriad and fascinating. No matter what the subject, the storehouse of the mind is opened and a million relics of a full life are there from which to select and choose. There are human experiences, memories, dreams from both night and day, fantasies, people real and imagined, places one has seen with the naked eye and places one has hungered for in the spirit, scents, snatches of long-forgotten conversations, old and troublesome emotions one had thought packed away, the memory of a caress, dislikes, hatreds, love and fear, serenity and passion, all waiting to help you in the telling of your tale. Many of these are unrecognised, but sometimes one is able to see through a finished story and know how old and how characteristic are some of the things contained therein.

Even superficially the events gathered behind a story are interesting, the whys and wherefores of the background, the actual experience that touched off the idea, and the means used by the writer to add substance and drama to a happening, an episode, a fantasy, or an idea. The writer appears in many guises throughout his stories, and each of them has a meaning and a reason, some valid relation to his character or person or the kind of human being he is.

This book is intended to be neither an autobiography nor a self-analysis, but rather a glimpse into the workroom of a professional story-teller, somewhat like wandering through the studio of an artist where you will find displayed some of the ingredients he uses in his work scattered about, his paints, palettes and canvases and lay figures, old works and new, good ones and bad.

Such a visit it seems to me might be interesting merely from the point of view of curiosity; it might also be helpful to the beginning writer and perhaps even furnish here and there a hint or a clue as to how to go about confecting saleable fiction. Yet I am offering it only as entertainment. If any of it should prove to be instructive, so much the better then.

Over a period of twenty-five years I have written some hundred and thirty published short stories, novelettes, serials and books, of these short stories I have selected twenty, ten of these written before or during the war and ten between 1945 and today. To each of these I have written a preamble or introduction which, to the best of my recollection is the story behind the story, the background of the idea, the reason for writing it, the design, the method, the things that animated me or for that matter whatever came into my head about it as I looked back. Whether these writings are true or false is debatable. When I write about motivation or emotions connected with the telling of a story which happened years ago I am trying to write not as I feel and think today, but as I hope I remember I then felt and thought. I am most certainly no longer the person I was when I began to write, nor do I write in the same style or upon the same subjects. Some of the things I write about my stories may be exaggeration and some even delusion, but everywhere I think I have managed to embed some kernel of truth.

Half of these preambles were written years ago when first a version of this volume appeared in the United States in 1946. I have now edited them and brought them up to date in the light of being older and, I hope, that much more experienced and knowledgeable.

There is a question I am always asked and it is not confined to the layman. It is: 'How do you work?' The content of this question varies from the vacuous probing of the ninny who wants to know whether I have to wait for inspiration and write on both sides of the paper to my colleagues who are as interested in my working hours and methods as I am in theirs.

Briefly then I work from half-past nine in the morning until twelve-thirty or one, break three hours for lunch and rest and return at three-thirty for a two- or three-hour session in the afternoon.

Up to two years ago when an illness suddenly robbed me of the use of my fingers I did all of my work myself at the typewriter, punching out first and second drafts and then sending the corrected and interlined material to my agents for copying. And incidentally the illness which affected the nerves of my hands was occupational. Forty years of bending over a hot typewriter had caused changes in the vertebral column at the neck, pinching the nerves. Faced with a loss of output and recovering in the hospital from an operation to ease the condition I engaged a secretary and in a few months had taught myself to dictate.

The use of my hands was restored, but I am now accustomed to dictating, like it and find that it has increased my output and I can work longer hours. It is also better for my dialogue. Say a silly line to your secretary and even as you are saying it you know it won't do. She may have been trained never to turn a hair no matter what idiocies you might utter, nevertheless you know that she knows the line is a dud and you kill it before it has a chance to go any further.

When I was typewriting my own material physically and was working to develop the plot or an idea of a short story I used to talk to myself on the typewriter, rambling on, setting down thoughts and ideas, praising or cursing them, calling myself names, etc. This had the effect of unblocking myself. Original and valid ideas then would float up from the subconscious and present themselves, and I have solved many a difficult story in this fashion. Today I can achieve the same effect by rambling on to my secretary, dictating my thoughts upon the subject. Pages and pages of these notes are then discarded, but they have accomplished their purpose of letting through the story I really want to tell.

Short stories are initiated from ideas, the tickle of an absurdity, 'Wouldn't it be funny if . . .', an item in the newspaper, a story told by a friend, an emotion or a character one encounters. The difficulty then is to translate this beginning germ or in-

cident into a fully fledged dramatic plot preserving brevity and unity.

This is the hardest work of all, for it requires thinking. I begin by writing trial synopsis and plot outline, adding, discarding, changing, messing about until a clear line for the beginning, middle and climax begins to emerge, after which a final synopsis is written.

Next, this final synopsis is broken up into scenes and so many pages allotted to each scene and transition of the story. The average length short story is limited to between five and seven thousand words. Five thousand words is about seventeen type-written pages. This does not give one much room to turn around and calls for all the tricks of economy, brevity and suggestion which is the nature of the art of short-story writing.

When I am satisfied that I can tell my story within the allotted space I spend two or three days writing character sketches, setting down all and everything I know about each of the characters in the story. Like the iceberg seven-eighths of this material remains submerged and doesn't show, but the characters have now taken on life for me and I am able to think and speak and act as they might.

The above is the work part, then comes the fun part, the writing. If the story has been properly constructed, this can be a joy and a delight. It is at this time that one makes little discoveries and adds those small touches which are often the contribution a director makes to a moving picture, and which help to bring story and character to life. After I have written the first draft I let it cool for two or three days, or a week, by which time I can detect the soft spots and weaknesses. The second writing usually eliminates these. I write double space and one side of the paper, margin of twenty, two hundred and fifty words to a page. This makes for quick and easy reading by the editor.

Final corrections are made with pen and the story forwarded to my agent who has it copied and bound and sent to the publisher for whom he thinks it is best fit.

I sit at home chewing my fingernails, waiting to hear if all this effort and planning is to be a success or a failure.

These stories represent a span of time from 1933 to 1958, a distance of a quarter of a century. Whether the later ones are an improvement over the earlier stories in style and content must be left to you. The subject matter changes in the later years as I found myself drawn towards Europe and my outlook tended to become more European and less carpentered to the American

B

market, an outlook which, incidentally, began to bring me rejections from American magazines which heretofore had been happy to publish my work.

There are two ways of reading this book, for I hope either enjoyment or instruction, and I don't know which to recommend, whether I should suggest that you read first the preambles to these stories and then the stories, or first read the story and then afterwards return to the little pieces in front which give the inside story.

Perhaps the second is more to be recommended since the story will have had its effect, if any, and you will then perhaps find it interesting to find how some of these effects were achieved and how the whole business came into being. However, should you not be able to resist reading the preamble first, or generally prefer it that way, I promise you that none of them 'give away' or reveal the point so as to spoil the story that follows.

In selecting stories for this, the British, edition of this book I have omitted several of my favourite stories which appear in the American edition as being somewhat too American in subject matter, baseball, etc., to appeal to British readers and have substituted tales of more international flavour.

Herewith then some examples:

McKabe

••

MCKABE *is the first fiction story I ever sold to a 'slick' magazine,
the same being the 'Saturday Evening Post' which had been my
goal ever since I started writing. The publication date I note was
August 12, 1933, at which time I was thirty-six years old and I
should say that I had been seriously attempting to crash the
portals of this magazine for some fifteen years.*

*The fulfilment of this ambition was not at all as I had imagined
it down through the years, namely the submission of the story
with the usual stamped, self-addressed return envelope, the sus-
penseful wait and the arrival of the letter containing a cheque.
On the contrary it was quite different and most business-like.*

*At that time I was Sports Editor of the tabloid New York 'Daily
News.' I had sold articles on sports subjects to several of the large
national magazines and I had acquired an agent, Mr Harold Ober.
I went to him with my idea and he arranged an appointment the
following week with Mr Thomas Costain, then a 'Post' Editor and
later himself a novelist. If you are interested in how stories were
and are merchandised in the U.S.A. it is the custom of the 'Post'
Editors (the magazine is domiciled in Philadelphia) to make
weekly shopping trips to New York to visit the offices of the
literary agents who at that time showed them their authors' manuscripts or discussed ideas or projects with them. Costain listened
to what I had to say and when I had finished simply commented,
'Write it.' This was no commitment or guarantee to buy. The 'Post'
never does, but it was an encouragement.*

*The ingredients of this story are a mixture of a kind of hero
worship I gave to the working newspapermen and reporters and
editors on the city or editorial side, the factual event of the killing
of the notorious gangster, 'Legs Diamond,' and my admiration for
Rudyard Kipling and a desire to imitate one of his short stories
entitled* THE DEVIL AND THE DEEP SEA.

*The background for this story, and one other in this volume,
is New York's first tabloid newspaper, the 'Daily News,' founded*

by the late Captain Joseph Medill Patterson of Chicago. The era is the lush period between the two wars.

The 'Daily News' at that time was quite different from the mammoth of today boasting the largest circulation in America. When I first went to work for it in 1922 it was young, virile, vigorous, rough-neck and rowdy. Tough and sensational it was fighting tooth and nail for circulation and a place in the community.

I think that newspapers, like people, like everything in nature on earth, are young, grow up, change, age, and pass. I am glad that I lived with and was a part of the 'Daily News' during its ebullient youth. It was the greatest shop in town in which to work and turned out some of the best newspapermen and women of the era.

Behind these people, animating them, supporting them, egging them on, was the then young Captain Joseph Medill Patterson, publisher of the paper, just home from the wars, with a record of socialism and liberalism behind him in Chicago, a man filled with the gusto of living, who had a sense of sparkling mischief without malice, whose understanding of the mass mind of the American public was infallible, and who never lacked the courage to admit when he was wrong. Working for him meant fun and excitement as well as good pay, and most of the men on the other sheets would have given a right arm to become a part of the 'News' organisation.

The newspaper as well as the people who worked for it used to fascinate me, and long before I thought of it as background for a series of fictional stories I used to duck away from the sports desk and roam through the other departments, watching, asking questions, getting the foreman or heads of departments to explain their work to me, trying to familiarise myself with the daily miracle that took place before my eyes, the smooth amalgamation of highly differentiated parts of a human and material machine leading to the inevitable climax of going to press on time.

I wandered through the darkrooms of the photographer's laboratory, where they could whip you out a print in less than five minutes after the cameraman had come bustling in from the scene of the accident or crime, the photo-engraving department, where pictures were turned into metal cuts to be laid next the type, into the library, where the intricate files were kept, files on the lives and misdeeds of hundreds of thousands of people, down to the composing room, where the chaffering batteries of linotype set the type for the paper and the headlines were autotyped. I spent time in the inferno of the stereotype room, where the plates

*for the presses were cast, and from time to time when the battery
of presses looking like the innards of an ocean liner or a battleship would begin to turn over slowly, commence to roll, and then,
picking up speed rise to an earth-shaking crescendo of noise and
fury, I would be standing up on the iron balcony, hanging on to
the vibrating steel rail, drinking in the sights and the sounds and
the smells as the pink papers with their black headlines poured
forth from the hopper and were stacked for the delivery room.*

One of my favourite people on the 'News' was Gene McHugh,
night editor, a bush-haired, hollow-eyed genius with ulcers, tough,
wise, decent, full of city-savvy and news instinct.

The morning of the day before Christmas in 1932 Gene was
on the lobster shift, running the paper between the hours of midnight and 8 a.m. His job was to supervise the final edition, which
was put to bed at four o'clock in the morning, and prepare the
schedules for the day men.

Shortly after six o'clock in the morning Gene received a telephone call from our Albany correspondent to the effect that Legs
Diamond, notorious bootlegger and gangster, had been mowed
down in a hail of machine-gun bullets in an Albany lodging house.
It was a clean and sensational scoop, but might just as well have
been delivered in Choctaw for all the good it could do either
McHugh or the 'News.' Because our run was off for the morning,
the linotypers, stereotypers, and pressmen dispersed, and the
printing plant shut down, to all practical purposes.

This was the problem that faced McHugh. The earliest he could
hope to get this temporarily clean beat into the paper was the
next day's pink edition, which went to press at six o'clock in the
evening. But by that time the afternoon papers would have killed
the story.

But McHugh was a newspaperman from his toes to his flying
thatch, and the fact that he couldn't get this news on to the street
in his edition galled him more than his ulcers. He knew it was
impossible. And yet a stubborn and invincible spirit surged within
him. He went to work.

Two hours later he had a paper on the street. It was an odd-
looking specimen but it told the news and served it up exclusively.
It was one of the really great scoops, beats, or whatever you wish
to call it, of the era.

There were several of Rudyard Kipling's short stories that were
special favourites of mine, and one of these was that epic of man
against machinery, THE DEVIL AND THE DEEP SEA, *which appears*

in the volume called THE DAY'S WORK, *in the authorised edition. If you don't remember it, it will pay you to look it up. It is the story of a little British steamer caught pearl-poaching in the East Indies and brought to bay with a five-inch shell through her engine-room. It deals with her chief engineer, Mr Wardrop, who attempts the impossible, namely to bring order out of the horrible tangle of steel, copper, and iron junk and repair the damage sufficiently to escape.*

The analogy between this story and the story of McHugh, Wardrop's problem and McHugh's problem, struck me at once. Here was a chance to try to emulate a writer who was a hero to me and attempt to write a story like that.

Emulate should not be confused with plagiarise. The theme of man against the elements is as old as literature, and that of man against machinery at least as old as machinery. McHugh sang in my heart as Mr Wardrop must have made Kipling's blood course faster. To put it mildly, the two stories and their treatments are entirely different. Rudyard Kipling remains undisputed champion, but I was able to achieve at least one lifelong ambition, and that was to make the 'Saturday Evening Post.'

But it is one thing to be told by the great personage of a 'Post' Editor, 'Write it,' and quite another to do so. I immediately was seized with a most virulent case of 'Post' fever, a disease similar to buck fever which grips hunters the first time they find a deer in their gun sites.

I destroyed page after page, tore up lead after lead. Everything I had ever learned about writing a short story I had forgotten. Here was opportunity beckoning and I was cowering miserably from it.

Eventually the nerves were conquered. After all Mr Costain had liked my story when I told it to him. All I really had to do then was to tell it to the readers the way I imagined it had happened.

After that it wrote itself in three days and I turned it in and a week later heard the news which was to change the pattern of my life.

I pity all who have never known the thrill of 'making' the 'Post,' or similar publication, for the first time. Like the exquisite moment of the first solo flight in an aeroplane it can happen only once; it can never be experienced again and it can never be forgotten. The Messrs E. McHugh, R. Kipling, T. Costain, H. Ober and the 'Saturday Evening Post' are hereby thanked.

As a final footnote to this history of a new start in life, the 'Post' paid me five hundred dollars for the story. Following its publica-

*tion I was sued for libel by a printer whose real name I had in-
advertently used, though in connection with another character,
a bit of sheer aberration on my part but indicating how closely
I was working with real characters. I won the libel suit, but my
lawyer's bill for the successful defence was nine hundred dollars,
which left me with a four-hundred-dollar deficit on the deal and
the determination to be careful in bestowing names on fictional
characters in the future.*

McKABE

The city room was nothing but a feeble pulse in the somnolent
body of the paper when, a few minutes after six-thirty in the
morning, the day before Christmas, the number three telephone
on the city desk of the *New York Morning Blade* jangled. The
paper had gone to bed hours before, when, at 4 a.m., the last
edition had come thundering off the block-long battery of presses.
The emergency crews had been released and sent home.

Gene McKabe, lobster-shift editor, looked up from the overnight assignment sheet on which he was working, preparatory
to turning it over to the day relief, when and if it should decide
to show up. McKabe was a thin, greyish, old-looking little man
at thirty-eight, who suffered from stomach ulcers and inferiority.
Irritably he flipped the receiver off the hook and prepared to
take a story from some tipster that two milk wagons had collided
on a slippery street, or that a drunk had fallen down a flight of
steps and was lying in the gutter. This was the usual run of news
that came to McKabe in the early hours, stories in which he
played no great part beyond weighing their importance in reporting them to the day shift for coverage. Well, someone had to
take the trick from midnight to morn.

McKabe mumbled: 'Desk – McKabe,' into the mouthpiece, with
his mind half on his assignment sheet and half on the dull pain
that gnawed at his middle at that time of the morning. The *Blade*
operator said: 'A Mr Giller is calling you from Albany, New York,
and wishes you to pay for the call.'

'Oke!' grunted McKabe, and wondered what could be getting
their Albany correspondent, a not too alert individual at best,
out of bed at that hour of the morning.

'Will you accept the charges?' repeated the operator.

'Yes, yes, yes,' said McKabe. 'Put him on.' He checked off an assignment for one of the day photographers to make some pictures along the Bowery and instinctively glanced around the deserted local room while he waited. A Negro janitor was hauling off huge wire baskets laden with paper and trash. Two char-women were on their knees in the aisles between the battery of rewrite desks. The art department was empty. The big horseshoe-shaped copy desk was untenanted. Monk, the lobster-shift office boy, the only other person in the vast room besides himself, had pushed two of the reporters' desks together and was lying atop them with his coat rolled up under his head, his shirt open at the neck, his mouth a gummy cavern, snoozing and snoring in an unlovely manner. The long-distance operator said something in a distant, far-off bleat, and the *Blade* operator replied in her singsong: 'We are ready with Mr McKabe. He is on the li-yen.' McKabe heard Giller's voice, at first indistinct and then clear and plain as the operators closed their keys. It was shaking and surcharged with excitement. He said:

'Hello! Hello! Desk? Who is this?'

'Hello, Giller – McKabe. What's biting you?'

'Who is it? . . . Mac? Listen, Mac. They got Feet Schindler up here a half an hour ago. Blew his head off.'

'What?' said McKabe, and glued the receiver more firmly to his ear. 'Lemme have that again.' Instinctively his eyes leaped to the clock over the desk. Six thirty-seven. The *Times* and the *Tribune* had shut down at five, the *American* and the *Mirror* a half-hour later. But the afternoon papers——

'Listen! Wait,' said Giller, his voice sounding odd with the pressure of excitement. 'Hello, Mac? They got Mimi, his girl, too, and Little Hymie and Joe Colonno. It's a slaughter.'

'Sweet Peter!' said McKabe. 'Wait a minute.' He called over to the sleeping office boy: 'Monk! Hey, Monk!' Then he threw a telephone book at him, which struck him in the chest. Monk sat up, bleary-eyed and indignant. McKabe bawled at him: 'Get on extension 457 and help me check this story.'

Monk ambled over to the desk, working his mouth, and picked up pencil, paper, and the receiver from the extension of McKabe's phone on the other side of the desk.

'Shoot!' said McKabe, his own pencil poised.

'Listen,' said Giller. 'I'm coming home about a hour ago from a little party at my wife's sister's. I'm a little stiff, see?'

'You're not stiff now, are you?' asked McKabe, suddenly suspicious.

'Listen,' replied Giller's voice, and its deadly earnestness convinced McKabe. 'After what I just seen, nobody could be stiff. So
the wife is inside and I'm just putting the car away when the
World War busts loose on the other side of town. It's 'way on the
other side, but it's so clear and quiet I can hear it. Machine-guns.
It takes me a half-hour to find it.'

To himself Monk carefully repeated the address Giller gave,
and marked it on his sheet.

'The state troopers were there already. They were all dead.'

'Who was dead – the troopers?'

'No, no! Feet and his doll and all of them. They made a clean
get-away.'

'I thought you said they were dead.'

'No, no, no! The mob that done it made the get-away. They
drove up in a car, walked up two flights, and machine-gunned
'em. Feet and Mimi and Little Hymie and Joe Colonno must 'a'
come up from Kinderhook and took a room in this joint. It's just
a rooming house. I guess they were all celebrating Feet's acquittal.
They caught 'em cold. There was a lot of busted gin and whisky
bottles around that got shot to pieces.'

'How many in the mob?'

'I dunno. They made a clean get-away in a car——'

Monk edited this statement automatically and wrote: 'Clean
get-away in high-powered car.'

'—but from the slugs that's in the bodies and the walls, there
must 'a' been at least four of 'em pumping submachine-guns, and
maybe a coupla lookouts. The walls was all shot to pieces, and
the lights. Feet and the girl were sitting on the bed when they
got it. Joe and Hymie were at the table, drinking. The floor is all
blood and plaster out of the wall and ceiling and pieces of glass.
They didn't take a chance on Feet getting away this time. Got
all that? Is that something? None of the other guys are out here
yet. We got an hour's start. Is that something?'

'Yeah,' said McKabe. His eyes went to the clock again. It now
showed a quarter to seven. 'That's something, all right. But what
the hell good does it do us? We're locked up. The run's off. The
crews have all gone home. We're dead. Get it? Feet's been
knocked off for the afternoon papers. That's your luck and mine.
The devil himself couldn't get out a paper at this hour. I'll rout
O'Rary out and fly him up to get some pix. Stay on it. Call me
back in an hour.'

There was a pregnant silence from the other end of the telephone.

McKabe hung up the receiver and chewed at his pencil, his

eye on the clock again. His face went suddenly ash-coloured and he swore. Excitement always made his stomach bad. Monk hung up the receiver to his extension and blinked across the desk at McKabe, who sat looking old and shrunken. The copy time-clock stamp went 'click' as another minute popped itself into eternity. Six forty-seven – the day before Christmas. Merry Christmas, Feet. Blown to hell. Feet, Feet, Feet. The name marched through McKabe's skull and trailed behind it black ribbons of headlines. The enormousness of the story suddenly struck home. Feet Schindler, the headline pet, big-time racketeer, killer, booze and dope runner. Feet, the much-shot-at, who had survived five murderous attacks and who carried enough slugs in his skinny body to founder him, whose latest escape from death had been a seven-day sensation, and whose acquittal the afternoon before of a charge of hijacking and abduction was still smashed over the face of the extra-final edition of the *Blade* which lay face-up on McKabe's desk. It read: 'FEET ACQUITTED.'

It was wrong. It ought to be shrieking: 'FEET MURDERED, FEET SLAUGHTERED, FEET BUTCHERED.' The date, 'December 24, 1932,' on the logotype made 'FEET ACQUITTED' stale and a lie. It was six forty-eight the morning of December 24, and Feet, the king cobra of the muscle and roscoe men, was lying in a welter of plaster and broken glass and his own blood in a cheap rooming house in Albany. Yesterday he was acquitted. Today he was dead. Fresher news! Hotter news! His moll was dead with him; Mimi, the pretty, red-haired *Follies* girl, and Little Hymie and Joe Colonno lying in the same room. Six-star, extra-final edition. The latest news. December 24, 1932. FEET ACQUITTED. Acquitted nothing! He was either roasting in hell or standing before the last bar of justice confirming his killings. Feet! Feet! Feet!

McKabe looked up at the clock again. The corpse of the paper was three minutes colder. Six-fifty. 'Call the pressroom,' said McKabe. 'See if you can raise anybody.'

Monk looked at a card stuck under the glass top of the city desk, stuck his pencil butt into the dial face, and spun it around to 346. As he did so, McKabe was dialling 342, the composing room, 3 – 4 – 2. Wait . . . Click . . . Ring . . . ring . . . ring . . . ring.

The phone in the empty office of the composing-room foreman rang again and again. Outside, the vast floor loaded with steel and lead, with the orderly rows of linotype machines set up at one end and the make-up stones with the half-broken forms of the paper resting thereon, was dark, empty, deserted. The purplish-blue, overhead mercury lamps were out. One electric drop-light that hung over one of the type saws cast deep shadows that reached to the linotypes and darkened the silver-lead pots in which was nothing but cold metal. A single red standing light gleamed over one of the machines and lit up a few of the rows of the keyboards. It had been turned on by the operator to indicate that the machine was out of order.

Three hours earlier, hot type had been dropping from the clacking, chaffering, spinning machines, as line after line of silver-lead was set by the flying fingers of rows of operators. The telephone began to ring in the empty room. This was a 'swing' morning because of the impending holiday. The day shift wouldn't be on until eight. The telephone stopped ringing.

It rang in the pressroom in the empty office of the pressroom foreman, who an hour ago had ordered the presses stripped, seen them washed down and oiled, and gone away. Outside, the great presses that stretched for a full city block lay dark, gleaming, and silent. They looked like the turbines of a gigantic battle cruiser. When they ran at full blast, they made a noise like sheet iron falling down a mountainside. The floor and the steel gallery that ran around them, and the entire building, trembled. Men, oily and grimy, walked the catwalks between and around them. The papers poured from them like chaff from a hopper. Governors spun, rocking beams rocked, levers and pistons moved back and forth in their complicated counterpoint. The paper whirled white through the cylinders and came out grey-black with news and pictures.

Now they lay quiescent, sinister mountains of machinery. The overhead lights gleamed from the polished brass and steel and from the oil on the steel floors to which they were anchored. There was in the vast and seemingly endless pressroom no motion, no sound but the regular ring-stop-ring of a telephone.

McKabe called a Garden City number and routed O'Rary, the flying photographer, out of bed, told him what had happened and ordered him to Albany to make pictures, and then telephoned to a reporter to meet O'Rary at Roosevelt Field and fly up with him to Albany and get on the story. The excitement bell in the A.P. and U.P. ticker room went: 'Ding . . . ding . . . ding . . . Ding-ding-ding-ding-ding.' Monk pricked up his ears and McKabe motioned him with his head in the direction of the room. When he came back, he had a narrow slip of white paper in his fingers – an A.P. flash.

It read:

6.52 A.M. FLASH. FEET SCHINDLER REPORTED SLAIN IN ALBANY. EDITORS: FOR YOUR INFORMATION. MORE LATER ON VERIFICATION.

McKabe swore helplessly. Now it was out. Feet Schindler reported slain. More on verification! Reported nothing. He was an hour, two hours ahead of them all. He had the story. He had it in his mind's eye. His physical eye looked at the time again. It was five minutes to seven. He saw again the picture that Giller had drawn for him of that dreadful room in Albany. He could get it down on paper – short, pithy, exciting sentences. But it couldn't be cast into type. It couldn't be got on to the presses. He had a moment of complete madness when he contemplated making twenty carbon copies of the story and getting it out on the street – getting something out on the street. Everybody would want to know. Everybody ought to know. Extra! Extra! Feet Schindler slain. Here's the story by Gene McKabe, on a piece of copy paper. Read it and pass it along to your neighbour.

The same Associated Press flash that lay before him was in the offices of the *Times,* and the *Tribune,* the *American,* the *Standard, News-Beacon, Chronicle,* and *Enquirer.* All the lobster-trick editors on the morning sheets were fingering the same slip of paper and cursing their inability to get the news on to the street. Lobster-trick editors! Forgotten newspapermen like himself who worked the shift from midnight to dawn. Not the most brilliant editors in the world, but good sound news men who knew what to do in case of fire, flood, or quake. Well, none of them could perform miracles and bring a corpse to life. With a good deal of scrambling, the day forces could get a morning paper out by seven o'clock that night, twelve hours later.

Not so the afternoon papers, due on the streets at ten-thirty in the morning. With a sickening sensation McKabe visioned the excitement and the activity in the offices of the *News-Beacon,* the liveliest of the afternoon sheets – editors on telephones to Albany; reporters piling into plane and car and heading north to run down the tip; rewrite men fingering through the clips on the dead Schindler, preparing a biographical sketch of his career; copy pouring into the composing rooms. Time, time, time – fleeting seconds and minutes. They would try to move their press time up, rout out their Albany man, locate the death house, interview the state troopers. Artists would be drawing diagrams and artists' conceptions of the slaying. The vast news-reporting resources of the Associated and United Press were hot on the trail by this time. It wouldn't be long before the bell in the ticker room would ring again, and the first details of the sensational slaughter would be clacked out on the automatic printers. And in the meantime the radio might kill the story.

McKabe jumped to his feet. 'Watch those phones,' he said to

Monk. 'I'll be back.' He ran over to the elevator and caught it
as the porter dragged a load of wastepaper aboard.

'Pressroom,' he said.

The operator looked at McKabe curiously. 'Gallery?'

'Floor,' said McKabe. His heart was banging against his chest.
His stomach was sore. In his throat was a curious, nervous,
excited feeling. He swallowed several times.

The elevator door slid back and McKabe half ran through the
door as though to catch the miracle he hoped he would find
before it vanished – rolling presses, pressmen, fly-boys – life and
activity. But the batteries lay there glistening, quiet, and oppres-
sive. There was no one on the floor. The catwalks of steel were
empty. The massiveness of this cold, silent machinery laid hold
of McKabe's heart and made him feel the way he felt when
he contemplated high mountains – alone, insignificant, helpless.
Mountains made men want to scale them. These cold, hard,
motionless ranges of steel made a stubborn anger well up in
McKabe's heart and throat and brought tears of rage to his eyes.

He stood, a pygmy, on the steel floor, a little, thin man with
bushy hair, now half iron-grey, eyes sunk into hollows, unshaven,
sloppy-looking, his tie pulled down from his shirt, his waistcoat
flapping unbuttoned, pockets bulging with pencils, shaking his fist
at the dead presses and then pounding his forehead with the heel
of his hand. Men had made these machines, but they wouldn't
run without men. He, McKabe, willed them desperately to run,
and not a gear, not a cog, not a lever could move. He began to
curse them. His voice came clattering back to him from the high
vault two storeys above. His eye caught the ever-present clock –
seven-three. Then his ears caught a scraping noise halfway down
the room. If it were only one pressman – one of anyone who knew
what handles to pull, what buttons to push to make those giants
roll again – somehow McKabe knew he might do the rest. He
ran down that catwalk between the two rows of presses like a
sprinter, his feet rapping sharply on the floor.

It was another porter, plunking trash into his wire basket and
dragging it along the floor.

'Hey!' shouted McKabe. 'You!'

The porter, a Swede, looked at him curiously. 'Vat?' he
said.

'Ah, hell,' said McKabe. 'Nobody here?'

'Nah,' replied the Swede. 'Dey close up, hour ago.'

'You don't understand anything about' – nodding his head at
the presses – 'these?' McKabe hoped vaguely that the man might
be an apprentice or an ex-pressman filling in to keep working.

'Haw, haw!' laughed the Swede. 'I keep away from dem. Vat you looking for – pressmen?'

'My God, yes,' said McKabe. 'Do you know where any are? Maybe there's a couple still washing up.'

The Swede shook his head. 'Proply you find a coople across the street.'

McKabe grabbed the porter's arm. 'Across the street? The speakeasy?'

'If dey get drunk enough, dey stay there sometimes.'

'Wait a minute,' said McKabe. 'What day is this?' He knew, but he couldn't bring it into his mind.

'Huh?' said the Swede, and looked at him. Then he fished into his wire basket and pulled out a paper. The black headline on it hit McKabe like a physical blow. It read: 'FEET ACQUITTED.' The Swede looked at the date line 'December 24, 1932' – and said: 'You haff a coople drinks already? Tomorrow iss Christmas.'

December 24. The day before Christmas – the day the cashier paid the Christmas bonus. Some of the crew might hang around and wait – hang around in the neighbouring speakeasies.

'O.K., O.K., O.K.! Thanks!' said McKabe. He was already running down to the end of the room. He ran to the elevator, pressed the button, and then, without waiting, pushed through the door to the iron stairs that led to the street.

A twinge of pain caught him and stopped him, weak and gasping. It passed. Two steps at a time, he ran down two flights to the bottom and out into the street.

McKabe crossed the street to the speakeasy and never felt the cold or the slight morning drizzle. He burst through the ground-glass door so precipitately that the bartender stopped wiping glasses and rather casually dropped his right hand down below the bar, but restored it when he saw who it was, and said: 'Hello, Mac. Merry Christmas. Don't come in quite so fast, old boy.'

Larkin, the sub-foreman of the pressroom, Farley, an old-time pressman, and a man whom McKabe did not know were sitting around one of the wooden tables drinking Scotch highballs and eating cheese sandwiches. They were all drunk. McKabe paused, looking as though he had seen the Angel Gabriel, mopped his brow, and said: 'Sweet Peter, I'm glad to see you fellows.'

The three looked at McKabe owlishly and a little resentfully, until Larkin recognised him and said: 'Oh, h'lo, Mac, ol' Mac, ol' Mac. Merry Christmas. Will ya have a li'l' drink?'

McKabe shook his head, made the usual gesture towards his stomach, said: 'I can't drink likker. It murders me. Listen, are all you pressmen?'

Larkin shook his head. 'Billers here' – nodding towards the stranger – 'is a sub-make-up. He jus' come on from Milwaukee. Wife's cousin . . . Billers, shake han's with Mizzer McKabe.'

'Can you set type?' said McKabe eagerly, without acknowledging the introduction.

Billers nodded his head solemnly that he could, but said: 'I ain't in a long time, I'm a make-up.'

'Listen, you birds,' said McKabe, his voice choking with excitement. 'I want you to come on back with me and help me get a paper out. Feet Schindler——'

Larkin interrupted indignantly: 'What the heck are you talking about? 'S shut down. Closed up. Can't get no paper out. Siddown and have a drink.'

'No, no! Listen, fellers,' said McKabe earnestly, his sunken eyes wide and pleading, and dropped into the vacant chair at the table. 'Listen, there's a whale of a story. We got it. They knocked off Feet Schindler and his doll and everybody. Listen, we could beat the afternoon papers out——'

'Ah, forget it, Mac, and have a drink,' said Larkin. 'You can't get a paper out.'

'The hell I can't,' said McKabe, blazing suddenly and banging the table so that a slab of cheese jumped the dish. 'If you two can plate up a press, Billers can set the story.'

Larkin wiped his mouth with the back of his hand. 'And who's gonna cast the new plates? Ya gonna have a new One and Three, ain'tcha? Ya can't get a edition out with a rubber stamp. Have a drink and forget about it.'

'Stereotypers!' said McKabe. 'Aren't there any stereotypers in here?'

Farley peered intently around the empty room and said: 'No.'

McKabe screwed his eyes shut and ran his fingers through his hair. Suddenly he pointed a bony finger at Larkin. 'What's that joint where the stereotypers usually hang out?'

'It's just over on Second Avenue, but there won't be anybody there now. Most of the boys went up to Ed's house to play pinochle. Ferget it, Mac.'

McKabe was up out of the chair. 'Listen, will you fellers stay here a minute till I get back?'

Larkin said: 'You're damn right we'll stay here. We're gonna stay here till tomorrow morning. We're——'

McKabe was already heading for the door. He heard Billers say: 'Who is that screwball?' as he went through the door. He started for Second Avenue and the speakeasy frequented by some of the stereotypers and compositors.

The place was deserted except for the sleepy-eyed bartender, who was hanging up his apron. He didn't bother to turn around when he heard McKabe's footsteps, but merely said:

'Closing up.'

'No, no. I don't want a drink,' said McKabe. 'Are any of the stereotypers here?'

'Naw. They been and gone. If you'd come a minute sooner, Otto was here. You know Otto? He just left.'

'Which way did he go?' McKabe knew fat Otto Schommers, who worked in the foundry, making the mats from which the plates were cast. The bartender shrugged his shoulders. McKabe ran out into the street. It was deserted. Helpless, he ran a few steps first north, then south, stopped and swore bitterly. Then, two blocks away on Thirty-ninth Street, he saw a squat, solitary figure standing on the corner beneath the elevated. A trolley car was coming up the avenue, northbound. McKabe broke into a run for the figure, shouting, 'Otto! Hey, Otto! Otto Schommers! Hey, Otto! Otto, wait!' He didn't even know if it was Otto. Or if he had seen or heard him. The trolley clattered closer. McKabe gave one more yell: 'Otto! Hey, Otto!' The car blotted him from sight. McKabe ran on. The trolley moved away. The squat figure was still there. It was Otto.

'Otto!' McKabe reached him and caught him by the arm. 'Otto! Where you going?'

Otto paused. 'Home. Where you think? You make me miss my car.'

'Listen,' said McKabe between gasps. 'Will ya come back and cast a couple of plates? Hell of a story. Wanna get a paper out. Gotta. Will ya, Otto?'

Otto gazed at McKabe placidly. 'Sure,' he said. 'It's O.K. with me. I'll cast 'em. If I ain't too drunk. Anything you say.'

McKabe looked at Otto's fat and pudgy face. 'Otto, I could kiss you. We'll pick up Larkin, Farley, and Billers on the way.' He put his arm around fat Otto's shoulder and they turned back down the street.

It was seven twenty-four when McKabe shepherded his group through the plant door. The block-long double battery of giant presses no longer filled McKabe with quite the same awe. He no longer stood so terribly alone before them. Two of these men with him could master them.

Larkin took his handkerchief from his lips and said: 'Now just what is it you want us to do, ol' boy, ol' boy?'

'Plate up,' said McKabe. 'Get the plates back on again. I'll write the story. Billers can set it and make it up. We'll send down a new page 1 and 3. Otto says he can make the mats and cast them alone. You get those plates on the cylinders; I'll do the rest.'

'Plate up with what?' asked Larkin with sarcasm. 'I told you the paper was dead. The plates have been destroyed. Come on back and forget about it. The plates have been melted up already. We don't keep 'em. You can't do a miracle, even if it is Christmas, Mac. I could 'a' told you that.'

McKabe said: 'Oh, God,' and clung to the handrail of number ten press. Farley began picking his teeth. Billers did likewise. Otto looked fat and placid.

'All right! All right! That won't stop me. We'll cast 'em all over again.' McKabe shouted it and then turned to Otto. 'Whaddya say, Otto? Cast the whole damn thing over again except 1 and 3.'

Otto shrugged his shoulders. 'It's O.K. with me. Anything you say. I'll cast a million of 'em. It don't mean nothing in my life. I get time and a half. I hope the mats is all right.'

McKabe clutched his head. 'The mats. Holy jumping – Otto, you look. I can't.' Otto waddled placidly off in the direction of the stereotype foundry. McKabe pounded his skull with the heel of his hand again. His stomach was afire. 'If those' – he broke into profanity again – 'mats aren't there——'

'You'll have the mats remade out of forms that is broke up,' sneered Larkin. 'You're off your nut.'

McKabe didn't hear him, or if he did, he gave no sign.

They stood around, silent and gloomy, until Otto came waddling back down the iron walk. His features were as expressionless and placid as ever. It was impossible to tell whether he had good news or bad. All four stared at him.

'Well?' It was McKabe who spoke.

'Yeah, the mats is there.' Otto scratched his head. 'You want I should begin casting? It takes some time.'

McKabe looked up at the pressroom clock. It was seven thirty-one. 'How long?'

'I dunno. Maybe a hour. I gotta work alone.'

'Can't Larkin and Farley help you?'

'We're pressmen, not stereotypers,' said Larkin. 'You get us the plates; we'll slap 'em on. It'll take Otto a couple hours to cast up all them plates for a thirty-six-page paper. The afternoon papers will be on the street. The *News-Beacon* goes in at half-past ten. Why don't you forget about it? What the hell is this hot story, anyway, that can't wait until tomorrow?'

'Come on,' said McKabe. He steadied himself on Otto's shoulder and the five went off to the foundry.

Otto divested himself of his coat, vest, tie, and shirt and worked naked from the waist up. He threw a switch and the foundry became bathed in blue mercury light. Larkin and Billers and Farley looked bilious, and Otto like a fat imp from inferno. He looked at the temperature of the molten metal in the casting machine, pressed on a button, and the huge pile of pipes, cylinders, cauldrons, beams, and dials came to life and hissed and groaned and clanked, shuddering. Otto cast a blank test plate to try out the machine and the metal, picked it off the revolving casting cylinder with hands clad in asbestos gloves, and shoved it back into the melting pot again. He worked with a sure, deliberate leisureliness that soothed rather than aggravated McKabe. The dead giant was stirring – the first faint flutter. McKabe watched Otto. From a pile in one corner of the foundry Otto took a brown mat, shaped like a half cylinder, dimpled and corrugated with type impressions, baked stiff and hard like a biscuit. Otto ran his fingers deftly over the inside surface. 'Page 2,' he said, and slipped it into the casting cylinder, made an adjustment, locked it into place, and pressed a yellow button. The machine hissed and roared. Metal parts moved against one another noisily.

The cylinder made a half turn, and to its outside clung the curved metal plate with the negative type faces on the outside. Otto plucked it off, steaming hot, and carried it to the shaver and pulled the lever. Steel knives pared little curls of silver from the inside. The plate slid on down over the cooler. Jets of oil and water shot up into the inside.

'Come on, you punks, and grab it,' said Otto. 'What you want me to do – put it on the presses for you? I'm a stereotyper, not a pressman.'

Larkin laughed. 'Stick it on the conveyor,' he said. 'We'll catch it outside.' He and Farley turned and walked out. Otto set the plate on the moving rollers that led to the pressroom, and the thing travelled solemnly out through a hole in the steel wall into the pressroom. A tremendous excitement took hold of McKabe. The moving plate seemed to release him from a stupor into which pain and discouragement seemed to have sent him. Time, seven forty-three. 'At-a-boy, Otto!' he shouted. 'I'll get the story out as quick as I can! . . . Come on, Billers!'

They went upstairs in the freight elevator, stopped at the sixth floor, the composing room, where McKabe unloaded Billers. He had an uneasy feeling that all might not be well there, but after his victory in the pressroom, he lacked the courage momentarily to investigate personally.

'Go on,' he said to Billers. 'Get familiar with the place. I'll rush

the copy down in short takes. The 36-point machines are over
in that far corner. The 72 and 96 is hand-set.' It was seven forty-
four by the composing-room clock.

'O.K.,' said Billers; 'take your time. I can't start until eight
anyway.'

The elevator door started to close. 'What?' screamed McKabe.

'You heard me,' said Billers. 'Union rules. Keep your shirt on.'

The elevator door shut. McKabe cursed Billers so that the
elevator man turned and stared at him and then had to remind
him that they were at the seventh floor. McKabe staggered out
of the elevator and over to the city desk. It seemed to him that
he had been gone for hours. He expected to see it piled high with
A.P. and U.P. copy, but it wasn't. The press associations were
evidently having trouble on the story. Monk was asleep at the
desk, his head buried in his arms. McKabe shook him until he
awoke, blinking stupidly.

'Come on. Get on the job. Hustle out to the library and get me
all cuts on Feet Schindler – the big ones.'

Monk dragged his leaden feet. McKabe yelled: 'I said hustle!'
and threw another telephone book at him. Monk ducked and kept
on going at no faster speed. McKabe inserted a sheet of paper
in the swinging typewriter at the city desk and from sheer force
of habit typed in the upper left-hand corner: 'Schindler slaying,
McKabe REW Giller'; wrote: 'By Eugene McKabe' in the centre
of the page, and then exed it out. He was an editor and had no
authority for a by-line. He then wrote:

> *Silent night, Holy night. . . The world sleeps.*
> *Only the Holy Christ child keeps lonely vigil.*

*The carillons of St. Anthony's on the hill in Albany, New York,
rang out the old hymn in the cold, clear dawn before Christmas
and then were drowned out by the roar of four submachine-guns
exploding simultaneously in the dingy top-floor room of a cheap
boarding-house at——*

McKabe checked his notes to make sure of the address.

*The slugs that poured from the flaming cannons obliterated
Feet Schindler, the king cobra of the racket men, tore his girl,
Mimi Fredericks, to shreds, and blew the life out of two of his
henchmen, Little Hymie and Joe Colonno, in the greatest underworld slaughter since the St Valentine's massacre in Chicago.*

McKabe stopped and read it over and liked it. It was a good
lead. He knew that if old Bill Waters, chief of the copy desk,
were in the slot, he would probably cut out the stuff about the

Christmas hymn and the carillons. But he wasn't. McKabe was rewrite, copy desk, and editor in one. His head drooped and he braced himself on the typewriter, and then realised that the telephone on the city desk was ringing again. It shocked McKabe to consciousness again. He got the receiver off the hook and to his ear, and was surprised to hear his own voice saying somewhere inside his head: 'Desk – McKabe.'

The voice at the other end said: 'Hello. Hello. That you, McKabe? This is Billers, down in the composing room. Listen, you can't set no type here. The machines is all cold.'

'What? What the hell are you talking about?'

'I said: This is Billers, in the composing room. The lead in the pots is all cold. You can't set no type here.'

McKabe shouted into the telephone: 'I'll be down!' and hung up. Wrath cleared his head. Not set type? Not get that paper out? He would go down and beat Billers to a mush. He got up and made for the stairs. He saw Monk issuing from the library and called to him: 'Bring 'em down to the composing room, and bring that copy out of my typewriter.' He half fell down the flight of steps and burst into the composing room, a dishevelled madman, frightened the wits out of Billers, who was sitting on a make-up stone reading the paper and smoking a home-rolled cigarette.

'Now, what the hell is this?' gasped McKabe.

Billers nodded his head towards the silent rows of linotype machines.

'Them lead pots is cold. You can't set no type.'

'Well, heat 'em up!' snarled McKabe.

Billers spat into a type rack. 'Take you two hours,' he said.

'The hell it will! Stoke 'em up. Force 'em!'

'Can't. Gotta bring it up gradual. Else the lead won't set. Them machines is cold. Here, come over here and take a look.'

He and McKabe went over to the first of the linotype machines. Billers rubbed some oil and grease from the face of a small dial on the side. The needle registered two hundred and ten degrees.

'How much should it be?'

'Between six hundred and six-fifty. Take you two hours. You gotta bring them up gradual or you can't set no type. Might take a chance in a hour and a half. Don't figure it no use trying.'

McKabe looked helplessly up and down the rows of dead machines with their white keyboards grinning like mocking ivory teeth. A few hours ago they were hot. Men were sitting at them and sending the brass letter casts tinkling into the casting racks, moulding the bars of type, line after line. A few hours ago——

McKabe grasped at the thought. 'Wait a minute,' he said. 'Maybe they weren't all shut off at the same time. Maybe some or one worked later than others. We could bring that up. Come on.'

Billers came reluctantly, saying: 'They're cold, I tell you.' They went down the first line, scanning the temperature dials. One of them was up to two hundred and seventy. The second row of machines was stone-cold. McKabe was moving ahead of Billers. He had learned to read the dials. At the fourth machine in the last row he let out a whoop.

'Hey, Billers, four hundred and fifty degrees.'

'It'll take you an hour.'

'Make it in a half.'

'Takin' a chance she won't flow.'

'I'll take it. Boost her. Pour it to her.'

Billers looked at the machine. 'That's 14-point Vogue. That's an advertising type. You can't use that.' He saw the look in McKabe's eye and hurriedly pressed a switch. There was a low hum from the machine. Billers looked at an indicator, adjusted something, and shrugged his shoulders. 'It's O.K. with me. Only we don't do things like that in Milwaukee. I'll set it in 36-point Old English, if you say.'

'You're damn right you will . . . What are we going to do about inside heads?'

'Nothin',' said Billers. 'Them machines is all damn near froze. You got hand type, ain't you?'

'Yeah, 72 and 96. We'll smack the word SLAUGHTERED across page 1. Maybe we've got some 120-point. Come on, let's take a look and see what's in the pup.'

They went over to the corner of the room where the Sunday predate edition lay on the make-up stones, locked in the forms. McKabe's practised eye skimmed over the reverse type: BROKER IN LOVE-CULT TRAP. KISS SLAYER TO BE EXECUTED THIS WEEK. GOVERNOR ILL AT ALBANY. WIFE SUES RICH MATE. CHARGES BLONDE IN HIDE-OUT. TALE OF KENTUCKY VENGEANCE. CITY SLUMS BREED GANGSTERS. BABE RUTH NOT MURDEROUS HITTER OF YORE. The Sunday-feature headlines ranged from 36-point Bodoni to 48-point Chelt and Century. McKabe whipped out a pencil and began to scribble on the back of an envelope. Finally he handed it to Billers. It read: 'TRAP GANGSTER AT ALBANY HIDE-OUT – EXECUTED IN MURDEROUS VENGEANCE.'

'Here,' said, 'fix that up. She'll go in two lines of three-column.' Billers looked at it stupidly. 'The machine is cold——' he began.

'Dig it out of the pup and saw it up!' howled McKabe. 'It's all in there. What the hell kind of printers do they have these days? Here, pick out that BROKER IN LOVE-CULT TRAP, and saw off the TRAP. Get it?'

Billers mumbled something about Milwaukee, unlocked the form, lifted the line out, and took it over to the saw. McKabe teetered back to the make-up desk, where Monk waited with the cuts.

'Gimme,' he said. He spread the metal likenesses of the dead gangster out before him on the desk. There was a big three-column cut of Feet's head with a cigarette drooping from the weak mouth. He wished it were five columns. There was another three-column full-length of Feet and his girl Mimi. Three and three were six – one column too many. Across the bottom of page 1 of the edition was a five-column cut showing Feet and Mimi and Little Hymie and Joe Colonno in the courtroom at Kinderhook. It was too deep, however. From the other end of the room came the ring and whine of the metal saw as Billers cut through the headlines: 'Wee-e-e-e-ow! Wee-e-e-e-e-ow!' McKabe held the cuts stupidly in his hand for a moment while a spasm of pain swept over him. 'Wee-e-e-e-ow!' McKabe came to life again, fighting the pain down, ripped open the desk drawer, and took out a large white sheet the size of the front page, criss-crossed with red lines into squares and marked: 'Dummy – Page 1.' He laid the three cuts on the sheet and with a pencil and rule marked off the overshoot on each. He cut Feet out of the deep three-column, leaving Mimi in two-column size, with a few pieces of Feet on the border, and laughed at the idea of Feet being dismembered again. He cut the legs off all of them on the five-column courtroom scene. Then he hobbled down to Billers.

'I can't find MURDEROUS,' said Billers.

'On page 34, Sports,' snapped McKabe. 'Never mind that a second. Crop these cuts for me where I got 'em marked. Saw 'em off. Step on it.'

'R-r-r-r-ring! Wee-e-e-e-ow!' McKabe caught 'Schindler Separated from His Sweetheart' as the saw bit through, and fired the piece into a nearby hellbox. Billers cropped the other one.

'That's page 1,' said McKabe grimly.

'Ain't you gonna have nothing tells who they are – whataya call 'em – captions? Or anything?' asked Billers.

'Hell with the captions,' said McKabe. 'Everybody knows who they are. When I smack that line SLAUGHTERED across the top of the page, they'll get it. Get these lines sawed up.'

McKabe returned to the desk. He dared not exult. It was too

soon. If the lead didn't heat up, if something went wrong with the casting or the presses – two men, and both drunk, to plate up – But in his ears already rang the cry of the newsboys: 'Extra! Extra! Special Extra!' A sudden panic laid hold of him. What newsboys? Where would he get them? What good was a newspaper on the pressroom floor? He grabbed the telephone on the make-up desk.

'Hello, honey – McKabe. Listen, get me Jim Dixey, the circulation manager, at his home. Hurry it.' He heard her dial the call. A man's voice answered the telephone sleepily.

'Hello, Jim. This is McKabe. Are you awake? Get me now. Hell of a story. Feet Schindler and his mob knocked off in Albany. I'm gonna get a paper out and——'

'Wait a minute – wait a minute. Who is this?'

'McKabe. I——'

'What's the matter? You drunk, McKabe? What time is it? You can't get a paper out now. Why the hell didn't you call me earlier?'

'Listen, you dumb Irish——' raged McKabe. 'Did you hear me tell you I was going to get a paper out? You and every other dumb so-and-so have been telling me I can't for the last hour. I'm getting it out, I tell you – getting it out!' His voice rose hysterically.

There was a silence from the other end of the wire. Then: 'At-a-boy, Mac. How soon you going to be running?'

McKabe looked up at the clock. It was twenty-one minutes past eight. 'Half an hour with any luck, three-quarters, maybe sooner. The afternoon papers can't move up more than forty minutes.'

'You gimme the papers. I'll get 'em around.'

McKabe was suddenly suspicious. 'You ain't humouring me, are you? I tell you I ain't drunk – I'm——'

'Listen,' said Dixey. 'If you're drunk or kidding me, when I get there I'll beat your head off. Go ahead, get her rolling.'

Get her rolling. Rolling, rolling, rolling – those dumb, immovable, lethargic giants below. 'Billers! Billers!' bawled McKabe. 'Come on down here! We got to get her rolling!'

Billers came strolling until McKabe bawled: 'Move!' at him. Then he shuffled. They went over to the linotype machine. The lead in the pot was a liquid, glistening silver. The dial read six hundred and ten degrees. Billers sat down at the keyboard, shrugged his shoulders, and said: 'I don't think she'll be any good. It come up too fast.' Then he ran his fingers over the keys lightly. The type casts tinkled musically into the rack. McKabe leaned over to the casing to read the line: 'Now is the time for all good men to come to the ai——' Billers stepped on the pedal; the machine hissed and clacked, chuttered, and then delivered the silvery bar of type. McKabe pounced on it. It was so hot it burned the ends of his fingers, but he held it. Billers scrutinised it. The type face was a little pock-marked, but legible.

'Let's go!' shouted McKabe.

'O.K.,' said Billers. 'You got the copy?'

'Sweet Peter!' said McKabe. 'The copy! Here, I'll dictate it.'

'Dictate it? You mean, tell me as you go along? I never done that in Milwaukee.'

'You'll do it here. Set it in two columns. You ready? I'll go slow.' He remembered every word of his lead: 'Silent night, Holy night——' What he hadn't been able to write upstairs through fear and exhaustion, he now told to the printer at the machine. They were a mad pair – this McKabe, gaunter and greyer than ever, his eyes nearly disappearing in the shady caverns of the sockets, his chair dishevelled, his lips pulled away from tobacco-stained teeth, seated on a stool, doubled over, telling in short, bitten-off sentences the story of the shambles in Albany, and Billers, the nondescript printer, a big, scraggly man with a large, expressionless face running pudgy fingers delicately over the hair-trigger keys, unemotional and uninterested.

Then followed a period that to McKabe was the blackest – the make-up. Billers had resolved himself into a slow-motion picture. He refused to be hurried. He was that most dreaded of make-up men – an old maid at the stone. He puttered, he fussed, he straightened, he measured, he went on long expeditions down to the end of the composing room for rules and dashes. Often when on the make-up trick, McKabe would dream a nightmare in which the edition was an hour late and he stood in front of an empty page while printers wandered about and did nothing to fill it. All make-up editors are subject to the same dream, which wakes them in a chilly sweat, reaching for their watches to see if it is really past edition time.

Billers was the dream come true. McKabe pleaded, argued, bullied, screamed, raged, begged. Billers moved unhurried. Against his lethargic movements the hands of the clock spun around the dial: Seventeen minutes to nine . . . sixteen minutes to nine . . . fifteen minutes to nine . . . fourteen; thirteen. What if by some miracle an afternoon paper had managed to get on the street with his story?

'What you want to do with this divorce story? We need more room,' Billers would ask.

'Yank it out. Get it out of there. Come on, Billers, for God's sake, hurry a little.'

'You can't throw it out without you break up page 4. It jumps to page 4.'

'I know it does! The hell with it!'

'You gonna let the jump ride without what goes ahead?'

'Yes . . . Yes . . . Yes!' Once Billers had slid his make-up rule into his pocket and said: 'I don't got to let you talk to me like that. I don't work here anyway. I quit.'

McKabe practically went down on his knees to him. The composing room was new to Billers and he had to look for everything he needed. The inside drop heads that McKabe had taken from the pup had to be resawed to fit. Five minutes were wasted looking for the 120-point type for page 1. Once the half-crazed McKabe picked up a paragraph of type and jammed it in the page, and Billers quit again, and meant it.

'You touched type,' he said flatly. 'I quit. That's against the union.'

McKabe chased him, a heavy leather type-levelling mallet in his hand. Frightened, Billers came back. At five minutes after nine the two pages were finally locked up; page 3 a solid mass of black display type with crazy, odd-sized headlines, no two words in the same type; page 1, sawed-off, captionless cuts beneath the one startling word. Otto poked his round, sweating face through the composing-room door.

McKabe greeted him eagerly. 'O.K., Otto. Just locked 'em up. All set, down below?'

Otto shook his head. 'I didn't dare tell you,' he said, 'but Larkin and Farley said what was the use and was gonna go home, unless I come right up and told you. Page 20 is lost. We can't find the mat.'

McKabe only nodded his head. 'O.K., Otto. Shove these two pages through. Get going!'

'But whatta you going to do about page 20? The mat's gone.'

McKabe laughed loudly. 'Go in without it. It's only the editorial page. Do you think you're gonna stop me now?'

'But you gotta have a plate, Mac.'

'All right, cast a blank one. Cast page 18 twice. Cast the calendar. Cast anything.'

'It's gonna look funny.'

'Hah!' exploded McKabe. 'If you want to see something funny, wait till you see these two pages. But it's a paper, Otto! Shove it through!'

McKabe and Billers went over to the steam table and watched Otto lay the composition mat over the form, cover it with a blanket, and send it humming through the steel rollers, which exerted two tons of pressure and stamped the impressions of the reverse type into a positive on the mat. Otto started to dump the mats down the chute to the foundry, but McKabe stopped him.

'Don't do that! Something might happen to them. We'll carry them down.'

Otto shrugged his shoulders. They rang for the elevator. While they waited for it, McKabe was sick. Billers held him up and said: 'Why don't ya take it easy now and lie down?'

'Stop it, will ya?' said McKabe when he could talk again. 'She ain't rollin' yet.'

It was seven minutes after nine by the foundry clock. Under the blue mercury lights McKabe looked like a corpse. He held on to a steel table while Otto methodically sent the two precious mats through the mat-former, which shaped them into half-cylinders, oiled them, and then dried them on the gas-heated scorcher, which turned them out looking like well-done waffles. He put them through the automatic plater. The hot lead hissed into the cylinders. The machine chaffered. Six minutes to a plate. Nineteen minutes after nine. McKabe clung motionless to his support, his deep-sunk eyes following every move Otto made. How much had those afternoon rags been able to move up their edition time?

'You got any choice what page you want to duplicate?' Otto asked. He had to ask twice before McKabe heard him. He shook his head. Otto selected one at random.

'Page 18. Moider mystery,' he said. 'They can read it twice.' He slipped it into the automatic moulder and then stuck his head down by the door through which the plates travelled and bawled: 'Starter coming!' McKabe pricked up his ears at that, but was too far gone to exult. The pain from his stomach had exhausted the last of his strength. Otto looked at him as he whipped the plate from the cylinder and sent it through the shaver and cooler. He gave it a final inspection and set it on the rollers. It sailed out of the foundry. McKabe followed it with his eyes.

'You don't feel good, do you?' said Otto.

'I'm all right. What can go wrong now?'

'Plenty,' said Otto, 'but maybe your luck will hold out. Want a hand in?'

He went to McKabe and slipped his arm around his shoulder and they hobbled on to the pressroom floor. It was nine thirty-one. Farley was in the bowels of the number-four press, plating up. Larkin stood at the row of red, yellow, and blue buttons.

'You're plenty lucky,' Larkin said. 'Number 4 had paper on her rollers. Me and Farley never could have got the rolls on alone. . . . What's the matter with you?'

'He don't feel very good,' Otto explained.

'This is a hell of a looking page,' commented Farley from inside the press. 'What do you want to print a thing like that for?'

The dull remarks in the quiet pressroom brought some strength back to McKabe. 'Roll her!' he shouted. 'Get her rollin'! What the hell are you waiting for? You got your paper! Roll her!'

Larkin shrugged his shoulders and pushed a red button. The white light bulbs alongside the press turned to red. A bell rang long and loudly, and as it stopped the sound changed to a low, sweet hum, which grew higher and higher in pitch. The wheels began to turn slowly and smoothly. Countless rocker arms, pistons, tappets, and levers went through their appointed motions. The sheets of paper, wide, flat, and white, stretched over the rollers and spindles, began to travel to their common meeting-place, dead white until they reached the turning cylinders, passed over them, and came away grey with print.

McKabe could see the individual pages as they travelled past his eyes. Then the hum grew louder and the press started to clatter as it speeded up. The printed paper turned to grey ribbons that hurled themselves from all directions into the vortex of the machine. The noise became a battery of machine-guns, and then, as the press rolled into high, turned into deep, rolling thunder that flooded McKabe and went to his core like a symphony. He still stood swaying in the centre of the now quivering room. He couldn't even see the astonishing rows or aisles of neatly folded papers that began to climb irresistibly from the mouth of the press, even rows with every fiftieth one turned crooked to mark the count. He didn't see the black headline, SLAUGHTERED, or the weak face of the dead Schindler, or Otto and Larkin and Farley and Billers, each with a paper, looking through it and shaking their heads.

He felt and heard rather only the sweet, shaking rumbling of the rolling press, and seemed to hear, too, the orchestration in it, the clattering of the trucks bearing the extra edition to the news-stands, the cries of the newsboys: 'Hyah! Special extra!' The rumble of the subways, the chaffering of the submachine-guns that, a few hours ago, had blasted the life out of four people, the scream of the stricken girl, the motors of the vanishing murder cars. All of these he heard in the counterpoint of the whizzing, whirling, spinning, pounding machinery. Papers! Extra! Murder! Exclusive! Paper? Yes, sir. Special extra. Two cents. Only the

Blade's got it . . . Silent night! Holy night! Feet Schindler and his girl and two bodyguards butchered . . . Noel. Noel . . . Only in the *Blade*! . . . Give it to 'em! Bang-bang-bang-bang! Extra! Extra!

Dixey, the circulation manager, came into the pressroom, rubbing his hands.

'O.K., kid. You've done it,' he said to McKabe. 'The country edition of the *Standard* is up, but it hasn't got a line. The *News-Beacon* won't be up for half an hour. It's a screwy-looking paper, but it's news.'

McKabe began to laugh softly and to himself at first, and then, gaining like the press, louder and louder. He dropped to his knees and swayed there, still laughing. 'Ha, ha, ha, ha! Ha-a, ha-ha-ha-ha!' His long, bony finger was pointed again, but this time at number four, the giant of steel and copper and iron and brass, the glorious rolling press that was thundering out his story, twenty thousand an hour.

'Ya big bum, ya!' he bawled. 'Ya big bum! I made ya roll!'

Flood

••

FLOOD *is one of a series of newspaper stories written as was*
MCKABE *around the fictitious 'Daily Blade' which was really the
tabloid New York 'Daily News.' In this series the same set of
people appear in different stories, not always playing a leading
role, but forming a kind of a cast of characters who eventually
became familiar to the readers of the 'Saturday Evening Post.'
Two of the principles in these stories were Perry Brown and
Rusty McGowan, reporters on the Blade. It was an accepted fact
throughout these series that Perry and Rusty were engaged to
be married.*

    FLOOD *was one of those stories that keep on happening inside
of you all the time they are being written, and that is about the
most I seem to be able to remember about it, which is strange
because I know the piece meant a lot to me during the time I was
writing it and I carried it around the country with me, doing
snatches here and there and never quite being able to live outside
its atmosphere.*

    *This was a different kind of experience and led to a different
kind of story. Many, in fact most, of these newspaper stories were
founded upon actual news events, explosions, fires, kidnappings,
destructions, and the tales were often based upon true adventures
that some of my reporter friends experienced in covering these.
But while the flood itself was a natural cataclysm the things that
happened to Perry Brown during his abortive covering of the
story were things that were taking place somewhere inside of me,
or once the story had begun to take shape were dredged up from
dark and obscure corners of the subconscious.*

    *A psychiatrist would probably be able to reveal the sources of
this story in a jiffy, but I suspect that the revelations would
probably be less interesting than the story itself which has remained one of the few favourites of mine of all those I have
written. I write 'few' advisedly for usually I find a return to stories
I have written a most painful experience.*

More interesting, I think, and particularly to the would-be writer or student of writing is the lesson I learnt from FLOOD *and one which was to save me a good deal of time and money.*

At the time I wrote FLOOD *I was still suffering from the delusion that to be a writer one had to have experiences, and since I had decided that I didn't wish to be merely a writer of sports stories, a field in which I had some fourteen years of experience, I needed to broaden my field and thus came to the conclusion that the way to broaden it was to be a reporter myself and thus come into daily contact with something spelled 'life' but in that context usually pronounced 'laife.'*

Captain Patterson, publisher of the 'Daily News,' must have thought me utterly mad when in 1937, having concluded a successful summer abroad as a freelance writer and sold everything I had written, I returned to the United States late in October back to the 'Daily News' which I had quit as the highest-paid sports writer in the country and asked them to give me a job at the Guild minimum, which was $70 a week, as an ordinary city-side news reporter and leg man. Having written successful fiction about newspaper reporters for three years I was now determined to turn the clock back and become one myself.

Captain Patterson smiled and complied with my request and so off I went bucketing about the country covering strikes, and murders, labour leaders and politicians, burglaries and trials and all manner of things, and all the while FLOOD *was gnawing at my vitals and wanting to be written. And it had nothing whatsoever to do with what I was doing or seeing those days, but only with emotions and fantasies that were going on inside of me and which I felt a deep-seated urge to express. None of the things in* FLOOD *ever happened beyond the natural catastrophe after which the story is named, nor up to that time or since had I or have I ever seen or covered one of those disastrous Mississippi floods.*

But how fatuously proud I was of myself when at last I was really a reporter, taking assignments from the city desk and earning my $70 a week. And when one day, thanks to the fortunate scoring of a beat, Captain Patterson raised my salary to $100 a week I was as pleased and excited as the day I landed my first short story in the 'Saturday Evening Post,' and went bucketing on with even greater energy to try to absorb more 'life' and more 'copy.'

And all through this period I was stealing time during train or 'plane rides, or in grubby hotel rooms late at night after I had filed my copy on whatever I was covering to work on this wholly imaginative FLOOD *story, with which its people and its theme of*

*comfort a woman can bring a man gave me no rest until it was
finished.* FLOOD *apparently got itself written in spite of myself and
it took me another year before I was able to appreciate the idiocy
of my behaviour and realise that writers listen to or look at what
goes on within them. Writers write.*

*This truth should not be confused with the necessity for legiti-
mate research for accuracy of background in telling a story. And
I never fail to research a story idea or novel thoroughly, either by
travel or reading or study, but I wasted several years, I think, in
finding out that it is a little silly to place the horse before the cart.
First one ought to have something to say and an overwhelming
desire to say it. There is then time enough to go about acquiring
the knowledge and experience to enable one to say it well.*

FLOOD

Nobody ever found out what happened to Perry Brown on the
flood assignment down through Ohio, Kentucky, and Tennessee.
He came back to the *Blade* office at half-past eleven one night to
get his mail and had very little to say.

He had been gone fifteen days and had filed exactly four stories.
There had been one good one from Cincinnati on the fire that
had devastated the business section, and two from Louisville
before all the wires went down. And one night a radio amateur
located in Winesville, Kentucky, had made an abortive effort to
transmit a story to the *Blade* short-wave receiver, purporting to
come from one Perry Brown, but there was bad static and interference, and the amateur suddenly went off the air and could not
be located again.

There had been a hiatus of some seven or eight days when they
did not hear from him at all and were a little worried about him,
but then came an appeal from Memphis from Perry for funds,
although there was no story. And shortly after that he came
home.

Reyburn, managing editor of the *Blade,* was curious and asked
Perry Brown, in a friendly enough fashion, what he had been
up to, and to give an account of himself. Perry looked up from
the envelopes he was examining. He was pale and looked older.
He was a big man, and bulky, but he was thinner, and his clothes

fitted him less than they ever did; seemed to hang on him instead.
He replied by asking Reyburn a question: 'Where's Rusty?'

'She's still in New Milford on the Agathy trial,' Reyburn replied.
'She was worried until we heard from you from Memphis. What
happened to you? You look as though you had been put through
a wringer.'

'Nothing,' said Perry curtly, and began to stack his envelopes.
Reyburn grinned at him. 'Didn't like our flood, eh?' he
said.

Perry Brown swore bitterly, and Reyburn suddenly saw that
something lay behind his eyes. Perry then said: 'I wish to God
you had never sent me out on that story,' stuffed his mail into
his overcoat pocket, and went out of the office. And that was
the last thing anybody ever heard him say about the assignment.
A week or so later he seemed quite normal, except that when
Rusty McGowan was in the room with him, he never took his
eyes from her.

After they had covered the flood and the subsequent fire in
Cincinnati, Perry Brown and Al Vogel, the fat photographer, went
to Louisville, where they became separated. Vogel was having
his troubles getting his pictures back out of the flood area, and
Perry was having his own problems piecing together a coherent
story out of the chaos of rising water, fear, and rumour. The city
officials and the Army engineers were working against growing
terror and panic, and the press was not welcome.

There was a curious quality to this horrible rising of the Ohio
River that defied Perry. He had covered floods before and had
seen those dreadful misshapen islands in muddy water, made
by slanting roof tops of houses showing just above the surface,
but about this one there was a cold, frightful relentlessness that
he could not get on to paper. From that moment he arrived he
never moved without fear in his heart. The ceaseless downpour
of rain from heavy grey skies helped this. Unless the rain stopped,
the end of the world was at hand. Water beneath, water above,
Perry felt the stratum in which he still lived and breathed, and
witnessed death and life, narrowing, closing in.

Everything that was done seemed helpless and futile because
of the rain and the rising river. He watched whole families,
miserable, frightened, shivering, panic-faced, moved to higher
ground, and knew that if the rain did not stop, soon there would
be no more higher ground, that earth water and sky water would
meet and the world in between would cease.

Perry had got a break when he encountered a colonel of

engineers he had met on another story, and the colonel had remembered him and let him ride south with him, skirting the flood, in an Army car, and so deeper into new flood area than any other newspaperman had been. And it was while floating in a small hired rowboat over the remains of a little town called Winesville that Perry first experienced the vanishing conscious-ness of any other world beyond that one which was drowned in moving water, death, and desolation.

A unit of newsreel men who somehow, too, had penetrated to Winesville had captured a corpse. It had caught their cameras unprepared on its lonely, bobbing ride, ferryless, across the Styx, and they were hiding it close to and screened by the gunwales of one of their boats until they could retrain their lenses properly. It had been an old Negro dressed in overalls and a cotton shirt. Their camera boat was held fast to what seemed to be a brick wall rising out of the water, but wasn't, because it was the second storey of a bank building. There was a window just around the corner with gold lettering on it: A. A. Clakins, d.d.s., Crowns, Bridgework, Office Hours 9 a.m. – 3 p.m.

The newsreel men were frightened at first when they saw that Perry knew, and clustered around in their boat until they recog-nised him. He had seen them before. They were a crew from Imperial Picture News. He lifted his face out of the collar of his slicker, in which it had been buried, and called over: 'A little ghouling, boys?'

One of the cameramen, a big chap, with the rain streaming down his face, called back: 'How'd you get here? Hey, nix; row off a little. Don't look. If one of those soldier boys got wise to us, he might do a little shooting. They killed a looter about a mile down, an hour ago. We're just gonna float this guy by again for a shot.'

'Jeepers,' said Perry, 'and we're supposed to be hard-boiled.'

'What the hell,' said the cameraman. 'He don't care any more. Row off a little, willya?'

Perry put pressure on his oars, moved the boat across what had been the main street, and with short tugs kept the nose of the skiff in the current. Two of the camera crew in another boat began to row slowly up the street. One of them was leaning over the side of the boat, holding on to something in the water. They just kept on rowing, and pretty soon the man who had been leaning over the side was sitting up straight, and a dark object came floating down with the stream, turning over and over with a queer, hapless grace. The large cameraman in the other boat had his right eye jammed against the rubber-cupped finder of his

C

camera and was grinding rhythmic circles, panning his lens just a little ahead of the floating body.

It was then that Perry Brown suddenly was astonished to find himself seriously wondering wherever they were going to show the pictures they were making. Who would look at them? The earth was laid waste by water. It was impossible to think of dry streets and moving-picture houses, and men and women standing in line waiting to buy tickets, and automobiles passing, and boys on bicycles, and traffic policemen standing at intersections. He looked down the watery avenue of what had once been a town. There was the top of a curved electric sign sticking up above the water, with the letters *BIJOU* legible in red and orange-coloured electric bulbs. Perry's quick mind supplied the *U* that lay just beneath the yellowish surface of the stream, and his imagination created an unbelievable, forgotten picture of the Bijou Theatre on Saturday night, with slick-haired boys, and girls with bright-red lips crowding the lobby and being sucked in through the portals as the water was now sucked down the main street.

The dark rotating object passed his boat and kept on going. The movie men, their shot recorded, were letting it go. Two militiamen in a boat, with rifles slung across their backs, shouted up at the newsreel men: 'Hey, you guys! Lay offa them kinda pictures!'

The big cameraman waved back. 'O.K., O.K., buddy!' and they started to row away, but Perry noticed that one of the other men was grinding away at the camera with a long-focus lens. The militiamen stopped Perry's boat and examined his military pass. It was then three o'clock in the afternoon. The grey rain was falling slantwise because there was a wind that was beginning to freshen into a gale. An old motorboat came chugging past. A man in a black slicker with a red cross on his arm was at the wheel. The boat was low in the water with the weight of its burden of men, women, and children wrapped in sodden blankets. Only the men and the children were looking ahead. There were four women in the boat, and all of them were gazing backwards in the direction from whence they had come.

Perry let his boat drift with the sluggish surge of the flood stream. He heard some yelling and guided his boat in the direction from which it came, down a waterway that had evidently been a side street off the main thoroughfare. There was a cluster of boats there manned by natives in thigh boots, slickers, and caps. They were evacuating men, women, and children trapped on the upper floors of houses. The first rise of the water must have been extraordinarily rapid in Winesville, from the number of people trapped in houses and driven to the second storey and, in some cases, the roof.

The yelling was coming from a man who was hanging out of a window a few houses down. The water-level was about five feet below the sill. He was gaunt and unshaven, with sparse grey-black hair, dressed in trousers, collarless shirt, and an open vest.

He had his hands cupped to his mouth and was bawling: 'Get a doctor, quick! I gotta get a doctor! D'ya hear down there? Get a doctor! She's gotta have a doctor! Get a doctor over here!'

Nobody paid any attention to him. Perry asked one of the men in the rescue boats where he could find a doctor. The man shrugged. 'Dunno! I ain't seen a doctor for nine hours. We could use a dozen of them. They had 'em at the city hall, but that's under now. That guy's been yelling for three hours. Wife's gonna have a baby. We've had a call in for a doctor with the Red Cross soon as they can spare one. They're all busy.'

Perry Brown rowed over beneath the window. The man leaned down eagerly.

'For heaven's sakes, hurry, doc! It's almost here! Make your boat fast to the bottom of the shutter! I'll give you a hand up!'

Perry called up: 'I'm not a doctor. They've sent for one from the Red Cross. I'll try to get you one.'

The man suddenly lost all control and began to scream curses at the top of his lungs, interspersed with cries for a doctor, as though the very loudness of his voice would bring him what he wanted. He was completely in the grip of panic. From behind him within the room came a woman's cry. Perry wanted to dig his oars into the water and pull hard and keep on pulling until he no longer heard those cries. He found himself thinking suddenly of white-tiled operating-rooms and nickelled tables and instruments, and cool surgeons in white, and blessed anaesthetic. But that was a dream of ages yet to come. This was the Deluge. So must Leah and Rebecca and Mary have cried their agony in lonely huts when God was angered and His waters covered the earth.

The man reappeared at the window, his face livid. He had a shotgun in his hands. He screamed: 'Damn you, doc! Get in here or I'll blow your head off! I'll blow your head off! D'ya hear?'

The shotgun, at the time, didn't impress Perry. His mind was already made up. He fastened the painter of his boat to the shutter and shipped his oars. He said: 'Put that gun away, you fool, and give me a hand.'

The man reached down and hoisted Perry up over the sill like a child, and Perry was a big man. A woman lay on a white iron bedstead over in a corner of the room. Her face was white and wet with sweat, and her mouth was twisted, her untidy hair damp and loose. Perry took off his coat. His knees were trembling and he was afraid that he would not be able to walk. When he was a cub reporter he had many times seen interns arrive, drop off the backs of still-moving ambulances and make kerbstone deliveries in streets, taxicabs, or drugstores. His mind, suddenly, with amazing clarity, reviewed for him those things which must be done. He moved over towards the bed rolling up his sleeves . . .

Some time later another man came through the window. He had a small black bag with him. He saw Perry and said: 'Ah, doctor, I see you got here ahead of me.'

Perry said: 'I'm not a doctor. I did what I could. For heaven's sakes, take over. I want to get out of here.'

The doctor shrugged his shoulders, looked surprised, and said: 'There isn't much more to do except get 'em out of here. The water's still rising. . . . H'm'm'm. That isn't a bad-looking boy.'

Perry went out the window and dropped into his boat. He felt sick and shocked. When the world went back to the waters from whence it came, no one took death or life seriously any more. He dug his oars into the water, now choppy with the high wind, and let the rain sting into his face. He paid no heed to the direction in which he was going. He didn't care. He was himself close to panic. He felt his tiny boat bobbing under him, and imagined it was the dead streets beneath, struggling to free themselves from the choking water. Chairs floated alongside in the water, and signs, and barrels and boxes, and soggy lumps of feathers that had been chickens. The incessant rain was heavy and made his oar handles slippery. He grated one of them against a piano that was floating on its back, with its ivory teeth showing, and nearly lost it. A dressmaker's dummy stuck its torso half out of the water, and he passed a waterlogged perambulator.

He was conscious that he was suddenly making unusual speed, but not aware why. He thought it was just the desperate power he was putting into the short oars that were always coming out of the wooden rowlocks. It was not until too late that he discovered that he had been rowing directly towards the river. The Army men had warned him against it. With the river gorge under him, he found himself sucked along and helpless amid the forlorn flotsam of the flood. He tried to stem against the current, nearly turned the boat over, and finally spun around in a dizzy circle, caught in a whirlpool. The wind had lashed the surface of the water into wavelets that were dangerous, because they hid the debris and floating objects that might upset him. Between rain clouds and twilight, it was getting dark.

Perry tried pulling across stream, and was succeeding when the current caught him again and whirled him into the top of a tree that showed just above the surface. A branch struck him a glancing blow on the back of the head and knocked him flat on his face in the bottom of the boat, less than half conscious. When he sat up again, his nose was bleeding. The boat was turning around and around with the current. Both oars were gone. It was still raining. It was dark. Only occasional objects rising from the surface of the water were darker than the sky and the horizon, and therefore faintly distinguishable.

There were no sounds but the rain and the wind and the rush of the stream beneath him, and the scraping of his sodden shoes on the bottom of the boat as he shifted his position. He had a tin dipper in the skiff, and he bailed it fairly dry, and then lay down in the bottom of the boat for better security of balance. He felt that he could no longer sit up in the black void through which he was plunging without falling over out of the boat.

He then gave way to the curiously gentle and soothing sensation of being a lost atom, utterly without power to help himself or shape his course. When his boat banged and scraped against solid objects, he found himself wondering vaguely what they were, and once he struck against something that was soft and there followed a great splashing. At that time, and during that passage, he was not afraid, because there was nothing of which to be afraid. Perry had found that fear was very often occasioned by responsibility and having to do something about something. There was nothing he could do in his present situation but wait for morning. He must have slept for a while – how long he did not know, because the luminosity was worn off his watch dial and it was pitch-black when he woke up. The nearest light seemed to be miles away on an elevation, and he caught the flash of a distant airways beacon.

He was not afraid even then; had no premonition of danger or disaster until his boat suddenly bumped, grated, rolled over, and was gone. Even in the fraction of a second's time occupied by the disaster, Perry was somehow prepared for the cold shock of the water, and kept his head above the surface. He began to fight for his life immediately. He lashed out in the darkness with his left arm and smashed his hand against something wooden and solid, hurting it and running splinters into the palm. He moved his legs automatically to keep his head above water, twisted around, and thrust out more gingerly with his right hand.

He encountered solid wood again, but ridged. His fingers sought for something to cling to, but the current was sweeping him onwards. Then his grasping right hand and arm suddenly thrust through a void; the ridged wood was no longer there, and the next moment he felt a hard blow on the muscle of his upper arm. Involuntarily he contracted it. The palm of his hand came into contact with a smooth surface.

His arm was around a projection of some kind – what, he could not imagine; but the desperate passage was momentarily stopped. The current sucked and tore at his legs and body. He held fast. He tried to think. It seemed impossible to marshal thoughts against the vindictive tugging and sucking at his body, the cold heavy grip of the water, sluicing rain, and the blackness of the night. He was a thinking animal, but the attacks upon him were all physical and came out of darkness. He finally said aloud to himself: 'I still have my hat on. That's funny.' Something floating past batted him violently on the shoulder and nearly dislodged him. And now that he was no longer moving through the water, he was badly frightened. His right shoulder felt numb and he did not know how long his strength would hold. He manœuvred to get his left hand up to reinforce his right in its grasp of the unknown projection. His fingers closed over what seemed to be a narrow strip of wood with an indentation running down the centre in which lay what seemed to be cord.

His fingertips suddenly created a picture in his mind, and his free hand, hurt though it was, wandered avidly to verify it. It was true. His right arm had been thrust through the open window of a half-submerged house – probably the second storey – curled around the side, and his hand was touching a wall. Cautiously he felt for the sill with his elbow. But it was more than two feet below the surface, and he could not reach it and keep his head clear. Was there room overhead? He felt for it, but apparently the entire window was out. He thrust against the powerful current with all his strength, pulling with his right arm, pushing with his left, kicking desperately with his legs against the heavy drag of shoes and pants and enveloping slicker. He banged his knee against the sunken sill, but found a purchase on it and got a leg over, and suddenly the pressure on his body was gone. He was in still water up to his waist, but his feet were on solid flooring. He was inside a room of some sort. His legs and whole body began to tremble with fatigue and nervous reaction. He was so cold that his teeth chattered. But he could think again. The immediate danger was over, he knew.

Was there another floor overhead, or was he at the top of the

house? Was there any way to reach the roof? Was the water still
rising, and how quickly? He felt that the last was not immediately
important, because remaining in the icy water much longer
would kill him eventually anyway. He knew that somehow he
must go higher, where it was dry. It was at that time that he
first heard the scraping sound from overhead, or thought he did.

Perry waited and listened. He heard rain falling on a roof, and
the rushing and gurgling of the flood outside, and his own splash-
ings as he moved closer to the window and jammed his legs up
against the space below the sill to steady himself. He tried
desperately to stop the chatter of his teeth. He thought that it
might have been the branch of a floating tree scraping against
the side of the house. Then he heard it again. It did come from
overhead and inside the house. If there were human beings above,
they might help him.

He called out into the darkness: 'Hey! Hey! Is there anybody
up there? Can you hear me?'

His voice sounded dead to him. He felt that it had hardly
carried beyond the confines of the window-frame, that the darkness was stifling it.

He heard no reply, and called louder, so that his throat hurt
him and his voice cracked like that of a boy. 'Is there anybody
up there? Hey! Is there anybody there? Can you hear me up
there?'

He heard the scraping sound again and then, directly over his
head, the noise of a window being raised. Then a woman
answered him. She said: 'Who is it? Who's there?'

The voice was low and rapid, as though the woman's heart
were in her throat, as though she were frightened, yet eager. It
was throaty and half whispered. She called again: 'Is anybody
there?'

Perry Brown stuck his head out of the window, holding on with
both hands to the lintel. The rain drove into his face. He could
see nothing.

'I am!' he shouted. 'Can I get up there? Where are you? I lost
my boat! I caught the window as I was being swept by! Is anybody up there with you?'

The woman replied: 'I'm alone! Where are you from?' Her
voice was heavy and languid, with the speech of the district.

Perry called back: 'I'm a reporter! Newspaper! I got caught
in the current! My boat rolled over! Is it dry up there? Can I
get up?'

'You can try! I'm in an attic room! Reach up!'

Perry, feeling his way carefully, climbed to the underwater

sill, his back to the flood. The water pulled at his legs again. He
held on to the side of the window with his right hand and felt
above him with his aching left. He touched a woman's hand and
arm, newly wet with rain. Then, out of the water-laden darkness,
something curious fell athwart his face, startling him. But it was
soft and had a strange, damp fragrance. In the blackness his
perceptions sharpened. He realised that it was a woman's hair.
The arm was firm and round, the hand rough. He pictured the
colour of the hair. Because of the darkness that surrounded him
he saw it as glossy black. He took in his the hand that he had
found in the darkness, and it gave him a queer strength and
comfort.

He said: 'Howdy. My name's Perry Brown.'

The woman said nothing, but he thought he heard her sob, or
cry out softly. Her fingers in his were suddenly limp. Perry said:
'Buck up, sister. There's two of us now.' He released her hand
and reached above. He felt the sill of a small window. It was
not far above his head. He wondered whether he could make it,
with the water below sucking and dragging at his legs, and
hampered by the weight of his wet clothing. Then he found an
iron bracket sticking out from the side of the window, tested it,
and found it firm. If he could make it on the first pull-up, he
might scramble through before his strength failed.

He said: 'Better duck back inside. I'm going to try to make it.
I'll either make it on the first try or not at all. When I say "Three,"
that's it.'

He relinquished his grip on the side of the window with his
right hand, seized the iron bracket, and grasped the edge of the
sill above as firmly as he could with his injured left. There was
not the least glimmer of light to aid him. He had to rely solely
upon the picture he had formed in his mind by his sense of touch
as to what lay above. He was not afraid, although he had a perfect
mental image of what would happen should he miss – felt himself
gasping and struggling in the water, turning over and over,
beaten and ground and crushed by the vicious flotsam in the
current, or swirled under water.

He said: 'This is it, sister – one, two, three,' and with all his
strength kicked off and pulled upwards. He felt the upper sill at
his chest and threw his head forward into the opening of the
window, at the same time striving to get a bend in his arms to
brace himself through.

But the drag of the water had been too much and robbed his
spring of a needed few inches. He hung there, gasping and fighting, kicking, his arms aching and cramped, and he knew that in

another moment there would come a weakness that would be
the end. There was fire shooting before his eyes, and his chest was
aflame. In terror, he cried out: 'I can't make it!'

Then hands grasped at his collar and shoulders and tugged. In
the moment's respite he battled for breath, gave a last kick, and
found he was braced on his numbed arms. The tugging continued.
The upper half of his body lay across the sill, inside the room.
He waited for a moment and then dragged his legs over after it,
and collapsed on the floor and lay there, trembling and sobbing
for breath.

After a while he recovered a little and said: 'Thanks, sister.
Where are you?'

He sat up and felt the woman brush up against him, and
found her hand and clung to it. She was trembling. He asked:
'What's the matter?'

Her voice came out of the darkness close to him, low and
desperate: 'I'm hungry. Have you any food?'

'Jeepers,' said Perry, and clapped a hand to his coat pocket.
He always made it a point to carry chocolate bars with him.
They kept him going when he was unable to get regular meals
or any meals at all on an assignment. He still had two, wet, soggy,
but intact. 'I've got some chocolate. How long since you've
eaten?'

'Two days, I think. I don't remember.'

Perry broke off a piece of a bar and peeled the wrapper from
it. He put it into her hand and said: 'Go easy, sister. Eat it slowly.
You've got to. I'll give you more a little later, but you've got to
start easy.'

He heard her eating it in the darkness. When she had finished,
he asked: 'Better?'

She said: 'Oh, yes. Yes. Give me more.'

'No. Later. You've got to go easy. It'll hurt you if you eat too
much now.'

'When can I have more?'

'Soon. Soon, sister. Be patient. Who are you? How did you get
stuck here?'

There was a moment or two of silence. Finally the woman
answered: 'I wouldn't leave. The others left when the water
started rising. I hid. I couldn't leave.'

The heat of Perry's exertions had worn off. He was cold, and
a chill shook him. He thought for a moment and then said: 'Sister,
I've got to take my clothes off. They're wet. I'm freezing.'

The woman's voice answered him: 'Yes, you must take them
off. I have a blanket you can take.'

Kneeling, Perry stripped off the wet, heavy garments. He heard the woman closing the window. He rubbed himself as best he could, trying to get dry and warm. He heard the woman say:

'Where are you?'

'Here,' said Perry, shivering and stretching out his hand. He felt a rough blanket and took hold of it. He wrapped it around himself. The woman took his hand and led him. She said: 'There's a mattress over here in a corner. You can lie down there.'

His feet touched the mattress. He knelt first, feeling its length and direction, and then lay full length upon it, huddled in the blanket. The rain was like the distant roar of surf on the roofing overhead. Another chill rattled Perry's frame. He shook from head to foot, and his teeth began to chatter again. He pulled the blanket around his neck and tried to stop it, but could not. The cold came from deep within him, from his mind as well as his shocked body, and from the pictures he was making in the darkness of the things he had seen that day. Now his heart was frozen with fear as his body was with chill.

He heard the woman speak softly from close by. She said: 'You're cold.'

Perry said: 'Y-y-y-y-y-es. I'm s-s-s-sorry. I can't s-s-stop it.'

Then her voice came out of the impenetrable darkness again, deeply and quietly: 'I'll warm you.'

He felt the blanket tugged gently, and relaxed his grip. He was shaking terribly, and his bruises were throbbing. The woman quickly lay down alongside him, pulled the blanket over them. She was wearing a dress of some material that had the texture of cotton, open at the neck. Perry felt her warmth through it. Her arm was under his head. His shaking continued. Once she said to him: 'Sh-h-h,' as though speaking to a child. His shaking stopped for a moment and he secured a respite before it began again. The woman held him closer. Perry's head rested in the hollow of her neck and shoulder. The fits of shaking were fewer now. They came at longer intervals. The fear was easing from his heart too. A strand of her hair touched his face. Her arms were strong and warm and brought him deep comfort; helped to banish the dreadful pictures from his mind as the cold was slowly leaving his body.

He had strange powerful thoughts as he lay there, warmed and soothed. Who was his unseen companion in the darkness? A woman. Or woman disembodied, the essence of womanhood? He had not seen her. He did not even know her name. She had spread wings over him. She warmed, sheltered, and comforted

him, shielded his body and was tender to its hurts. As a boy, in
reading, the phrase '*Mater Omnium*' had stuck in his mind. His
own mother had died when he was very young. But he had
remembered her and, as a child, in his daydreams he would picture
himself held to her bosom, wrapped within the folds of her robe,
warm and safe and in refuge. Was this, then, she? Was he, Perry,
a child again and dreaming, as he sometimes did, of the reality
of his dream? '*Mater Omnium, Omnium Mater*' – the words
chased themselves through his head. Mother of all, mother of
the world, mother of man. Through the darkness came only the
strong womanhood of this person he could not see. He was warm
now and drowsy, hovering between consciousness and sleep.
Journey's end – the end of the world – one man and one woman
left alive. He said, in a half whisper: 'Thank you!'

'Sh-h-h-,' said the woman once more. Perry fell asleep. When
he woke up, the room was full of grey murky light and it was
grey out of doors and still raining. The woman was kneeling by
the window with her back to him, looking out. He saw that she
had blue-black hair that hung down to her waist.

Perry said: 'Good morning,' and she started, and then turned
around. Her face startled him. She was not beautiful. Her
features were so heavy-boned as to be almost coarse. She was
young – could not have been more than twenty-six or seven. Her
eyebrows were black and strongly marked, and there were hairs
between them. Her cheekbones were high, and more prominent
because she was thin. The nose was long and straight, the mouth
large, full-blooded. The jaw line that ran from ear to chin was
slanting, bony, hard. Beneath her cotton dress swelled large
breasts, and she was tall and wide-hipped. He was shocked,
because he was a romanticist. He knew that he had expected
standard beauty. Her eyes, too, were quite dark, her skin pale
and roughened.

She said: 'You all right?'

Perry sat up and wrapped the blanket around him. 'Thanks to
you. I guess you saved my life last night. A couple of times.'
They were in a small bare attic chamber. The roof came to a
flat inverted V, directly overhead. In it were two trunks, a
battered chair with but half a back to it, and the mattress upon
which he lay. A cooking-pot with a lid on it stood on the floor.
Perry asked: 'Who are you? What's your name?'

'Mary Rud. Rudscienski. They call us Rud for short.'

'Polish?'

'Not me. My husband. I come from around here.' She said it
with a kind of pride.

'Where is your husband?' Perry wished then that he had not asked, but the girl shrugged her shoulders.

'He got out, I guess – with the kid. He made a sort of raft.'

'And left you here?'

She shrugged her bony shoulders again. 'I don't know. He called. I wouldn't come. This is my home. I just couldn't leave it. See, it was my home. I hid. I looked out the window after. The raft was spinning around. It was half sinking. I guess he couldn't hang on any more to the house. Maybe the current took him away. Maybe they're all gone.'

Perry realised that in a matter-of-fact way she was saying that her husband and child might be dead. He felt again that she was a primitive, but in a different way from the experience he had had the night before. The capacity to suffer deeply called, to some extent, for breeding and imagination. This girl must have been bred close, close to the soil, to be so strangely immune to disaster. She had made her choice, and it had been to remain. He had come upon that trait before in the flood. The men got out quickly enough, but the women, many of them, had to be removed forcibly from their homes to save them. Their homes. It was all they had that was stable and unchangeable and that repaid them love for love. The girl's inarticulateness moved him to a queer compassion for her.

He said more softly: 'And then what happened to you – after?'

Mary Rud stirred and shifted her position, so that she sat on the floor with her back to the window, her hands in her lap, and her head tilted a little to the side at an angle that suddenly struck Perry as inconceivably tender and childlike. It softened the harsh jaw line, and the blue-black hair fell to the floor past her shoulder.

'I had to come up here. The water came faster than I thought it would. I moved some food to the second floor, but it was all washed away. I got a pot of water up here. It's most all gone now. I had a half a loaf of bread, but that's gone. Have you any more chocolate?'

Perry broke off a piece of a bar and gave it to her. She bit into it quickly with good white teeth, stopped suddenly, and held it out to him, saying: 'You?'

Perry shook his head. 'I had a big meal yesterday afternoon. Go ahead. You need it.'

But she stopped eating and sat there looking at him with her large dark eyes. Finally she asked: 'Where are you from?'

Perry told her at length. When he told her about New York, her eyes grew larger. She could not understand why folks in New

York should be interested in what happened to people on the
Ohio River, but she wanted to hear stories about the city –
fabulous ones. She had never even been to Louisville. She had
been born and raised on a farm. For a while she had worked as
a waitress in a café in Winesville. As she told of this, Perry, whose
mind always made pictures when he was listening to anyone,
saw her, short-skirted, full-breasted, in white apron or overall,
with her black hair coiled in a knot at the back of her head and
a pencil stuck into it, carrying a tray full of dishes, her hips swinging as she walked, and men at tables turning their heads to watch
her passage. There she had met Jan Rudscienski, the farmer she
had married. She was then nineteen. She said that he was good
enough to her. She seemed to dismiss him with that. Perry, city-
born and bred, was amazed at her casualness. It was his first
experience with the placidity and resignation of those whose
constant struggle is with the soil and the forces of nature.

The blanket wrapped around him, Perry went to the window
and looked out. To the left, and under water, he saw the slanting
top of the roof of a small porch. It was this that had upset his
boat the night before. It was still raining. There was water as
far as he could see, but no houses. There were the branches of
many bare trees rising from the flood about the house, and these
had entangled debris of every description – barrels, troughs, gates
floated off their hinges, crates and boxes and hencoops. The water
was a dirty yellow in colour. Perry raised the window. There was
no sound but the falling rain and another like the sighing of
wind through a leafy grove, which was the water rushing through
the light twigs of the trees, and another, which was a deeper
gurgling as the stream bent its way around solid objects.

Perry asked: 'What's around on the other side?'

'Water,' replied the girl. 'The nearest house is three miles.'

He looked down at the window below, from which he had
climbed during the night. It was gone. The top of the frame was
barely showing level with the surface of the water. 'Hey,' he
said, 'it's gone up since last night. It's still rising.'

The girl was not surprised. Of course it was going up. She had
been watching it rise for days. She had come to accept it as
natural. It would continue to go higher and higher.

Perry examined his clothes. They were damp, but he decided
to put them on, hoping the heat of his body would dry them.
He turned his back and climbed into them laboriously and,
curiously, without self-consciousness. They chilled him at first,
but he moved about briskly and managed to warm them a little.
He looked into the waterpot. It was a third full. He had a bar

and a half of chocolate left. He went over and knelt at the window beside the girl and said: 'Look, kid; we're in a nasty spot.'

He was kneeling with his hands in his lap, she sitting with hers folded, and so they looked at each other. She said nothing, but there was sympathy and a wonderful warmth in her eyes, and a little twisted smile played at the corner of her mouth and disappeared. If he was worried and afraid, she was sorry and wanted him not to be. She was inarticulate, but not with her eyes and body.

Perry thought that she had leaned ever so tiny a fraction closer to him. He could not help himself then. His hands still in his lap, he leaned forward gently and kissed her lips.

That night they huddled again in the darkness and became as one, naturally and without question. But their union was compounded more of pity and loneliness than passion. When they awakened late in the morning of the second day, the yellow waters outside were still rising.

There was no telling how high the water would go. When it came pouring into their attic room, it would drive them to the roof. If it continued to rise, it would sweep them away. The rain never stopped. Perry managed to fill the waterpot with rainwater, but they faced starvation. The remaining bar of chocolate was reduced by half. Perry rationed it, managing to give her the large share of the small amount they dared eat. She had been without food longer than he and already was growing weak.

Mostly she lay on the mattress, while he told her stories of New York. She would lie very quietly and listen to him, and sometimes ask him questions. She knew a smattering about moving-picture stars from movie magazines and occasional visits to the Bijou in Winesville. Her knowledge was limited and bounded by her life. She talked seldom, except to ask him for more stories, but she spoke with simplicity and directness always. And her growing weakness lent her a beautiful dignity.

Perry was amazed to find how beautiful she had become. Each of her strongly marked features had grown dear and tender to him. He was continually discovering beauty where he had seen none before. It was the same face that he had first seen when she turned around in the grey light of the flood morning, but now he found something clean and moving in the slanting line of her jawbone. He loved the heavily drawn eyebrows and the long straight line of her nose that dropped straight from her brow. It reminded him of heads of Minerva he had seen. Her hair was his delight. And her hands, to him, had lost all their roughness, when sometimes she held his head between them.

He never thought of the world he had left, but only of the
small one he inhabited now, and the woman who was a part of
it and of him. They had so little, and what each had they shared
completely. Even as she grew weaker, her fund of tenderness
and womanly compassion seemed never to end. Her mouth grew
softer and more childlike as it drooped with hunger. Sometimes
her dark eyes were glassy.

They never spoke to each other of love. That, too, seemed to
be a part of the lost dead world. Perry felt, somehow, in their
isolation, that the word was reduced to an absurdity. Once, his
mind took him back to a night-club in New York – small tables,
men and women crushed knee to knee, mingled smell of per-
fumes, food, and bodies, the crashing of dishes and the sighing
of a band, and a woman with yellow hair and a red mouth, wearing a black satin sheath dress, standing in the spotlight cater-
wauling about love:

> Life's just a game and we play it,
> But I've got to keep hearing you say it,
> Tell me it's love; tell me it's love.

She sang it with her arms outstretched in a pleading gesture.
Men and women at the tables looked at one another, their lips
moist and eyes sparkling. Love, love, love. They had to hear the
word a thousand times over, read it in print, see it in pictures,
to believe it.

The girl had interrupted his thoughts with a half-whispered
'Is there any more chocolate?'

Perry held her then tightly in his arms, shaken with tenderness
and compassion. Also he gave her the last of the chocolate bar –
a scrap hardly more than an inch, because he hoped it would
lessen in her the awful pangs he felt tearing at his own vitals.
She ate it and sighed and clung to him.

Just before nightfall Perry thought that they were going to die,
that even the small remaining corner of an expiring world was
due to become blotted out. The yellow torrent of water was a
scant six inches below the level of the window-sill. Sometime
during the night or early morning it would spill into the window
and invade their room, cold, stinking, lethal. Flight to the roof
was now out of the question. The girl was too weak to help herself. Perry knew that his own strength was insufficient. Morning
would find them standing waist-deep in icy water. The next night
would find them dead.

Perry didn't tell Mary what he had seen. And that night
which was to be their last, he found their positions reversed.

Now it was he who still had strength and compassion and human warmth to give.

As long as there was the faintest of grey light to see, and long after it was gone, Perry strained his eyes to see her face, to catch the last line of the beauty of her features.

The window was open. There was no use in trying to stem the monster when it came for them. He heard the rush and gurgle of the water outside, and once the excited chattering of a bird. In the far distance he heard another rushing sound, higher in pitch than the rain and the torrent. As he listened it was accompanied by the drawn-out, throaty wail of a locomotive, and it made him draw the girl only closer to him. He refused to believe it. And yet, for a moment, he found himself thinking of Rusty, and the *Blade* office, the city room of his powerful, vital newspaper, with the typewriters clacking and the telephones ringing, and the editors and reporters busy at their desks, and outside the throb and roar of the city.

But of those realities he thought as he had thought of the night-club – as things of a thousand years ago, memories bred in him rather than remembered; as once when he had walked the Roman walls of a border city in England he had felt suddenly that he had been there before, that time and space were non-existent, and that there, where he stood on the ancient stone and mortar, gazing down into the tangled underbrush at the wall's base, he had stood once in another age, with the hair on his neck creeping as it was creeping then, awaiting an enemy.

Rusty he had loved in the past and would love again. She was dear to him for what she had been so many centuries ago. In the darkness with this woman in his arms he was again close to the ages that came out of darkness and returned to it. This brief passage, then, was over, and he was not unhappy, because he was not alone. He knew that not at any time did man face any terror more fearful than to be alone, and was grateful. The girl was asleep when he kissed her good-bye. Soon he fell asleep too. When he awoke, the sun was shining in through the half-open window. The room was still dry. He got up and looked out. The yellow waters were still below the level of the sill. The sky was cloudless, blue, and brilliant. He heard a scraping sound from around the corner of the house. A rowboat appeared, and then another, a large, flat-bottomed barge. There were men in them. One of them wore a Red Cross brassard on his arm.

'Hey!' called Perry. 'Hey!'

They saw him and rowed over to the window.

The man in the small rowboat was a powerful fellow with

blond hair and huge hands. His name was Jan Rudscienski and he was the husband of the woman who lay asleep beneath the blanket in the corner of the room. He looked at Perry without suspicion, but asked: 'How you get here?'

Perry told him briefly. He grunted and climbed into the room and asked: 'Is she hokay?'

'We're – she's starved,' Perry said. 'We haven't had any food except a little chocolate I had.' He seemed to be thinking and talking like the normal human being he had been, except that he was weak with hunger.

Rudscienski leaned out the window and called: 'Hey! She's here. Bring some o' that soup.'

A Red Cross man came in with a vacuum bottle. He went over to the girl and raised her head. She opened her eyes for a moment. Expressionless, they travelled to Perry, to the man who was her husband, and to the man who held her. She drank a little of the hot broth and closed her eyes again. The Red Cross man gave some to Perry, who drank sparingly.

Mary opened her eyes. 'Is Alvis all right?' she asked.

Her husband replied: 'Yup,' and then said to the Red Cross man, 'We better get her out o' here.'

They lifted her across the sill and into the Red Cross barge. In the sunlight Perry noted how blue-black her hair and brows were, and again saw the firm pillar of her neck. He put on his slicker and climbed into the barge too, and they rowed away from the house, Rudscienski following in his boat. There was no wind, and it was warmer. Perry saw high land that had previously been blotted out by the rain, a mile or so away. He heard the sound of a motorboat. It came over to examine them. In it was his friend, the colonel of engineers, and two or three other officers.

'Hey,' said the colonel. 'So there you are. We've had an alarm out for you. Are you O.K.?'

Perry nodded his head.

'Want a lift?' asked the colonel. 'We're going down as far as Owensboro. You can get transportation out there.'

Perry nodded again. He was feeling too sick to talk. He drank another cup of broth while the motorboat came alongside, and then, with the help of one of the officers, climbed in. They cast off immediately and headed south. Perry stood up in the boat, propping himself by the gunwale, and tried to call good-bye, but his throat was dry and his head swimming. Mary Rudscienski opened her eyes for a moment and saw him. A half smile visited her mouth for the shadow of a moment and then vanished. Perry waved, and Jan Rudscienski and the Red Cross man waved back. Then the farmhouse came between them.

'For God's sake,' said Perry Brown, 'has anybody got a drink?'

'Not officially,' said the colonel. 'Give him the unofficial bottle, Joe.'

One of the officers passed Perry a half-full quart bottle of rye whisky. He drank a good third of it and did not remember very much after that.

Once, when he returned to a consciousness that, for a few seconds, was not fraught with memories of Mary Rudscienski, he found himself in bed in a hotel room. A Negro bellboy was standing at his side, gazing at him with large eyes that showed their cream-whites.

'Where am I now?' Perry asked.

'De Acropolis Hotel, Memphis, suh.'

'How'd I get here?'

''Deed, Ah don' know, suh. Yo jus' came here, Ah guess. Ah been takin' care o' you, suh. Yo clothes is all cleaned and pressed, and I had yo underthings washed. Yassuh, boss!'

'Have I eaten anything?'

'Guess so, boss. You et everything Ah been bringin'. Ah been takin' care o' you, boss!'

'Is there any more whisky?'

'Fetch yo some, boss.'

While he waited, Perry's eyes wandered about the room. There was a telephone on the bedside table, and a Gideon Bible. A Whistler print hung on the opposite wall. He got up and went to the window and looked out, and was shocked when he saw no limitless expanse of turbid yellow waters with the naked tree-tops breaking the surface. The street below was crowded and noisy with traffic, cars and trucks, and hurrying people skipping between them. There was a five-and-ten-cent store directly opposite, and for a while he watched the women thronging in and out the doors. The sanity of the familiar store sign and the display of merchandise behind the plate-glass window was healing.

He remembered times in the last few days when he had awakened so full of a nostalgia for something that was gone beyond recapture that there was no fight left in him. Miserable beyond comprehension, he drank quickly, only for the anodyne of unconsciousness. As a boy, Perry had often for a day been haunted by the escaped beauty of a dream. What had happened to him in the flood-bound house had already taken on the quality of a dream, but it still shook him, physically and mentally, beyond bearing. Perry Brown was a reasoning animal, but it was not

either with or against reason he was fighting, but against a terrible
sense of loss of something that had been beautiful. At times he
was half driven to the insane determination to find Mary Rud
again, to try to ease the pain by once more pressing his cheeks
to hers, to feel the softness and sweetness of her mouth, and to
close his eyes in the peace of her arms.

But he knew that that really was not his loss. He recognised
that he had been in a world to which he could never again return;
that he was shut out from it as though what had taken place had
occurred on another planet, hundreds of light-years away. It was
then that he would drink again.

The view from the window helped. People, cars, policemen,
newsboys, stores, and the wholly concrete and soothing display
of bottles and paper flowers and cheap glassware and knick-knacks
in the five-and-ten opposite – this was, after all, a world he had
known and loved and could live in. It was still there. With a
sudden rush of tenderness and shame he thought of Rusty, with
her copper-coloured hair and grey-green eyes, and wide mouth
with the half-humorous smile. Somewhere, busy, keen, alive, she
would be on the trail of a story. When she saw him again, her
face would light up with that look he loved, half amused, half
tender, and wholly loyal.

He shook himself and went away from the window. The objects
in the room no longer looked strange to him. They no longer
hurt him. This was where he belonged. He picked up the receiver
of the telephone and replaced it again; then lifted it and sent a
telegram to the office to send a hundred dollars.

The bellboy came back with a bottle of whisky. Perry paid him
for it and then gave it to him with a ten-dollar bill, saying: 'You
keep it, son. I don't want it. Beat it. Tell the porter to get me
space on the night train for New York.'

Three hours later he put on his clothes, paid his bill, and went
home.

Did you see the Coronation?

This in every sense of the word is a period piece. To the modern generation it will appear as dated as the bustle or the Lambeth Walk. The Coronation referred to was that of the late King George VI which took place in 1937, and, of course, the language spoken by the two characters involved, Swing and Audrey, a pair of débutantes from Chicago, is as obsolete as beatnik talk will be ten years from now.

Yet I could not resist the temptation to include this story in this volume for Swing and Audrey are old friends and stories about them ran in the 'Saturday Evening Post' from 1937 through to 1945.

The characters are based on two young ladies I met while crossing to England on the S.S. 'Statendam' early in 1937. Great heavens, that was twenty-three years ago and I still keep thinking of them as débutantes in spite of the fact that both are long married and have children of their own. In fact I attended Swing's wedding in Chicago.

They were eighteen when I first encountered them on the 'Statendam,' and bound for England to spend the spring and part of the summer as paying guests in Devonshire, later to be joined by Audrey's mother on the Continent. Swing and Audrey are not their real names. We met during the course of a progressive bridge game in the ship's lounge, and when we introduced ourselves, they announced that they were 'Two débutantes – from Chicago!' – just that way with a kind of swing and rhythm to it and also a great sense of importance and fitness, the way one might say: 'Doctors – from Edinburgh' or 'Painters – from Paris.'

One was a quiet, dreamy, bookish child, the other a lively, bouncing, merry, and athletic little cricket. And they spoke a jargon such as never before had assailed my ears, a compendium of débutante slang and young things' idiom full of such aptness, toughness, and gaiety that I was captivated. I just wanted to listen to them talk so that I too might learn this marvellously expressive language which could convey ideas and shades of meaning from which apparently ordinary English-speaking peoples were quite hopelessly cut off. It had a considerable vocabulary all its own, and eventually when we became fast friends – a friendship that has included their families and lasted down through the years – they helped me to compile for my own use a kind of débutante dictionary, which was constantly enlarged and added to as new expressions came up.

But there was more to them than glossology, for in addition to superb manners, good breeding, and sweet natures there was their outlook on life.

Daughters of wealthy and prominent families in Chicago, they had made their débuts, or 'come out' simultaneously – up to that moment the crowning event in both their lives, for which they had apparently pointed from the cradle. They were clothed and cloaked in débutantehood. They accepted its majesty like training for the throne, which, once achieved, from then on armoured them both against all and any troubles, from minor emotional disturbances to major cataclysms that included fire, flood, and earthquake. Their thinking and feeling, everything they did or that happened to them, were seen or evaluated from the point of view of two who had had the great good fortune to be brought up as débutantes – from Chicago. Nothing was impossible to a girl who had gone through that mill, or could be expected to faze her. All life could be rationalised to fit into some compartment of this training. It gave them an impregnable and wholly charming self-assurance.

That was the spring of the Coronation of the late King George VI and which, oddly enough, I attended in the capacity not of a reporter, but of a photographer. An English friend of mine, Tom Noble, at that time Studio Chief and Art Director for the Kemsley newspapers, had need of every camera and operator that could be marshalled for that event. I had a Leica. I got to see the Coronation. And I should say that one of the milestones of my career in which I took the greatest pride was the appearance in the 'Daily Graphic,' at least for one edition, of one of the pictures I took. Was there ever a clown who didn't want to play Hamlet?

The débutantes came up to London for the Coronation too and pronounced it just too, too divine, and we all went together to the Coronation Ball.

Somewhere during this period developed the itch to involve my two débutantes in the Coronation in a short story. Somehow I had to get Swing and Audrey into Westminster Abbey. The fun of writing fiction, of course, is that if you work at an idea long enough there is nothing one cannot do and within a week I had *what I thought was a fairly watertight sequence of events. I had rented my cottage in Devon again and when Audrey's mother joined them in England they all came down to Salcombe and stayed with me for a week, during which time I pursued my studies of their language assiduously, and* DID YOU SEE THE CORONATION? *was the result.*

The plot of the story is pure fiction. No such thing happened, of course, but with Swing and Audrey on the loose in England, it could have happened. The girls and their speech, however, and their outlook upon life and the infectious and sometimes touchingly gallant youthfulness that animates them are, I think, accurately reported. They were always helpful and considerate and breathless and wriggling with zest for life and always about to perish with excitement, I mean absolutely pass out and quietly die from hysterics over whatever was going on or happening to them.

The decision to use the device of having one of the girls narrate the story was made for verisimilitude and credibility as well as from the fact that it enabled me to write the entire story in the queer private language of the young things of that day.

There is used in this story likewise a trick, an opening gambit, which formula I shamelessly pinched as developed by Mary Roberts Rinehart in her wonderful Tish stories running at that time.

This opening gambit appears to be almost an incoherent and scrambled rehearsal of difficulties and problems, plus a veiled forecast of what is about to happen in the story.

This type of opening serves a double purpose. It is a come-on to hook the interest of the reader, and at the same time it serves as a kind of innocent blind in which to bury four or five 'plants,' ridiculous or innocuous-sounding statements all of which have a later bearing in the story. You encounter the principles of the 'plant' nearly every time you go to the theatre to see a play. When, for instance, in the first act a character goes over to a desk, opens a drawer, takes out a pistol, examines it to see if it is loaded, replaces it, and closes the drawer, you can be sure that before the evening is over someone is going to be shot with it. It is a cardinal rule of story writing, and one, as I recall, that is taught in all the courses, that the reader must be put into possession of all the facts. You are not permitted to spring surprises on him in the professional league.

It has always seemed to me that a little such technical knowledge would increase the average reader's enjoyment of a story. A skilful plant enhances rather than interferes with the narrative and it is fun after finishing a story to check back over it and see whether the author has played fair with you throughout. If he hasn't, you are entitled to complain twice – once to the writer and again to the editor who let it go through. That's what editors are for.

I wrote the story during the time of the girls' visit and read it to them when I had finished it. They corrected a few minor philological errors and then announced that they just couldn't bear it, it was just too, too divine, they meant absolutely extra amusing. I hope you find it, even at this late date, somewhat the same.

DID YOU SEE THE CORONATION?

Did you see the Coronation? Wasn't it just too snappy for words? It was so divine when that old love of an Archbishop lowered the crown on top of the King's head. I simply wept. I've never been so touched in my life. Swing said the King looked as though he were trying to duck, but then Swing simply hasn't any reverence for anything. She was perfectly furious, and didn't want to come at all first, because they had made Edward abdicate, but then, after all, what was the use of being in England and not seeing the Coronation, especially when it was so easy?

Wasn't it too ridiculous, all the fuss they made about how hard it was to get seats, and all the crowds and everything? Why, we had no trouble at all. Well, practically none, unless you count Swing's getting the hiccups just as the Queen was being crowned, and, of course, being so close – that is, standing right behind her, almost – it was really awful for a moment, until she suddenly caught a glimpse of that perfectly dismal Captain Fizz, and that frightened her so she stopped. Oh, and then, afterwards, when Captain Fizz chased us into the Sultan's carriage, it was a little awkward for a moment. I mean it might have been, but the Sultan turned out to be extra-genial, even if he was a coloured man. And Swing made such a hit with him when she worked his fly-swatter for him. He wanted to marry her right away. I just had a picture of Swing breaking in on the family in Chicago, with an airy 'Hello, darlings; this is the Ambeok of Negotora, Sultan of Amu Penang. We're going to be married.' Can't you just see

their faces? Oh, and of course Captain Fizz turning out to be
who he was was rather fortunate, because our families never
would have understood it if we had gone to jail, although the
jails are quite different over here, and they never put anything
into the papers, even if it's true.

You see, we never would have been at the Coronation at all
if Swing weren't such a fiend at bridge, and, of course, I always
hold the cards, and that nasty Major Putrington and his wretched
wife trying to take advantage of us just because they knew our
families had plenty of chips – I mean it served them right – and
so, when we did have the chance to buy two tickets for the
Abbey cheap, it seemed as if we ought to do it.

And, of course, when Captain Fizz kept trying to put us out,
it really wasn't his fault, because he didn't know who we were
then, and although it was Swing's idea to take the sandwiches
with us, it was mine to give some to the pathetic old gentleman
who looked so tired and hungry, and, of course, when he turned
out to be the King's uncle, we were almost as surprised as Captain Fizz was. I mean Captain Fizz knew he was the King's
uncle, but not that he knew us, and Swing's reaching down and
retrieving the Queen's handkerchief helped, too, because when
she dropped it, all those stiff English women just stood around
with egg on their faces. And now, because the Queen smiled at
her, Swing is giving herself airs just as though she had been
presented at court, though we could have been if we had wanted
to. Perhaps it would be better if I explained everything.

You see, we are débutantes from Chicago.

Swing and I came out together in Chicago. It was the biggest
party of the year. We had three floors at the Palmer House.
Never saw so many college boys boozed at one time in all my
life. Well, after that it was a plenty hectic season; we just had
to keep going, and, of course, Swing and I acquired a couple of
stooges, awfully nice boys, and we really were more than a little
fond of them – I mean we were serious, even though we were
only eighteen – and then – well, I mean our families stepped in.
So that's how Swing and I came to be parked in Devonshire
together for six months to cool off, at Grammorton House, Fenley
Moors, Little Downey.

Well, we had been plenty free with the family chips last
winter, so we didn't at all mind being put on an allowance. I
guess Swing will come into ten or twelve millions when she
comes of age, but you would never guess it, to be with her, and
though Dad isn't exactly a pauper, he has always made me count
my pennies. You see, Swing is really Janet Pierce, and Mr Pierce

– Harriman Pierce – is the owner of the Harriman Pierce five-and-ten-cent stores, only I call her Swing, and I am Audrey Westmar, and if you have to look at our pictures in the roto-gravure sections all the time, it isn't our fault; we really only came out to please our families, and if you think it is an easy life being a débutante, you just try it some time.

So there we were, sort of under the thumb of Mrs Grammorton, down in Devon, and it really wasn't so bad, even if we did have to dress for dinner every night, and some of the other guests there were just too peculiar for words; but, of course, there was just no chance of our going up for the Coronation, because we had promised not to exceed our allowance and we knew every-thing was just frightfully expensive there and we really did want to see England, and it wasn't so bad being away from our stooges, because one good thing about a stooge that's anywhere half decent is that he'll keep. So we really just gave up the idea of the Coronation – that is, until the bridge game.

You see, we used to play bridge after supper with the other guests at Grammorton House, and, of course, we never play for more than sixpence a hundred, and somehow we always found ourselves at a table with Major Putrington and his wife. The major was old and maggoty and all sort of stringy, with a most dreadful wife. Swing said she always looked as though she were getting ready to answer a telegram that had bad news in it. So one night, about a week before the Coronation, the major asked us if we didn't want to increase the stakes, and we thanked him and said no, that we never played for more than ten cents a hundred back home, which was quite true, because once I played for half a cent a point, and Dad heard about it and nearly had a kitten.

Mrs Putrington gave us a sickly-sweet smile – Swing said later that it reminded her of eating pomegranates – and said: 'We understand here that in America one always plays for very high stakes.'

'Well, we don't,' said Swing, 'because we can't afford it.'

'Aha!' laughed the major, just like that. 'Aha, aha! Jolly good. Can't afford it. Aha! I say, that's jolly good. It's been so dashed dull here. Thought you might want to stir things up a bit. Can't afford it. Oh, you Americans! Aha! Jolly good!'

I caught the 'I-want-to-talk-to-you-alone' signal from Swing and went up to our room. She came up a moment later and said: 'How much money have you got?'

I said: 'Eight pounds. But it's got to last me until the end of the month.'

'Give it to me,' said Swing. 'I've got seven. That makes fifteen. We'll just have to stay home if we lose it. Our rent's paid here, so we can eat and sleep.'

I said: 'Oh, Swing, what are you going to do?'

She said: 'Play that pair of maggots. They've found out that our families are chip-heavy and they want to take us for expenses. Jolly good sport, milking two eighteen-year-olds. Let's go. And for heaven's sakes, Audrey, no psychics.'

'Oh, Swing, I'm nervous.'

'You hold them, I'll play them,' said Swing. 'Anyway, the Putringtons are still playing out of the book we threw away three years ago. I am ever glad I was educated as a débutante.'

When we came back, Swing said sweetly – she has beautiful manners: 'So sorry we kept you waiting. What stakes would you like to play for?'

'Eh? Eh?' said the major. 'Oh, I say, that's jolly good. London Club stakes. Pound a hundred suit you?'

I nearly fainted, but Swing said calmly: 'That's fine. Shall we cut for deal?'

Swing is a very deceptive bridge player. She looks as if she had no interest in the game at all, or were thinking of something else, or were half asleep. She is a tall, quiet girl with lots of dark hair and a faraway look in her eyes, and when someone bids, it always seems to startle her, but that doesn't fool anybody in our crowd in Chicago any more. But, you see, it completely fooled the Putringtons.

So that was how we got the money to go to the Coronation. Mrs Grammorton always makes everyone stop playing at midnight, because all the lights go out then, and the major had to give us forty-seven pounds, mostly because once Swing woke up out of what seemed to be a sound sleep, not having said anything but 'Pass,' and doubled their two no-trump bid, caught them with a weak suit, smelled out my strength, and set them 1400. When Mrs Grammorton found out the next day what had happened, she was plenty annoyed, and the major and his wife had to leave.

Mrs Grammorton put her foot down first at our going to the Coronation alone. You see, being English, she doesn't understand that American girls, especially débutantes, are different and can go anywhere by themselves; so we told her we had relatives in London, which was true, except that we weren't going to look them up, because, as Swing said, what was the fun of going to the Coronation if you went with relatives; so she finally relented

and said we could go. We called up the Harriman Pierce Stores
representative in London and he got us a wonderful room in a
lovely old house off Hanover Square. We rode up to London
in a third-class carriage and took our lunches with us to save
chips, as we figured whatever of Major Putrington's money we
didn't spend on the Coronation we would use for shopping.

Of course, nobody could get inside the Abbey without an
invitation, and the most we hoped for was to wait until the last
minute and then try to buy a cheap seat in a window somewhere
to see the procession, and Swing said from some of those
windows that had grandstand seats in them we ought to be
able to see the plumes in the hats as they went by, if they were
tall enough, and why didn't we wait and save our money, and
then go to the circus when we got back home instead.

We tried all over, but the good seats were all sixty dollars
apiece and the cheap ones twenty-five dollars each, and when
we thought of the tailored suits we could get in New Bond
Street for that, we simply couldn't make up our minds what to
do. So when the nice young Englishman we met at lunch at
Quaglino's offered to sell us two seats inside the Abbey for six
pounds each, which is sixty dollars for both, it sounded plenty
good to us. Of course, we didn't actually meet him. I mean he
was sitting at the next table and spoke to us after a while. Of
course, we don't speak to strange men unless they are obviously
college boys and not too tight, but Englishmen are different and
all sort of quite harmless.

So, when this man at the next table smiled and said: 'You
young American ladies are over for the Coronation, I take it,' it
seemed perfectly all right, so I told him we were, and when he
asked whether we had our seats, I explained just how things
were to him; he was really very nice, with sort of sandy hair and
pale-blue eyes and not much chin, but then, all the Englishmen
with chins are put right into the Army or the Navy. So then he
said: 'How would you like to sit right inside Westminster Abbey?'
So I said: 'That would be plenty good. Can it be done?'

He said he had two tickets and he couldn't go, but inasmuch
as we had none, he would be glad to sell them to us for a small
sum. He said he would give them to us, except that they belonged
to a friend who wanted to get rid of them. Of course we asked
to see them, and he explained that he couldn't show them to
us there, because in England it was a very great crime to sell
tickets to the Abbey, and there were so many people about,
but if we would walk a little ways with him, he would show
them to us. Swing kicked me and said: 'It sounds like a gyp,

but I kicked her back and said: 'Shut up; he hasn't got our money yet.'

So we left Quaglino's with him and walked down Bury Street towards St James's, and after a while he showed them to us, and even Swing had to admit that she was wrong, because they really were two tickets for Westminster Abbey, and they had the crown on them and everything, and the name of the King, George, with his number after it. They were really extra-official, engraved in gold. So we paid him, and he thanked us and jumped into a taxi and drove away. He really was very nice.

Well, we were simply perishing to think we were really going to be inside the Abbey for the Coronation, until Swing suddenly remembered about clothes, and, of course, we didn't have any court dresses, but, luckily, we had brought our white evening dresses up to London just in case we should meet anyone who would ask us out, and I said we could go to Selfridge's and buy some white elbow gloves and some white feathers to put in our hair, and Swing said that you didn't wear feathers to a Coronation, you wore tiaras; feathers were for presentations; so we had a fight about that, but we finally bought a pair of rhinestone tiaras and a few odds and ends, and then we got all the papers and read the instructions, and found that we would have to get up at half-past five in order to be at the Abbey at six-thirty in the morning, and Swing said that that was a lot of nonsense, that the ceremony didn't begin until half-past ten, and she wasn't going to get there until nine o'clock, which was early enough.

I said that the papers warned that nobody would be allowed through after seven o'clock, but Swing said that with those tickets we had we ought to be able not only to get through but to sit next to Queen Mary, which was funny, because the way it turned out, it was Elizabeth we were next to, and not Mary, and she is a lamb, and just as sweet as she can be, and I wished we could have given her some of our sandwiches, poor dear; she did look so hungry.

Oh, yes, I almost forgot about the sandwiches. You see, it said in the papers that guests in the Abbey would have to go eight or nine hours without eating, and of course Swing just hates to go more than three hours without a bite, and so we made up some sandwiches to take along, and then found we didn't have any place to put them, because we weren't taking any bags or anything, and I said we couldn't walk into Westminster Abbey carrying our lunch, and Swing said she wouldn't mind carrying her lunch and a bottle of beer, if they didn't mind, and then I saw her looking at my dress in a very strange way, and that solved it, you see, because although it was a very simple dress, it had two panniers of white satin at the side, and so we just cut the panniers open and put two sandwiches on either side and basted them up again, and it really didn't hurt the dress at all – in fact, it helped it a little, making it sort of old-fashioned, like a bustle.

I wanted to start early, the morning of the Coronation, but Swing said that was silly, that they just said that to frighten people and that we should be there in plenty of time, and so we didn't get up until eight o'clock and put on our white evening gowns, and, of course, no make-up at all, because it would have looked just too horrible in daylight, and our tiaras really were quite stunning; and so we left the house at a quarter to nine and found one of those funny little taxis cruising around – only this was an antique, and plenty decrepit; Swing said she was sure it had been used for Queen Victoria's Coronation – and we got in and told the driver to take us to Westminster Abbey.

He gave us a very funny look, though I'm sure it wasn't because of the way we were dressed, because people in England wear evening dress at some of the oddest hours, and then he said: 'Will I drive you right up to the haltar, miss?'

We said no, just to take us around to the front entrance. Then he climbed down from his seat and came and opened the door and looked at us for a moment, and shook his head and climbed back into the seat. He said we would be lucky if he got to within a mile of the Abbey, and then he started the machine's one lung and we drove off.

We seemed to be driving around for a long while, and all of a sudden we came down a narrow street and up behind a crowd and stopped. We told him not to stop, but to go right on, and when he said: 'Yes, miss, will I go hover or hunder the people?' Swing told him not to be a bore, but to blow his horn, because we had tickets, and it startled him so that he did, and a police-man came over and said: 'Here, what's all this? Going to the Coronation, Bertie? Didn't you read the regulations? Come on, out of it now, quickly.'

Swing said: 'Tell him we're débutantes,' but I let down the window of the cab and showed the policeman our tickets. He looked at them for a long time as though he were completely baffled, and even took off his helmet and scratched his head, and then put his helmet back on again before he said: 'Well, now, young misses, I've seen a lot of queer ones in my day, but this beats them all. Did you buy these tickets?'

I told him we had and had paid six pounds for them, and

wanted to go through because we were late for the Coronation, and would he please fix it so our driver could go ahead?

At that he gave us a most dismal smile and said: 'Well now, young misses, I am very sorry, but I am afraid you have been took in. You cannot go through here with those tickets, and the reason you cannot go through is——'

Well, we never found out what the reason was – at least not then – because at that moment there was a terrific honking in back of us from an enormous limousine that seemed to have pulled up behind us, and a voice shouted: 'Here, here, Jenks! What's all this? Clear the way here! This car must get through!'

The voice came from another policeman, only he was older and had a moustache and more stripes than our policeman.

Our policeman saluted and said: 'Sorry, sergeant. I was just explaining to these here two young ladies as how they couldn't go through because——'

'Never mind the two young ladies, Jenks! Come, come, show some life! His Grace's car must be let through! Lively now! Get that taxi out of there!'

Well, there was no room to turn around, so the policeman opened up a way through the crowd and waved us on through, saying to the driver: 'Hup, go on, Bertie. And see that you turn off inside, or I'll have your licence.'

So that is how we got through into the Coronation area, except that Bertie – if that was our driver's name – couldn't turn off when he got inside, because we were on a sort of a circle, or circus, as they call them in London, and another big limousine with a crest on the door shot out from the side and got in front of him and the big one in back of us closed in behind, and there we were, in a sort of procession of big cars. I asked Bertie which way we were going, and he said: 'To the Abbey, miss. I can't turn off now. I'm caught.'

'Well,' I said, 'that's where we wanted to go in the first place.'

'I wonder what's the matter with our tickets,' Swing said.

I said: 'Nothing. You'll see! The policeman was just being difficult. They all are.'

So that's how we got to the Abbey, and it was perfectly simple, and when we got there, our taxi had to wait in line while the people got out; and I must say, I never saw so many beautiful uniforms in all my life. Swing said they all looked like lion-tamers. And finally our taxi drew up to the little side door and we got out, and while Swing paid Bertie, I got out our tickets, and then we went up to the door, and there were two attendants there in sort of medieval costumes, and one perfectly stunning man in the most gorgeous uniform, with gold lace and a lot of medals on his chest and a red band around his hat and a short moustache and the most perfect white gloves; so we showed them our tickets and just prepared to sweep on by, when the two attendants stopped us, and they called to the stunning creature, and he came over and had a look at our tickets, and first he got red in the face and then he began to fizz in the strangest way, just like something boiling over, and he gave Swing and me an awfully black look and finally said:

'I say, look here. You know, you can't do this.'

'Can't do what?' said Swing. 'We're not doing anything. We're just going to the Coronation.'

The man fizzed again, and got quite purple before he said: 'No, you're not! What dashed cheek! Americans, I'll wager!'

I said: 'Certainly, we're Americans. We're débutantes from Chicago. And we have our tickets for the Coronation, and we want to go in. I know we're a little late, but you needn't be so fussy about that. So are a lot of other people.'

'Late? Late? I should think you are late. Dashed insolence. Look here. You'll have to go right away. Those tickets are no good at all.'

Swing whispered: 'Oh, oh. I knew there was something peculiar about that man.'

But I wasn't going to go away without an argument, so I said: 'Oh, yes, they are. We paid six pounds apiece for them. How dare you say they're no good when they have the crown and everything on them, and the name of the King and the Abbey?'

Well, this time the man really fizzed. He was so mad – you see that's why Swing and I named him Captain Fizz – and then he took the tickets and held them in front of us and said: 'Can either of you young ladies, by any chance, read?' So, of course, we told him we could, and then he said: 'Well, then, would you oblige me by reading this' – and he pointed with his finger. So I read out: 'Coronation of His Majesty George——'

'Yes, go on,' said Captain Fizz. 'And what comes after that?'

'Why, a V – a five,' I said – 'George the Fifth. What's wrong with that?'

'Oh, I say,' said the captain, after having fizzed terrifically. 'What's wrong with that? Oh, nothing, except that this is the Coronation of George the Sixth. That ticket was good twenty-six years ago, but not today.'

'Oh, come,' said Swing. 'Don't be a boor. What difference does it make? It's almost George the Sixth. And besides, we paid for them.'

'Can't be helped,' said the captain, fizzing frightfully. 'You must go right away from here, or I shall have to call a policeman. Look here, now; you're holding up all these people . . . Oh, I say; now you have done it!'

You see, he had turned around to see who was waiting. And, of course it was the people who had been in the huge limousine right behind us, and the man was sort of tall and greyish, and really wearing a most wonderful uniform, and as soon as he saw him, poor Captain Fizz turned quite red and straightened up and gave him the most intense salute, and the two attendants at the door who had sort of things like boat hooks in their hands, they got quite rigid and presented their boat hooks, and so, while they were saluting, Swing and I just walked on in, because, after all, it wasn't our fault they had put the number of the wrong George on the ticket, and, as Swing said later, if it had been King Edward, as it should have been, that never could have happened, and anyway we had paid for the tickets, and just because our families have plenty of chips is no reason why we should simply throw money away.

So you see, that's how we got into the Abbey, and it really was quite easy, and I could never understand why people made such a fuss about how difficult it was, because there we were, inside with the wrong tickets, and I'm sure we could have got in just as easily with no tickets at all.

Swing said we'd better find seats right away, so we started looking for some; but of course the Abbey was simply jammed – I mean I never saw so many people – and of course it was the most glamorous sight, and most of the time we just stood around and stared like a couple of goops at all the robes and the ermine and the jewellery, and every time we would get settled somewhere, someone in a different kind of uniform would come along and make us move out; really, I never felt so hunted in my life. We held on to our tickets, but we wouldn't let anybody see more than a little bit of them, for fear they would notice they were for the wrong Coronation.

And then, of course, we got lost in the Abbey; it's the most tremendous place you ever saw and just full of tombs, and we kept wandering around and hiding behind them whenever we saw anyone with a uniform who looked like an official, and finally we thought we saw an aisle leading down to a place that seemed to have some empty seats, and we thought maybe the people who had the seats wouldn't come, and anyway, if they did, we would be there first, because, you see, it was getting late, so we fairly whipped down the aisle and ran straight into Captain Fizz. I was simply terrified.

Well, you see, we had no way of knowing that the seats we had seen were the ones the King and Queen and the peers and things were going to sit in until they were crowned, or, of course, we never should have gone near the place, and all of a sudden there we were, surrounded by archbishops and things, and poor Captain Fizz was quite purple with rage, and we knew he was about to do something dreadful to us, because, really, I have never seen a man so mad in all my life; so we turned and streaked, only, in the excitement, we ran the wrong way, with Captain Fizz and a lot of men who looked like butlers or foot-men after us, and just then the organ began to play and then a lot of people in costume came walking up the aisle where we were.

First there were three sorts of heralds, right out of *Alice in Wonderland*, and then some men in the most beautiful costumes, carrying a lot of jewellery, and, of course, we would have recog-nised the Queen, even if there hadn't been six sort of butlers holding up her train, and all the little boys up in the gallery simply screaming: '*Vivat Regina Elizabeth!*' at the top of their lungs, and a lot of women walking behind her, and maids of honour in white dresses and tiaras. You see, we had walked right into the Queen's procession, and there was the captain right behind us, fizzing most horribly.

Well, everyone was giving us grim looks, and the captain had turned absolutely violet when Swing, who wasn't a bit upset – she never gets upset, which, I guess, is another good thing about the training of a débutante – said to Captain Fizz: 'Calm down now, and tell us what you want us to do, and we'll do it. If you hadn't hunted us so, this wouldn't have happened.'

Well, the captain's eyes simply started from his head, and the procession was practically on top of us when he found his voice and whispered: 'Fall in. For God's sake, fall in or I'm ruined.'

Swing grabbed my hand, and before I knew what was hap-pening, we were walking in the procession with the maids of honour, and it was all done so quickly that nobody really knew what had happened. I whispered to Swing: 'Swing, my knees are knocking together so hard I'm sure everybody can hear it,' and Swing whispered back, 'Shut up and keep going. We'll just do what they do. It looks as though we were going to have a good seat for this Coronation.' And later she whispered: 'Don't look now, but I think the King is walking right in back of us.'

D

Well, of course, we didn't really have a seat at all, because the ladies-in-waiting and maids of honour don't sit, but stand up around the Queen on either side; but, of course, we didn't mind standing a bit, because, you see, we were right where the Coronation was happening, and Queen Mary was sitting in a sort of a box with a lot of people right behind us, looking really royal. Somehow, when we were all arranged, we were standing almost next to Queen Elizabeth, who seemed to be a swell person, and she wasn't a bit nervous, and I was getting over being frightened, except that I whispered to Swing: 'If anyone starts counting maids of honour, we're lost,' and Swing said: 'No one's going to start counting, but if anyone looks at our feet, we're sunk.'

Well, of course, English girls have got the most tremendous feet, poor dears, and the maids of honour, who, we later found out, were all peeresses, seemed to have really extra large ones, so Swing and I hid ours under our dresses as best we could, and then the King came along with his glittering procession and his butlers, and I must say I have never seen butlers dressed so beautifully, and, of course, there were the crown jewels, right out of the Tower, close enough for us to touch.

So, you see, that explains how we got right up close to the Coronation; I mean if we had got any closer we would have been the Coronation, and somehow, just before the ceremony started, Captain Fizz managed to slip behind us and fizz: 'I'll see you in quod for this. And if you make any kind of slip, dashed if I won't strangle you both.'

Swing whispered: 'Don't be silly. Compared to the reception line at a débutante tea in Chicago, this is easy.'

Well, I was never so impressed with anything in my life as the way that lamb of a King – I think he is much more attractive than Edward – went through all the things they made him do. I mean they were always taking clothes off him and putting others on him, and praying over him, and giving him things to hold and then taking them away from him again before he could really ever get a look at them; and I suppose if he ever really wants to see the crown jewels, he'll have to go to the Jewel Tower and look at them there, because he would hardly get his hands on anything before some dear old Archbishop would dash up and remove it and give it to someone else, and then all of a sudden they handed him a whole lot of things at once, and I honestly never felt so sorry for anyone in my whole life, because he had a golden ball with a cross on it in one hand, and a sceptre in the other, and something else in his lap. Swing said the poor man looked exactly like a college boy at a tea party, trying to balance a plate on his knee, with a teacup in one hand and a sandwich in the other.

Then the Archbishop took a sort of golden duck and unscrewed his neck – or maybe that happened before – I mean there was so much happened – and poured some oil out on a golden spoon, and for a moment I thought he was going to give it to the poor King, who looked as though he was ready to submit to just anything, but instead he just dipped his finger in it and made his mark on the King.

Oh, and I almost forgot the part where the Archbishop introduced the King to everybody in the Abbey on all four sides, and everyone shouted: 'Long live the King!' and trumpets sounded and I just had shivers all up and down my spine.

It was while the Archbishop was fussing with the crown before putting it on the King – the poor old thing was so nervous it almost slipped – the crown, I mean – that the Queen dropped her handkerchief. Those English girls just stood there and looked at it, or were watching the Coronation; so Swing, who was nearest, picked it up and gave it to her and made her a little curtsy – one she had learned from a French governess when she was just a child – and the Queen gave her the sweetest smile, although right after it I could see she was looking a little puzzled, poor dear. I mean, after all, she was sure she knew all the maids of honour, and there we were, you see; but in the sort of glittery light in the Abbey, our tiaras looked just as real as the others, and I thought I heard the captain fizzing a little.

Well, then there was a lot more ceremony and praying, and I really thought it would never end, and it was really very touching to see the lords paying homage to the King, and while it was all going on, I noticed a really wonderful-looking man in the most gorgeous uniform, standing right near us, and he had all kinds of glittering stars on his chest and things hung around his neck, and I recognised the gentleman who had been behind us when we entered the Abbey, only he was looking sort of pale and worn and terribly tired, and once I thought he seemed to sway a little, and so I whispered and asked him if he was all right, and he said: 'Oh, yes, quite. Quite all right, my dear.'

But he wasn't at all, and I had a sudden inspiration and said: 'Are you hungry?'

He whispered: 'Starved, my child. Been up all night, you know. Forgot to eat. Silly of me.'

'Would you care for a sandwich?'

'Would I care for a sandwich? Good Lord, child, you don't mean to tell me you have a sandwich?'

So I kicked Swing a little, and she gave me the pin she had brought along for the purpose, and I picked the threads of one of the panniers in my dress and got it open and sneaked him a cheese sandwich all nicely done up in waxed paper, and he almost swooned when he felt it in his hand, and then he sort of backed around behind a pillar, and when he returned he was looking much better, and he whispered: 'God bless you, my child. I don't know who you are, but you are obviously an angel dispatched by Heaven. I say, might I send a friend? Poor Crommartin is worse off than I was. Would you have another?'

I said, by all means, and when he wanted to know how we would recognise the friend, Swing said out of the corner of her mouth: 'Tell him to say you said he was O.K.'

So after a while a tall thin man, in really the most gorgeous velvet cloak I've ever seen, backed over and said: 'One, two, three, four, five from the end. Righto, the little one with the light-brown hair. I say, my dear, Buckminster said I was O.K.'

So we gave him a sandwich, and he hardly waited to get behind a pillar to eat it, poor dear, he was so hungry; and, of course, he had a friend; so we fed all we could, until our sandwiches were gone, and one of them had to do homage to the King, and he knelt there for the longest time, and everybody thought he was trying to swallow his emotion, but he wasn't, he was trying to swallow the last of our sandwich before he spoke his piece, and I was so nervous for fear he wouldn't get it down, I nearly died.

Well, they finally got around to crowning the Queen, and I was simply petrified I'd do the wrong thing, but we just watched the other maids of honour – I mean the real ones – and did what they did and stood where they stood, and there really wasn't anything for us to do, because there were four peeresses who held a sort of gold awning over her, though Swing and I were ready to step in and grab it if they dropped it, because they didn't look any too certain, the way they held it, and really the whole thing went off beautifully, except just as that love of an Archbishop of Canterbury put the ring on the Queen's finger and started to say: 'Receive this ring, the seal of a sincere faith——' Swing got the hiccups, and the Archbishop turned right around and looked at her, and it frightened Swing, but not enough.

Well, just as the Archbishop went to take the crown off the altar to crown the Queen, there was the most awful silence in the Abbey – I mean you couldn't hear anything except, of course,

Swing's hiccup – and I'm sure it was the most awful moment of my life, except one night at a hockey game in Chicago when a Yale boy in our party fell right out of our box on to the ice, and both teams skated right over him, and Captain Fizz had evidently made up his mind to end it all and kill Swing first, because I saw him sidling towards us, around in back, with murder in his eye, and, luckily, Swing saw him, too, and it frightened her so she stopped the hiccups, and the Archbishop crowned the Queen.

So after the Coronation part was over and the procession re-formed, we thought perhaps we had better not go with them any more, so we just went part of the way to where we had met them in the first place, and then cut down one of the cross aisles, because we had seen a door at the end of it; only we weren't quite fast enough, because Swing's heel got caught in her dress and nearly threw her, and Captain Fizz came after us, and we could see that he was still simply furious, so we just picked up our skirts and ran as fast as we could, with Captain Fizz right in back of us, and we did get through the door and out into the street, but there were soldiers on either side, forming a lane, and police behind them, so we couldn't turn off; and Captain Fizz was fizzing and breathing right on our necks, and there was a carriage drawn up at the door, and we were so absolutely panic-stricken we just ran to it and opened the door and jumped in, just as Captain Fizz said: 'Got you!' Only he hadn't.

Because, you see, there was this enormous coloured man sitting in the carriage – I mean he was really very handsome – and he was dressed in the most beautiful golden cloak I've ever seen in my life, and he had a gold thing sort of like a pagoda on his head, and gold chains around his neck, and a lot of stars and medals besides, and when Captain Fizz yanked open the door of the carriage, he leaned forward and said in just the softest voice:

'Iss something wrong?'

Well, I've never seen anything in my whole life like the look on poor Captain Fizz's face, he was simply mauve with wrath, but he had to step back and salute, and while he was saluting and saying: 'I beg your pardon, Your Highness,' the carriage drove off.

So that was how we saw the procession after the Coronation. I mean that is how we were in the procession, since we really were, because we were in the carriage of the Ambeok of Negotora, Sultan of Amu Penang, and, of course, he was a savage, though he spoke the most wonderful English, because he had been educated at Oxford; but he was a perfect dear, and he said he was so glad to see us, because he had thought he was going to have to take that long ride over the Coronation route all by himself, and wouldn't think of us leaving, and he told us all about himself and all his wives and his jewels, and it was such a relief really to find someone who had more chips than our families, and we told him all about Chicago and being débutantes, and about our parties, and he was quite fascinated, and said he would like to come to Chicago sometime and visit us, and Swing said: 'Yes, do,' and he had a golden stick with a sort of a fringe and little golden tassels on the end of it, and it seems it was his royal fly-swatter, and Swing offered to work it for him, and he was so pleased, not that there were any flies, but he was used to being where there were and just liked to have it worked anyway.

The streets were just packed with people, and when we drove down the Embankment past thousands and thousands of school-children, they all cheered, and the Ambeok taught us how to bow to the plaudits of the multitude. Really we've never made such a hit – I mean even our families would have been proud of us if they could have seen – and we were just hoping that some of our Chicago friends would recognise us – I mean we really had something there, what with the Ambeok grinning and bowing, and Swing patting him on the neck every so often with the royal fly-swatter, and me waving graciously – they simply would have died.

We were a great success on Oxford Street and at the Marble Arch, and going through Hyde Park I suggested to Swing if she didn't feel we ought to be thinking about going soon, because we were headed right back towards Buckingham Palace, where we were almost sure to run into Captain Fizz, who obviously didn't like us, and maybe the Sultan could drop us off somewhere and we would get a taxi home; but Swing was having such fun working the fly-swatter and improving her technique – she said she was just beginning to develop a backhand – that she simply wouldn't think of it, so we kept right on, and going through the arch on Constitution Hill, the Sultan asked Swing to marry him and promised to make her his number-one wife, and Swing, who is a dreamy sort of girl, said she would consider it, and then the dear, who was really so polite, asked me to marry him, too, so that we could go on being together and teach his women how to be débutantes.

Anyway, we promised to look him up at the Savoy, where he was stopping, and have a glass of sherry with him, and the carriage stopped at Buckingham Palace, and we said good-bye and he went inside, and there we were on the sidewalk and no taxi in sight, just as we walked right into the arms of Captain Fizz.

I nearly died. He fizzed furiously for a moment, and then took us each by the arm, saying: 'Aha! Dashed well knew I'd find you. Unauthorised presence in the Abbey. Interfering with the Coronation. You won't get away this time.'

'We didn't interfere,' said Swing. 'We helped. Stop pinching.'

'Not pinching,' said Captain Fizz. 'Going to turn you over to the police. Dashed cheek. Just like Americans.'

'I'm going to trip him,' Swing whispered to me. 'You run.' But before she could do it, another state coach drew up and stopped, and the handsome grey-haired man to whom we had fed the sandwich stepped out. He saw us and came right over and said: 'I say, Fitzwarrine, what's all this?'

Swing whispered: 'I knew his name would have something with a fizz in it.'

The captain didn't salute this time. But he straightened up and said: 'Caught them, Your Grace. Unauthorised entry into the Abbey. Joining in the Coronation procession. Interfering with the Coronation. Going to hand them over to the police. Teach these dashed Americans a lesson. Can't come over here and mix in our Coronation. We don't go over there and join in their Inauguration.'

The old gentleman addressed as 'Your Grace' looked at us for a moment and then said: 'They're angels, Fitzwarrine. There's been some mistake. They're angels. They gave me a sandwich when I was starving. Crommartin had one, too, and Trevelyan. . . . You haven't another one, have you?' This last he said to me.

Fitzwarrine fizzed a little and then said: 'Sorry, sir. Duty. Unauthorised presence in the Abbey. False ticket. Dangerous characters, probably. No other alternative but to hand them over.'

The nice old gentleman looked at us again, and smiled and said: 'My dears, who are you?'

I said: 'We're débutantes from Chicago.'

'I'm Janet Pierce,' said Swing, 'and this is Audrey Westmar. And you can send us both to jail if you want to, and we'll tell how we were swindled trying to buy a ticket to the Coronation. And I want to notify the London office of Harriman Pierce Stores.'

'Eh?' said Fitzwarrine. 'Eh? Harriman Pierce? Oh, I say. Not Harriman Pierce's daughter. Oh, I say, how awkward! How very awkward!'

'Very awkward for you!' said the old gentleman, who seemed to be enjoying something, to Fitzwarrine.

'I say,' said Fitzwarrine. 'Now I'm dashed if I know what to do. Most embarrassing. Duty and all that. Unauthorised presence in Abbey. Ought to hand you over.'

'Well,' said Swing, who has an uncanny way of knowing when she is going to come out on top, 'why don't you?'

'It's all very well to say why don't you,' said Fitzwarrine, 'but it puts me in a dashed peculiar position. You see, I'm Lord Eilton.'

Well, of course, as soon as he said that, I knew we had something, because Swing knows an awful lot about her father's business, and Lord Eilton was the chairman of the board of the English subsidiary of the Harriman Pierce Stores, and besides, he owned several large factories in Manchester and the Harriman Pierce Stores bought just scads of things from him.

So then the nice old gentleman we had fed in the Abbey turned out to be the Duke of Buckminster, the King's uncle, and a perfect darling, and he finally said: 'See here, Fitzwarrine, supposing I post-authorise the presence of these two young ladies in the Abbey. Will that relieve you? Blessed if I ever want to have a Coronation again without them . . . You're sure you haven't another sandwich anywhere about you, my dear?'

Well, that just fixed everything, and Captain Fizz – I mean Lord Eilton – was plenty relieved, and he really is a love when you get to know him and he hasn't got a Coronation on his mind, because it turned out he was something dreadfully official at this one, and he took us through the lines and got us a car and sent us home, but not before he invited us to be in his box at the Coronation Ball at the Albert Hall the next evening and talked a lot about hands across the sea, and I am sure he is going to ask Swing to marry him – everybody does – and if he does, I hope she'll tell him she's engaged to the Ambeok of Negotora, Sultan of Amu Penang, but anyway, I've never met so many sweet people in all my life, and we did see the Coronation for practically nothing and with no trouble at all, and yet a lot of people we met afterwards told us they couldn't even get near to see the procession.

The Roman Kid

This, I would say, was an example of a bad story grafted on to a good idea, but I have included it in this volume for a number of reasons, one of them being that it was selected for Anthony Boucher's ANTHOLOGY OF GREAT AMERICAN DETECTIVE STORIES. At the time I was writing it I didn't know that I was writing a detective story.

Every student of writing, particularly those anxious to crack the American fiction market, should know how to write a formula story. In THE ROMAN KID I should say the mechanics of this art are so glaring that it is hardly possible to miss the turning of the wheels and the wheels within wheels. This particular formula is the famous one used to describe most American fiction stories in three sentences: 'Boy meets girl. Boy loses girl. Boy gets girl' and you will see that so conscious was I of this cliché during the composition and telling of this story that I called attention to it myself in the ending.

And while the romance of THE ROMAN KID is the purest U.S.A. brand escape stuff, the basic idea of it is founded upon fact and one that you could verify for yourself the next time you are in Rome if you will go to the Museo delle Terme near the old Thermal Baths and ask to see the statue known as the Sitting Boxer.

This is a life-size bronze of a bearded Roman gladiator. He is wearing a Roman version of the boxing glove, an iron cestus laced to his hands with leather thongs, criss-crossing his forearms to the elbow. He has a cauliflower ear, the boxer's trade mark, a bashed-in nose and face and arms portraying numerous cuts and bruises, extraordinarily vivid delineations of the damage that can accrue to a fighter during the course of a rough evening, particularly when the mittens are made of iron instead of leather.

The sketch from which the sculptor moulded the original clay must have been made in the dressing-room immediately after a bout.

I first encountered the Sitting Boxer in 1933 when I visited Rome to negotiate with the Italian Government for a team of Italian amateur boxers to come to the U.S.A. for an international amateur boxing match with the championship New York Golden Gloves team. I spent a considerable amount of time in research in libraries, museums and the American Academy on what passed for sport in ancient Rome.

At this time I had the good fortune to make the acquaintance of Prentice Duell, the Harvard archaeologist and painter. Professor Duell, a brilliant, tough and most un-Professor-like young man was so kind as to guide me in my research work and we formed a lasting friendship. Together we went to Tarquinia to study frescoes on the walls, to the Etruscan tombs many of them reflecting the sporting proclivities of the one-time occupiers; we visited Roman stadia, the Colosseum and the Circus Maximus, and it was he who took me to the Terme Museum to see the statue of the Sitting Boxer.

The statue had only recently been excavated at that time and not much was known about it or the sculptor. It was thought possibly to have been one of a group and there was also a theory that this was a representation of the boxing king of a Greek island who forced anyone landing on his island to try conclusions with him.

Now, to a sports editor and veteran boxing writer who had seen many hundreds of professional and amateur fights and boxing matches, the statue and the condition of the old pugilist's face and arms and body spoke volumes. Every muscle, his attitude, his hands, the battered ears, and the marks on his features told their story, a story that anyone who had spent as many hours as I at the ringside and in the dressing-rooms of fighters before and after matches could read.

For days I had been sitting literally at Duell's feet, popeyed at his erudition and knowledge of antiquity, drinking in the wisdom he had excavated from the ages. Now for the first time I was confronted with a situation where I knew a lot of things he didn't know, and the temptation to show off to him a little was too great to resist. With somewhat studied casualness I said:

'Well now, I can't tell you anything about the period to which it belongs or the artist who made it, but I can tell you a little about the big guy himself, what he was like and how he fought, and maybe even something about the chap who mussed him up. For one thing he was a southpaw.'

'A what,' said Professor Duell startled.

'A southpaw – side winder – a left-hander.'

'How do you know?' Prentice asked.

'Why it's perfectly clear,' I said. 'Look here,' and I showed him.

The results were even more than I had hoped for and in a moment Professor Duell was most satisfactorily playing Watson to my Sherlock Holmes. Some of my deductions may have been far-fetched, but they were all logical and probable and consistent with the law of the prize-ring and my experience. All of these deductions you will find in THE ROMAN KID.

I was tremendously impressed with myself and afterwards we hastened to the bar of the Ambasciatori for some old-fashioneds. After the third the Professor swore that some day he would put my revelations regarding the Sitting Boxer into a book on archaeology, and after the fourth I swore that I would return the compliment and put Professor Duell likewise into a book. He kept his promise. So have I.

It wasn't until five years later, while I was working as a feature writer for International News Service and wanted passage money to get back to England in the spring, that I thought of using the idea of the Sitting Boxer in a short story.

The hero, Tommy Thompson the sports writer who works for the 'Daily Blade,' is obviously autobiographical, but physically I made him into a friend of mine, the late Edward Neale the sports writer for the 'Associated Press.' Neale had resigned as a sports writer to go to Spain as a war correspondent. He was killed by a shell while reporting the civil war, the first of many famous newspaper reporters and war correspondents to die in this fashion. I envied Eddie when he left on this assignment. I was saddened when he was killed.

THE ROMAN KID

'Bon giorno,' said Tommy Thompson. 'Ubi est the——' he paused and then concluded that he had made sufficient concession to what he thought was the Italian language, and finished: 'Could a guy take a gander at the Tertullian Fragment?'

The girl at the desk of the Antiquity Room of the Museo Romano flinched a little and then cocked her bright head to one side and repeated slowly, with a reflective pause after each word:

'Could – a – guy – take – a – gander – guy – take – gander. Gander is the male of goose.' She stopped and looked at Tommy with the corners of her mouth drawn down and a sort of despair in her eyes.

Tommy suddenly realised that she had a face of infinite humour, and that the humour somehow managed to disguise its beauty, or rather made you less conscious of it. Unlike the Italian women to whom he had already grown accustomed during his short sojourn in Rome, she had masses of soft hair, the colour of early morning sunlight, large light-blue eyes, and a small nose. But Tommy felt that here was a person with whom one instinctively wanted to laugh. So he laughed.

'Excuse it please,' he said. 'Maybe I ought to talk English. My Italian is terrible. I wanted to get a squint at that fragment of manuscript by the first Roman boxing writer. I read a piece about it in the Paris *Herald*. They're supposed just to have dug it up and it's the only existing description of an early boxing match. Some Greek fed a Roman plenty of left hands and stopped him . . .'

The girl shook her head and said plaintively: 'Why did they not teach to me the right kind of English?' Her mouth was thin, wide, mobile, and slightly pathetic. She was tiny and dressed in a long, blue smock. 'I have taken very high marks in English, but it is the wrong kind. You are an American. Are you an archaeologist?'

'Who, me? Jiminy, no.' Tommy grinned again. He was a pleasant-looking man in his late twenties with a broad, wide-open face and a strange two-inch patch of grey that ran through his dark hair from front to back. 'I'm a sports writer. You know – boxing, baseball, and stuff. I do a column on the *Blade* in New York. But I'm a sucker for this ancient history. I'm supposed to be collecting a team of Italian amateur boxers to take back to fight our Golden Glovers, but I've been spending most of my time trying to find out what sports were like in ancient Rome. Very tough. If they had any columnists in those days, they buried 'em deep.'

The girl gazed at him, her face alive with intense interest. Finally she said flatly: 'Americans are wonderful people. Come. I show you.'

She led him down an aisle between massive bronzes and pieces of ancient frescoes to a small alcove where there was a little pedestal holding up a flat glass frame. Under the glass was a small triangle of stained brown manuscript that looked like a piece of old rag. It was six inches across the top and about four down one side. Tommy could discern faintly the black brush characters on it.

'That,' said the girl, 'is the Tertullian Fragment.'

Tommy stared at it and then said: 'Oh oh! I knew there'd be a catch to it. It's in Latin, isn't it?'

The thing Tommy liked about the girl was that she didn't crack. An American girl would have said: 'What did you expect it would be in, eight-point Bodoni, with subheads?'

Instead she said gently: 'I will translate it for you.' She leaned over the case, her eyes shining with interest and concentration, and read slowly in her fine, precise English with the slight accent that Tommy had not yet placed:

Falernus, the Senator, in his accusations, pointed to the scandal of the Emperor [Titus, the girl explained] who saved the life of Sinistrus his defeated boxer because of his love for Aula, the sister of the vanquished gladiator. All Rome, he said, knew that Sinistrus deserved to die because by his defeat at the hands of the Greek, Phistra, a small but nimble boxer, who by the quickness of eye and hand and the agility of his legs remained uninjured during the combat, while inflicting many wounds upon his taller, stronger, opponent, the Emperor's gladiator drew the laughter of the multitude, thus bringing discredit upon the purple. Nevertheless the Emperor, with a glance at the box of the patrician Reglus, where sat the girl Aula, and in the face of the tumult of the mob demanding death for Sinistrus, who lay bleeding from many wounds as well as exhausted by his efforts, signified that his life should be spared. These matters, declared Falernus, were common knowledge . . .

The girl stopped and looked up. 'It ends there,' she said.

'Gee,' said Tommy. 'The little guy just stepped around and popped him. A sort of a Fancy Dan. I'll bet it was a lousy fight. I never saw one of those that wasn't. Maybe it was a splash. Titus sends his man into the tank and then coppers on the bets. There was a dame angle in those days too, eh? Gosh, you know, you're wonderful. You translated that at sight.'

'Perhaps,' said the girl, 'you will return the compliment and translate for me too.'

'I apologise,' said Tommy. 'I didn't mean to be rude. Whenever I start to talk fight, I fall into that jargon. They were funny guys, those old reporters. They didn't care a hang about the sports and never wrote about them unless there was some political angle to it – like this guy Tertullus. I guess when your space was limited and there weren't any printing presses, you had to stick to things that were important. Nobody seems to know much about what a show was really like at the Colosseum because nobody ever wrote about them. I guess they just stuck up a copy of the results and the box score somewhere in the Forum and let it go at that.'

A tall, stoop-shouldered man came through a door that opened from a small office at the rear of the little alcove, and spoke to the girl in German. He was grey-haired, grey-faced, and weary-looking. He wore a gold pince-nez attached to a black ribbon. The girl answered him and then turned to Tommy: 'This is my father, Professor Lisschauer, the curator of the museum. Papachen, this is an American gentleman who is interested in the sports of antiquity.'

Tommy shook hands. 'Thompson is my name, sir. The *Blade*, New York. Sports writer. Your daughter was kind enough to translate the fragment for me.'

The old man had a pronounced accent. He said: '*Ja, ja.* Leni haff just tolt me. You do not read Greek and Latin?'

Tommy shook his head. 'I – I'm afraid what little education I have, I got the hard way. I mean I had to go to work when I was a kid.'

The old man looked at him puzzled and then glanced sharply at his daughter.

'Then how can you be a student of antiquitation? It iss impossible.'

Tommy felt uncomfortable. There was a detachment about the professor that shut him out completely. He did not want to be shut out. He tried to explain:

'I – I'm trying to get the feel of things. I mean the people of those days and what they were like. Behind all these inscriptions and statuary and stuff there were people – you know, human beings. They couldn't have been such a lot different from us. That fighter, for instance, I saw in one of those wall paintings in Tarquinia, squared off with his thumb stuck out ready for a left lead to the eyeball. You could just see him getting ready to say: "Excuse me, pal," and then cross the right while the other guy is still blinking. He must have been the Gentleman Jones of Etruria. Gentleman Jones is a light heavy we have around New York. Polite, smooth, and very sporting in the ring, but he loves to stick that thumb in the other guy's eye. What I mean is maybe those old-time sports were just like that . . .'

Professor Lisschauer looked baffled, shook his head, and said: 'The reading of the ancients requires years of study.' He sighed. 'And then sometimes it iss nod enough. You are wasting your time. You will excoose me please.'

He turned and shambled away. His daughter watched him go. On her face was pain and concern.

'Gee,' said Tommy, 'did I say something? I guess I'm just a dumb cluck. I didn't mean——'

The girl shook her head. There was a brightness in her eyes. Tommy saw that they were close to tears. 'Papachen iss in some trouble. That is all. He did not wish to be impolite. He thinks only of his work. Ach, if I could only help him . . .'

'Is it anything serious? I mean is there anything I could——'

Leni smiled. 'You are kind. I am afraid you would not understand. His integrity. His years of hard work. And then to lose everything.' She stopped. 'Forgive me. It iss private trouble. I should not bore you.'

She hesitated and then suddenly asked: 'Have you seen the famous statue of the *Resting Boxer*? It iss in the Museo delle Terme.' She raised her head proudly with a significance that Tommy did not understand at the time. 'It iss a discovery of my papa.'

'I haven't,' said Tommy. 'But I will. Do you suppose you – I mean, would you go along with me some time, to – to——'

'Take – a – gander – at it?' finished Leni.

'The once-over,' said Tommy.

'The once-over,' repeated Leni.

'A quick peek——'

'A quick peek.'

'You're on.'

'You're on. Does that mean yes?' Leni asked.

'Yes.'

'Yes. You're on.'

Their laughter joined and echoed from the quiet caverns of the museum. They took each other's hands on it. Something told Tommy that this was not the time to kiss her. But there was nothing to stop him from wanting to.

They met two days later, on a bright, clear, warm spring Sunday, and went to Alfredo's, where Tommy, entranced, watched Alfredo's showmanship as he manipulated the Fetuccini in the melted butter, and later they ate his famous sole in white-wine sauce and exchanged bits of information about their lives.

The Lisschauers were Viennese. Leni's father, a famous archaeologist, was the curator of the Museo Romano. Leni herself had studied with him for many years.

'Gee,' said Tommy. 'I knew there was something. My mother came from Vienna. My father was an American. And you can read the past as though it were a book. And yet you're sweet and simple. I've never met anyone like you. Shut up, Thompson, you're ga-ga!'

'Ga-ga?' said Leni.

'Soft in the head,' explained Tommy, and then added under his breath: 'about you,' continuing aloud: 'You must learn our beautiful language. I'll teach you if you'll help me with my ancient history.'

Leni looked at him curiously with her large eyes. 'You are a strange boy, are you not? You write about the sports and you are interested in antiquity. I thought Americans only cared about to make money.'

'I love it,' confessed Tommy – 'making money, I mean; but I don't let it get me down. What do you like to do besides read old Latin manuscripts at sight?'

'Oh,' said Leni, thinking seriously and counting on the fingers of one hand, 'I like to dance, to play tennis, to ski, to . . .'

'That's done it,' interrupted Tommy. 'There's a tea dance at my hotel at five. What do you say we go and step?'

Leni nodded her head violently in assent. They toasted each other in Lacrima Cristi on that . . .

They kept meaning to go to the Museo delle Terme all through the afternoon. But there was such a fine blue Roman sky and the smell of flowers in the air – Tommy could not be sure whether it was flowers or Leni, who was dressed in a simple white frock with a little girl's sash at the waist, and a big straw hat – and also they acquired a cab-driver named Pietro Dandolo whose fine brown horse was named Ginevra. Pietro sang snatches of operatic arias as he drove – sang them very quietly to himself. And although it was warm, he still wore his rusty blue coat and shoulder cape and battered silk hat, and he sang his orders to Ginevra instead of speaking them, which was why Tommy and Leni grew to love him. Tommy engaged him for the whole day.

He drove them through the Porta Pinciana and the fragrance of the Borghese gardens to the Plaza de Popolo. From there they crossed the Tiber over the Ponte Margherita and went rolling along the muddy river past the Castel Sant' Angelo, and the Salviati and Corsini palaces. It seemed so natural that all the time Leni's hand should be in Tommy's, and their fingers intertwined.

Tommy told Leni something about himself and the curious life he lived in New York – the constant round of prizefights, baseball games, golf and tennis matches. At fifteen he had had to quit school and start in as an office boy in the sports department of the *Blade*. His father had been a singing teacher who had been

ruined by the depression. Tommy's education had been continued by his father to the best of his ability. He had a talent for
writing and had become sports editor and columnist and lived
in an atmosphere of athletes, competition, and sweat. But in
Tommy too there was a reaching for beauty, and a sensitivity to
human beings and what made them tick. The bright girl at his
side was stirring a yearning in him, one that he felt unable to
express, except in the curious language of his life and his trade.
On her part, the girl was fascinated by the strangeness of this
American, his vitality and animation, but with her feminine intuition she already felt the hungry, incompleted side of his nature
and was drawn to it.

They recrossed the Tiber by the Ponte Palatino and drove back
through the wonderful, shining city, past the great Victor
Emmanuel monument and the Palazzo Venezio to the Ambas-
sadeurs, where they went down to the little café below and
danced Viennese waltzes and Tommy taught Leni American
slang and she came to look with a fond joy for the wide grin that
spread over his face when he interpreted.

'You're the tops. Get it? It means there was never anybody
like you ever before. You're the number-one gal.'

Leni repeated after him solemnly: 'I – am – the – tops.'

'Here's another one. Carrying the torch. When you're crazy
about someone – like "Baby, am I carrying the torch for you!"
Get it?'

'I get it,' said Leni, copying Tommy's intonation exactly. 'Can
I carry the torch for you too, or is the torch only for gentlemen?'

The whirling waltzes and the unity that comes from the perfect
matching of rhythm and movement finished them. By the time
they went to the famous Ulpia restaurant, hard by the Trajan
Forum, for dinner, they were in love. They sat close together in
the damp cool of the grotto below with the magic upon them,
their hands tightly clasped, listening to the little orchestra, the
guitars and mandolins and the blind violinist with the wonderful
throbbing tone. The old grotto was carved out of the tufa of the
buildings of the Forum. Dim lanterns faintly showed the garlands
of spring flowers, the hanging basket bottles of Chianti, and the
bits of old marbles and pieces of ancient friezes.

Tommy said: 'Gee, Leni, I've got a nerve to spring this on
you this way, but I can't help it. I'm going for you. I've never
gone for a gal this way in my life. Do – do I have to translate
that for you too?'

Leni took Tommy's hand and held it to her cheek and shook
her head that way, holding it. She said simply and directly: 'Oh,

strange, American Tommy. I am afraid that I going for you too.'

'I want to kiss you,' said Tommy, flatly. 'Would anybody care?'

Leni looked at him with her eyes dancing like wood sprites. 'This is Rome,' she said. 'The old gods would like it very much.'

They kissed each other. They kissed each other again until the sweetness was no longer bearable. 'Oh gee,' said Tommy, 'I heard the gods cheering . . .'

'I did too,' said Leni, 'only I think it was Benedetto.'

Benedetto, the enormous proprietor, waddled over to the table with a bottle of wine. He said: 'Bravo! Bravo! Signor, signorina, permit me, the compliments of the Ulpia.'

'Looka,' said Tommy, after they had drunk a toast with Benedetto, 'let's get this straight now. I love you. I'll never love anybody but you. I want to marry you. But quick. I want to take you back to New York with me. I never want you out of my sight from now on.'

Leni took his hand and said: 'Oh, Tommy. I think perhaps I want to also so much . . .'

And then the dancing went out of her eyes and she caught her breath sharply and let go of Tommy's hand. He could see that something inside her had gone limp.

'Oh oh——' he said. 'Trouble. What is it, Leni? Is there another guy?'

The girl suddenly was frightened and a little panicky. 'Oh, Tommy – I should not have let myself go so. It iss so different with us here. It has been understood for so long that I will be the wife of Professor Zanni. He is Papa's associate. I know that Papachen wishes it. And we here are different with our families. Papa is everything. He would not understand you. And just now, when he is in such deep trouble. Oh, Tommy, I shall die . . .'

Tommy spoke a little grimly. 'I get it. When I walk into Madison Square Garden or Twenty-one, I'm a big shot, but in this set-up Mr Thompson of the New York *Blade* is just John Mugg.' He paused, and when he caught Leni looking baffled again, said: 'Never mind, sweet, that's one I didn't want you to understand. Look, what is the trouble your dad's in? Tell me about it, Leni.'

Leni said: 'Oh, Tommy,' again, and then replied: 'It is about the statue of the *Resting Boxer*. The one – the one we did not see. Papa discovered it near the Fosso delle Tre Fontane. It was his great discovery. It is one of the most perfect bronzes ever found. Papa has written that it is in the style and manner of the

sculptor Præxus in the time of the Emperor Titus. Mussolini
made Papa a Commendatore because the statue is of the Golden
Age of Rome . . .'

'And so——'

'And so a Professor Guglielmo in Napoli has published a paper
on the statue, against Papa. He is a very important man in
archaeology. He has written that the statue is – how do you
say?– a——'

Tommy whistled. 'I get it. A phony.'

'Is false. Is a fraud. Three years ago the Manzini brothers were
put into jail because they had made and buried many statues
that were – that were phony, as you say. Now they are both
dead. Professor Guglielmo has written that the statue my father
has discovered is a fraud of the Manzini brothers.'

'Well, isn't your dad's word as good as his?'

'Guglielmo is an important man in Italy. He is high in the
party. And we are Austrians. And proof? What is there but that
which Papa has from his years of study, from his knowledge? . . .'

Tommy chewed on his lower lip. 'And unless he can prove
he's right, he loses his job. Nice. This guy you're supposed to
marry. Where does he figure in this set-up?'

Leni frowned. 'He iss terribly unhappy. He is afraid that Professor Guglielmo may be right.'

'Just a pal,' said Tommy. 'And if your father goes out, he goes
in.'

'Oh, Tommy,' cried Leni, 'how did you know?'

'It's got a familiar ring to it, sweet.' Tommy sighed. 'At this
point, enter our hero. And what does he do? He does nothing.
On account of he's just a dumb sports writer. It's a fine plot, up
to there.'

'Plot, Tommy?'

'Mmmm. Boy loves girl. Girl's father does not love boy. In
fact, he does not know boy exists. Girl's father is in jam. Buckety,
buckety, here comes boy on a white horse, rescues father. Father
says: "Bless you, my children." Boy gets girl. Only this one has
me stopped. Cold. As a hero I'm just a columnist. Let's get out
of here, Leni, and go for a drive. I want to cool my head off.'

They filled their pockets with sugar for Ginevra, the horse.
Pietro Dandolo was sitting on the box singing the 'M'appari' aria
from *Martha* to himself, so they fed Ginevra until he had finished
and then got in. Pietro said something in Italian to Leni and
started off.

'Where is he going?' asked Tommy. 'Not that it matters on a
night like this.'

'He says because there is so big a moon, he is driving us to the Colosseo.'

The indeed so big moon shone through the skeleton of the Colosseum and illuminated the simple white cross erected on the spot where the Christian martyrs died. Leni and Tommy wandered in through the main entrance, their arms about each other's waist, picking their way around the pieces of fallen pillars and slabs of tufa and marble cornices. The great shell of the ancient arena was deserted except for the many huge Colosseum cats who lived there. Sometimes the moonlight picked up their eyes and made them glitter. The shadows seemed alive with their slinking figures, and sometimes their shapes were outlined, sitting on the long, broken columns.

Leni and Tommy sat close together on a drum-shaped slab of broken pillar and soaked in the feel of the place, the ancient quiet, and the beauty of the rising tiers of tumbled stone and the silhouettes of the arches.

Leni began to speak in her soft, expressive voice. 'There, in the centre, is the box where the Emperor sat. There was a great purple cloth that hung from it. The patricians and the Senators were in the near-by boxes, according to their rank. In that little gallery above sat the courtesans. The plebs, the common people, were up at the top.'

'The gallery boys,' said Tommy. 'I guess a chump had no more chance of getting a ringside seat at this show than a guy named plain Joe Doakes could crash the first five rows at a heavyweight championship fight at the Yankee Stadium.'

'On days when the sun was too hot, or there was rain, there was a great canopy erected that covered the whole arena like a roof, a canopy of many colours.'

Tommy grunted. 'We're civilised. We let our customers sit out in the rain at Palmer Stadium and the Yale Bowl.'

'They could let in water and cover the whole floor of the arena enough to stage sea battles, of which the Emperor was very fond. Have you seen the excavations at the other end? In the time of Titus the floor of the arena was many levels below this one. We are sitting on the dust of twenty centuries.'

'I looked at them. You know what they reminded me of? – The basement of Madison Square Garden, our big indoor arena in New York, at circus time. Runways for the animals, cages, dressing-rooms. And nobody really knows very much about the shows they put on here, or what it was like, do they, Leni? There is the Emperor's box. There sat the big shots, there the girls. There was a canopy. Men fought with weapons and with their hands. Christians and slaves and condemned prisoners were torn to pieces by wild animals. And that's all.'

Leni sighed. 'It is all so long dead, Tommy. One must be so careful of the records one reads into stones.'

Tommy sprang up suddenly from the drum of the pillar and took a few steps into the arena. The floor was white with moonlight, and the grey patch that ran through his hair looked like solid silver. He spread his arms wide with his fists clenched and shook them and cried: 'But it isn't dead, Leni. Can't you feel it? All the people. There were people here. Thousands of them. Human beings. The place was alive with them. What's two thousand years? They must have been just like us. Leni, it drives me crazy. I want to see them. I want to bring this place to life.'

He stopped suddenly, shoved his hands deep into his pockets, and began to pace, and the dark shapes of the cats scattered to the deeper shadows. He spoke again. 'This couldn't have been so different from what we know – World Series day, or fight night at the Polo Grounds, or the Harvard-Yale game at New Haven. Crowds coming in to see the show, pushing and gabbing. . . . If you'll listen, you can hear the scrape of thousands of sandals on the ramps and that excited hum and chatter of a crowd going to a show. You would hear snatches of conversation. They must have talked in Roman slang as they went to their seats the same way we do – 'Who do you like tonight? What do you hear? I've got a good tip on the third prelim. A new guy down from the north – they say he's a honey, fast and shifty. He's fighting for the Blues . . . Is it true that Decius, or whatever he was called, is out of shape? They say he didn't train a lick. A wise guy. I heard the main go was in the bag. I got it from the inside. Friend of mine who knows the guy who trains the gladiators. I'm gonna have a couple of bucks riding on Drusus. He's a house fighter. Those guys haven't blown a decision yet . . .' Pushing and shoving, and sweating, and laughing . . .'

Leni was standing too, now, her face pale, reflected from the white ball of the nearly full moon that now hung directly over the black shell of the old arena. Her lips were parted with excitement. She did not understand much of what Tommy was saying, but the feeling of it was reaching her. 'Oh, Tommy. Please go on.'

'Crooks, gamblers, sports, pickpockets, actors, writers, just plain people out for fun, guys with their dolls, and the dolls dressed and made up to kill – I've seen their paint pots in the museums, big-shot gangsters, lawyers – Rome was lousy with lawyers, politicians, the regular fight crowd. Why you can work right back from the numbers on the portals, Leni. If they numbered the portals they must have had tickets that corresponded to the numbers.'

'Yes – yes, Tommy. They were made of bone, I think.'

'Then they must have had ticket-takers and directors and ushers. It was probably a political job. Maybe they even had programmes——' he grinned suddenly, widely. 'Can't you see the programme-sellers standing under those arches and on the ramps, and by the stairways hollering: "Get your programmes here. You can't tell the gladiators without a programme. Names and numbers of the Christian martyrs." '

He threw up his head and gazed around the great amphitheatre to the entrance arcades. 'And what about grub, and concessionaires? There never yet was a sports crowd that didn't get hungry and thirsty. There must have been venders selling things to eat and drink. What would the Roman equivalent have been of our hot dogs and peanuts and beer and pop?'

'Meat on a stick, probably,' said Leni; 'yes, and fruit . . .'

'They probably hollered just the same as ours: "Get it red-hot here!' and wine——'

'The *vinarii*,' interrupted Leni, almost breathless, 'the wine merchants. They carried it around in skins . . .'

'Red wine and white. Didn't they used to cart snow down from the mountains to cool it? "Ice-cold, ice-cold, ice-cold! Get your ice-cold *vino* here, ten cents a cup. Who'll have a cup? Sweet or sour, sir?" Noise, cries, excitement, and maybe the mob up in the two-bit seats stamping their feet because they wanted the show to begin. And the guys selling souvenirs. "Show your colours." The blue and the white. Hawkers, with blue ribbons and white ones. "Show your colours, folks. What's your favourite?" '

'Oh, and little clay figurines of the gods,' breathed Leni, 'for the good luck.'

'Sure. And statuettes of the favourite gladiators to carry or tie to your tunic the way the gals who go up to New Haven for the Army-Yale game pin a little bulldog or Army mule to their coats.'

'And girls selling garlands of flowers to throw into the arena to the victors,' Leni said. 'There they stand, with flowers in their dark hair, and the garlands over their arms . . .'

Tommy put his arm around Leni's shoulder in glee and pointed to the vast floor of the arena. "They had to get ready, didn't they? Set the arena for the show? There are the roustabouts – slaves, I suppose – marking off the combat areas, looking after the props, preparing the boxes of sand to cover up the bloodstains. There'd be the officials, and judges and referees and masters of ceremony, dressed up to kill and strutting like an A.A.U. official in his hard hat at a big track meet. Officials are all alike. The crowd is sifting to its seats. People are visiting from box to box, laughing and making bets. Whistling breaks out from the top tiers as a gladiator comes out to try the footing and look at the direction of the sun so that if he wins the toss he can get it to his back. I guess man could whistle from the time he had a mouth.

'And can you get an idea of the dressing-rooms below? The taping and bandaging and last-minute advice to the fighters, and the swordsmen limbering up and doing knee flexes and lunges and making passes with their short swords, and the boxers shadow-boxing to warm up, the way every fighter has since guys first put up their dukes, and whistling their breath out of their noses as they punched at the air. And I guess maybe down in the dungeons the Christians were on their knees, quietly pray-ing. And sometimes over the noise of the crowd and the cries of the candy butchers and wine-sellers and hawkers you would hear from deep down the impatient roaring of the beasts, the way sometimes when the circus is in the Garden and there is a sudden lull and you hear the lions from down below . . .'

Leni was crying: 'Oh, Tommy, Tommy, you have made this place of the long ago, so alive . . .' Her eyes were shining, and now she too stood with her head thrown back and her arms outstretched towards the slender white cross. 'These things were so. They were. Oh, they were.'

Suddenly she stopped short and spun around facing the man and cried sharply: 'Tommy!' and again: 'Tommy!'

Tommy was startled. There was such a strange look on her face. Her eyes were so wide. 'Sweet, what is it?'

The girl suddenly placed both hands to her temples and held them and spoke in German: '*Ach, lieber Herrje! Es ist nicht möglich – aber doch – doch——*'

'Honey, what's happened?'

Leni ran to him. 'Tommy, you must come with me at once. But at once. It is still early. You *will* come with me. I have had – oh how do you say it? Something inside of me, all through me.'

Tommy held her off. 'Is it a hunch, honey?'

'Oh yes, yes, Tommy. Is that the word? Something inside of me that has told me something.'

'Do you want to tell me about it?'

Leni shook her head. 'N-no. Not yet. But you will come . . .'

She took him by the hand and together they ran out of the

arena, frightening the cats again. Pietro was so startled that he stopped in the middle of the Toreador song.

'*Trenta,* Via Palestro, *e presto,*' ordered Leni. They scrambled into the carriage, and a surprised and startled Ginevra rattled them over the cobblestones and on to the smooth asphalt of the Via del Impero, at what, to the best of her recollection, was a gallop.

Leni said: 'I do not want to say yet, Tommy. Just hold me, please.'

The address was a private house, not far from the Museo Romano. 'Our home,' Leni said. She still had Tommy by the hand as she rang the front doorbell. A pleasant-faced elderly woman in a black dress and white apron came to the door. Leni said breathlessly in German: 'Ach, Liesel. Is Papa still up?'

The woman replied: 'He is not at home, Miss Leni. The Conte Alberini came. They both went away together. I believe they were to go to the Museo delle Terme.'

Leni wasted no time. She cried: 'Come. Oh, if it is not too late. *Presto, Pietro al Museo delle Terme.* The little door on the Via Gernaia side . . .'

Ginevra, thoroughly outraged, clattered them past the huge grey Station Centrale, whipped them around a corner on two wheels and deposited them before a tiny iron door in a high, thick wall. Leni seized a bell pull and jangled a bell wildly and then pounded with her little fist so that the iron door rattled and clanged.

The door was finally opened by an ancient attendant in a faded blue uniform coat.

'I am Leni Lisschauer, Professor Lisschauer's daughter,' Leni said. 'Is my papa here?'

The attendant nodded. '*Si, si signorina.* It is a little irregular. We are closed. They are all on the second floor with the Conte Alberini. You may come.'

He had an old lantern, and by its dim rays he led them, Leni still clinging to Tommy's hand, through a garden in which were many shadowy statues, to the dark and gloomy museum built on the site of the old thermal baths. It grew lighter as they went up the stairs to the second floor. The room at the far end of the museum was illuminated and they heard voices coming from it.

Leni, still towing Tommy, broke into a little run. They burst into the room. The four men there turned and stared.

One of them was Professor Lisschauer. He looked very old. The second was tall and dignified, with a black beard and a monocle. With him stood a short, fussy, baldheaded little man wearing pince-nez attached to a black ribbon. The fourth was a thin man with a narrow face and long black hair combed back from a high forehead.

But the thing that caught Tommy's eye was not so much the men, but the great bronze on a marble pedestal in the centre of the room. It was the figure of a naked man seated, his arms resting on upper legs, his hand encased in the iron-studded, hard-leather cesti worn by the ancient pugilists, with thongs extending halfway up to his elbows and ending in a tight leather cuff.

His head was turned to the right looking up over his right shoulder. He was curly-headed and bearded, heavy-muscled. He had been through a terrific battering. On his right shoulder and right elbow and in the criss-crossed thongs of the right forearm were three deep and gaping cuts. His ears were cauliflowered, ballooned, and cut. His nose had been smashed to one side and cut, his lips puffed, his cheekbone swollen and gashed. His eyes showed the heavy ridges of the professional prizefighter, and traces of old scars as well as new wounds. The cesti, which were thick and about two and a half inches wide, covering the knuckles and letting the fingers protrude, had sharp cutting edges, and the two halves were held together around the hand with narrow strips of iron.

The thin man with the lank black hair made a little movement towards Leni, but her father was the first to recover. He spoke to her in German:

'Leni! What are you doing here? Who is this man? Ah yes, he was at the museum. I remember. But why?' He stopped, turned to the group, and said in Italian: 'Forgive me. Count Alberini, I believe you have met my daughter. Professor Guglielmo, my daughter Leni.'

Leni introduced Tommy. The bearded, monocled man was Count Alberini, State Director of Museums and Art, the fussy little baldheaded man was Guglielmo. The thin, narrow-faced one with the long hair was Armando Zanni, Lisschauer's assistant. Then she turned to her father. 'Papachen – what has happened?'

'It is all over, my child. Count Alberini has accepted the statement and the testimony of Professor Guglielmo. The Manzini brothers were once known to have made a statue of a boxer. Zanni has had no alternative but to agree with him. I have given my resignation. The Count has been very kind. He brought Professor Guglielmo here from Naples to confront me and give me a last chance to prove my case. I could not.'

Leni turned to Tommy quickly and translated what her father had said, in pain and in panic. The Count was coughing discreetly and then spoke softly and deprecatingly in English: 'Your pardon. But this is indeed a very private matter. This young man——' He looked inquiringly at Leni.

The girl turned. 'He is an expert——' She was very close to tears.

Professor Guglielmo removed his pince-nez and cocked his head to one side and asked: 'Of antiquity?'

'No,' cried Leni, her young voice ringing bravely and defiantly through the room. 'No! Of life!' Suddenly she turned to Tommy and wailed: 'Oh, Tommy – Tommy! Do something! Make him live. Bring him to life for me the way you did the old people of the Colosseo. Tommy . . .'

Tommy caught her by the shoulders and said: 'I get it. Keep your chin up. I get the picture.' He faced the group of men. 'Do all of you gentlemen understand English?'

They all bowed. Zanni said: 'But naturally. It is a part of education.'

'Good,' said Tommy. 'Anything you don't understand Leni will translate for you. She's on to my jargon.' He grinned pleasantly at Zanni. 'Education sometimes has its limits. Leni, tell all these guys to keep their shirts on. I want five minutes with this old chap. Maybe I can help.'

He stepped out of the circle and walked slowly over to the statue while the four men and the girl stood watching him. He spoke to himself very slowly as he stood in front of the great bronze, his hands in his pockets, his head cocked a little to one side——

'The Roman Kid, eh? What a licking you took! . . . Gee, shave off those whiskers, and you could be Paolino sitting on the rubbing table in the dressing-room at the Yankee Stadium after Max Schmeling got through with him. What a pasting! . . . That's a lovely pair of tin ears you've got, my friend. You just never bothered to duck, eh? Oh what a job – what a job! . . .'

He commenced to circle the statue slowly, examining it minutely. He fingered the three cuts on the right side, went suddenly to the other side and examined the left arm, whistled, and said: 'Oh oh, side-winder!' He inspected the hands carefully and then hopped up on to the pedestal, fingered and examined the cuts on the face, the bruises and abrasions and scars. He jumped down to the floor again, and suddenly fell into a boxing stance, looked at the statue again and changed it, and then walked rapidly around it again. Once he addressed himself to Count

Alberini. 'These cuts,' he said, 'are definitely cuts? Not accidents? Ages of being buried, or being tossed around?'

'We do not believe it has been buried for ages,' the Count replied with a little smile, 'but the cuts and marks were all placed there by the sculptor.'

'Thanks,' said Tommy. 'That's all I wanted to know.' He made one more circle around the statue and then backed away from it with a little gesture of salute and said: 'Thanks, pal. There's been many a guy since your time who's had his ears pinned back just the way yours were.' He turned and faced the group, uttered something out of the corner of his mouth to Leni that sounded like 'Buckety, buckety,' and then said with a fine, studied, dramatic carelessness that delighted him: 'Gentlemen, what would you like to know about this guy?'

It was old Professor Lisschauer who grasped at the straw. He said: 'What? Iss there anything you can tell us?' There was deep despair in his voice, which made Tommy suddenly ashamed of his fine pose. He dropped it.

'Plenty,' he said grimly. 'In the first place, the guy was a southpaw.'

'A which?' inquired Professor Guglielmo politely.

'Portsider. He was left-handed. I'll bet most guys hated to fight him. Nobody likes to fight a southpaw.'

Count Alberini looked interested. 'So?' he said. 'How do you determine this?'

'Looka,' said Tommy. 'You can't miss it.' He stepped up to the statue, took a pencil from his pocket, and used it as a pointer. 'Here! Deep cut on right shoulder. Another on the arm just below the elbow. Another on the forearm inside the lacings. No cuts on the left shoulder or arm whatsoever. Here's how the orthodox boxer stands——' Tommy fell into the regular stance, left hand, left foot forward. 'Here's how this guy stood——' He reversed his position and stood with his right foot forward, right arm extended and curled, left arm bent at his side. 'Get it?' he said. 'The reason he has those cuts on the right arm is because that is the part of him that was closest to his opponent.'

For the first time light came back to Leni's face. The Count solemnly walked over to the statue, inserted his monocle in his eye, inspected the three cuts one after another, assumed the left-handed boxing stance that Tommy had taken, straightened up, slapped his thigh and said: *'Per Bacco!'*

'Uhuh!' said Tommy. 'And anyway, the guy's had a busted left duke – hand, I mean. That artist didn't miss a thing. Here, you can see the swelling where it knit badly. He used the left for the Sunday punch. That would be the one most likely to go. All right. He wasn't a boxer. He was a slugger. All he wanted to do was to get in close enough to lay in that left – which meant curtains. Get it?'

Guglielmo walked over, adjusted his pince-nez, and said: 'You can explain that?'

'Look at the ears on him,' said Tommy. 'Guys who can box don't get marked up that way. This guy's had a hell of a licking. All those bums who take five to give one wind up with pretzel ears and scarred eyebrows. He's got the musculature of a slugger too, and the legs. Here, look at all these heavy muscles behind the shoulders and down the back, and on the arms. The fast boxer and snap hitter has slender shoulders and tapering muscles. And anyway, the cuts on the arm again tell you that. Look here, professor, let me show you. Square off in front of me.'

He got Guglielmo in a boxer-like attitude. The little old man seemed to like it and tried to look fierce and belligerent. Tommy ranged himself opposite him in the left-handed stance, but with his right arm and fist completely extended in front of him, and the left cocked at his breast.

'I can keep you off in this way. But this guy fought with his right arm curled in front of his face like a shield as he shuffled in. That's how he got those cuts where they are?'

Guglielmo practised a little, transformed himself into a slugger, examined the statue, went into a pose again, straightened up, looked at Alberini and said: '*Mirabile! . . . E vero. . . .*'

Leni clapped her hands. 'Oh, Tommy, bravo!'

Professor Zanni shrugged his shoulders and said: 'In the realm of pure conjecture . . .'

Tommy threw him a look, licked his lips, and spoke again. 'Now if you'd like,' he said, 'I think I can tell you something about the guy who whipped him. The sculptor who did this made his sketches in the dressing-room or in the arena, immediately after the fight. Now——'

Zanni suddenly showed even, white teeth. 'Just a moment, my friend. How do you know he lost the fight? Perhaps he was the winner, no?'

'Zanni,' said Tommy, 'you ought to read a book. It'll broaden you. Do you admit that he was sketched immediately after a fight?'

'If the statue were genuine, I would. The artist has been so careful to include every mark with nothing omitted. But he might still have been the winner.'

'Then the sculptor would also have been careful enough to

include the victor's chaplet or garland which would have been
on this guy's head if he'd won,' said Tommy with his most
charming smile.

'Bravo!' said Alberini and Guglielmo in unison.

'*Herrlich!*' said Professor Lisschauer. He moved over towards
Alberini and Guglielmo. There was a little gleam of hope in his
tired eyes.

'Thanks,' said Tommy. 'All right, then. The little guy who
licked him was probably a Greek. He——'

It was Zanni who interrupted again with a laugh. 'Hah! No,
no, no, my friend. That is now pure fancy. You have the true
American imagination.'

'You sure root for the home team, don't you, Zanni?' Tommy
said.

'I do not understand this expression.'

'Leni does,' suggested Tommy. 'Maybe you've read a book, but
not the right one. There's one over in the library of the American
Academy I can refer you to. Professor Stoddard gave it to me.
It tells how the Greeks never punched for the body. They were
purely head punchers. This guy hasn't a mark on his body. But
look at his kisser. The Greeks, from all I can find out, were much
better boxers than the Romans. And make no mistake. The guy
who gave the Roman Kid his pasting was a little sweetheart. He
fought on a bicycle, and——'

Even Leni joined in the unison chorus: 'A bicycle?' They were
all hypnotised.

Tommy grinned. 'Excuse me. That's one I haven't taught you
yet, Leni. He fought in retreat. He knew he had to stay away
from this guy or get killed.'

'Why do you say a small man?' asked Guglielmo.

'Figure it out,' replied Tommy. 'Small men are fast. Big guys
are slow. This guy is still alive, isn't he? If his opponent had been
a big, fast guy with a punch, he'd be dead instead of sitting
there. You could cave in the side of a guy's head with one of
those things he has on his hands. But the Greek was fast enough
to keep away, and probably smaller. He either didn't have a
punch or he was afraid to get close enough to let one go. And
the direction of the cuts and bruises on the Kid's face indicate
that the Greek hooked, or punched up at him, and therefore was
smaller . . . Look at the condition of the right side of the Kid's
face, compared to the left. The Greek probably let him have a
few right-hand smashes when he had him woozy. But he was
a smart little guy and he knew how to fight a southpaw, which
is more than most of our fighters do today. He kept moving,

circling to his own left and the Kid's right, away from that deadly left hand, and as he circled and back-pedalled, he kept popping him with left hooks – look at the way his nose is bent, the size of his right ear, and the mess he made out of the right side of his face. Even so, he didn't want to risk getting close enough to finish him. He had the fight won, so why take a chance? He just popped him with that left until the southpaw collapsed from the accumulation of punches, loss of blood, and exhaustion. Afterwards——'

Leni suddenly placed her hand to her face and screamed.

Her cry echoed through the high, empty vaults of the deserted museum.

'Tommy! Tommy! Papa!' she was staring. 'The Tertullian Fragment! The description . . . Tommy! Papa!'

They were all talking and shouting at once, Alberini crying: *'Corpe di Bacco,'* Guglielmo saying over and over: *'Si, si, si, si, ma si, si-si . . .'* and Professor Lisschauer: *'Lieber Herr Gott. Aber gewiss . . .'*

'I don't get it,' said Tommy.

'The Fragment!' cried Leni. 'The description of the boxing match before Titus!'

'Holy smokes!' said Tommy. 'I had forgotten it.'

'The name – The name!' cried Professor Lisschauer. 'Sinistrus, the Left-Handed One. It iss. It iss. You haff here before you Sinistrus, Roman boxer of the Emperor Titus, defeated by the little Greek, Phistra, and granted his life because of the love of the Emperor for his sister Aula.'

It was not strange that Leni and Tommy should be hugging each other, but it was a little unusual that Lisschauer and Guglielmo should be in each other's arms, and patting each other on the back, until the little man suddenly stepped back and cleared his throat and said: 'I must have leave to speak. Count Alberini, Professor Lisschauer, I withdraw. I apologise. I have done a great injustice, though my intent was honest. I was wrong. The Manzini brothers have been dead two years. The Tertullian Fragment was discovered less than six months ago. They could not possibly have known of its contents. I hope that I will be forgiven. For my friend Professor Lisschauer I have the greatest esteem and admiration.'

The Count adjusted his monocle and said: 'Professor Guglielmo, it is no more than I expected from a man of your attainments and generosity. The resignation of Professor Lisschauer is of course not accepted.'

Professor Lisschauer somehow made a magnificent job of not

seeing where Leni had just been. He came to Tommy and said: 'I wish to thank you from the bottom uff my heart, and to make to you my apologies for my attitude and my ignorance in the museum that morning. We are all too far from the realities of life. You have shamed us all . . .'

Tommy said: 'Gee – don't – it catches me in the throat. . . . I'm – I'm just a dumb guy who happens to have been around fights and fighters all his life . . .'

There was a pause. 'I am so happy,' said Professor Lisschauer, 'I could to sing and cry. We will go to my house, all, and drink some wine. Mr Thomsen, Count Alberini, Guglielmo, Zanni.' He stopped. 'Where has gone Zanni?'

'Zanni,' said Tommy succinctly, 'has taken a powder.'

They all looked blank, but Tommy didn't explain. They moved off down the long aisles of glass cases and marbles and bronzes towards the stairs. When they reached the darker portions and the attendant went ahead with his lantern, Tommy did what was requisite.

'You know,' said Leni, when she could speak again, 'I – I think perhaps boy is going to get girl. . . .'

The Witch of Woonsapucket

People ask me frequently how I get ideas for stories. Sometimes I am ashamed to tell them because the genesis of the idea is frequently madder than the story itself. This happens to be the case with THE WITCH OF WOONSAPUCKET which was one of a series of business-golf stories I kept going in the 'Saturday Evening Post' over a period of years, all written around the personality and troubles of the advertising manager of a concern manufacturing golf equipment, an invented character.

The origin of this story goes back to the particular kind of noddy I am and the days when I was writing my sports column. I used to cover all the big golf matches, the National Open, the Amateur, the Women's, the P.G.A., and I had many personal friends among the golfers, men of whom I was genuinely fond, like Tommy Armour, Bobby Cruickshank, Bob Jones, Walter Hagen, Gene Sarazen, and many others.

I was never able to take my sports casually, but always rooted passionately for some individual or some team and suffered agonies when my side looked as though it might lose. I never bet a dime on any sporting event, with the occasional exception of a small wager on a nag, during my entire thirteen-year tenure in sports, but I always had a strong personal rooting interest in some team or contestant.

Well, one day (and this is where the narrative becomes embarrassing) I was following a golf match. If my recollection serves me, it was the Augusta Open Tournament, at Augusta, Georgia, and I was rooting this time for Walter Hagen, who was staging a comeback, to win it.

I was fond of Hagen. He was a friendly, uninhibited man loved by the sports writers for his faults as well as his virtues. He liked to live well and he was inclined to look upon the flowing bowl with honest thirst and friendly eye. He had not won a major tournament in too many years and there at Augusta it seemed as though he might crash back into the big time again. I remember wanting like the very devil to have Walter win this one because

*in addition to the personal element it would have made a great
sports news story. The comeback of the old ex-champion has
always been one of America's favourites.*

*The morning of the final round Hagen led the star-studded field
by several strokes and it looked as though he might be going to
turn the trick, but immediately he began to play he started to
slip – a stroke here, a stroke there – the sound championship form
which had been his through the early rounds was no longer
there.*

*This state of affairs was very much on the conscience of two
sports writers, a colleague of mine, the late Grantland Rice and
myself. There was a kind of a roadhouse night-club a few miles
outside of Augusta and thither golfers and reporters repaired for
conviviality in the evenings during the tournament. Hagen had
been celebrating there, remaining until four or five in the morning
and managing not only to appear upon the first tee in the morning
on time, but also to deliver a brand of super golf. Thus when at
the end of the two days' play he appeared to have the tournament
sewed up, so eager were Rice and I to see this achieved that we
devised a little plot between us.*

*That night we kept stealing drinks from him. No sooner would
he set his Scotch and soda down after having had a sip of it when
we would whisk it away. He would call for a fresh one and the
procedure would be repeated. Then we practically kidnapped
him from the club and took him back to the hotel and put him
to bed at eleven o'clock to get a full night's sleep.*

*The results showed how wrong it is to tamper with nature or
alter the winning rhythm, for apparently the shock of going to
bed and sleeping for nine hours proved too much for Hagen's
system and on the last day, in the dramatic finale with Hagen
playing in the same foursome with the eventual winner of the
tourney, neck and neck, strokes as I have indicated were beginning to slip away from him. I felt desperately responsible. Why
had not Rice and I left well enough alone? And so I tried to hex
his opponent.*

*I now present a picture of a grown man following a golf four-
some in a major tournament, muttering gibberish to himself.*

*Of course I wasn't really hexing, but in my eagerness to see
Hagen come through I thought how wonderful it would be if I
knew some magic words to say that would cause Walter's opponent to fluff a bunker lie, or roll a short putt eight feet past the
hole. And so, when matters became tense and the Hague's nearest
opponent was about to make a shot, the success of which would
put Walter still deeper in the hole, I made up words of magical*

E

gibberish in the sort of despairing, infantile hope that they might be the ones necessary, the words of power that would summon Beelzebub to joggle the fellow's elbow at the critical moment. These charms I mumbled to myself, well out of earshot of the contestants. This was strictly between me and Old Nick.

Well, here the long arm of coincidence consented to be yanked, and Hagen's opponent actually blew two strokes on easy shots he should have made, which, I must say, alarmed me somewhat as well as delighted me. Hagen picked up two sorely needed strokes and I was in a fair way to hang out my shingle as an operating wizard.

Then nature and form took their normal course. Walter's golf wouldn't stand up against his non-hangover jitters, and, magic or no magic, his opponent pulled himself together and went on handily to win.

Years later, while rummaging through the attic of my mind for an idea for a story in this series, I remembered my moment of complete idiocy at the Augusta tournament, and THE WITCH OF WOONSAPUCKET *was the result.*

Any reader for entertainment or student of fiction writing in possession of the egregious facts can see how this story was put together. Using nothing but the original notion of a guy trying to put a silent hex on a golfing opponent, the train of thought would move naturally from hexing to witches, to witch-burning, and thence to the vicinity of Salem, Mass., where the story is laid.

This is a formula story, a somewhat despised creation in literary circles, but I must confess I love the kind. They are fun to think up, fun to plan, and fun to write. They come as a lightening of the load and a blessed relief. They fall into the category of what is scathingly known as potboilers, and many a brimming pot I've boiled with them, but I am not content to rest upon the confession that I made frequent compromise sorties into lower levels of magazine taste in order to keep the larder stocked. There was never any writing down in these stories. I always wrote them to the best of my ability at the particular moment. But often I would get as much pleasure, and sometimes more, out of knocking out a Bill Fowler business-golf story, or a débutante yarn, as many of the other, more serious attempts in which I was trying to convey a burn, or a yearning or an honest emotion to paper.

For these pieces served two purposes. They amused and rested me and they also entertained the customers. They constituted a welcome change of pace for them and for me.

Sometimes I would receive scolding letters from clients asking:

'Why do you waste time on junk like So-and-So?' Why don't you write more stories like Whatsis?' naming some story that had appealed to them emotionally. But the formula stories also brought in approving mail, and if somebody wrote: 'I read that story out loud to my wife last night, and we both laughed until we were sick' I considered that there could not be much higher praise and my time and efforts had not gone unrewarded.

It is the characteristic of the formula story that the basic pattern of the story remains static. Only the scene and incidents change. While top magazines by no means restrict themselves to formula stories, every magazine has one or two pet formulas based upon trial and reader reaction. They vary. The 'Collier's' formula differed from the 'Post' type, which in turn is quite different from the ones favoured by 'Cosmopolitan' or 'American' or 'Red Book' or the women's magazines.

To me the word 'formula' in story means that certain ingredients, as in a prescription, are always present. Here, for instance, are the ingredients of the golf-business story: The hero and narrator, the young and not too bright advertising manager for a golf-equipment manufacturing firm, at the beginning of each story is given some near-impossible task by his irascible and demanding boss. This task is always complicated by circumstances, the honest stupidity of the hero, or the machinations of his not too ethical rival, the villain, who is the advertising manager for the rival firm. The story then moves out on the golf course among the pros, where trouble continues to pile up for the hero. Just when things look blackest, the hero does something dumbly honest, or despairing, or the villain perpetrates the final deed, in which he out-smarts himself, virtue triumphs, and everything turns out just fine in the best of all possible worlds.

It would be churlish to scorn the 'Saturday Evening Post' for never tiring of this one when the truth is that the readers served by the 'Post' are the ones who never weary of it. Like children listening to fairytales, the oft-told, well-remembered stories are always the best and the ones they wish to have repeated.

To the writer or story-maker the challenge comes in trying to fit new ideas, new backgrounds, and new characters into this pattern and keeping it ever fresh so that the reader is never aware he is reading a formula story. He just feels comfortable and knows he is enjoying himself. Often this work is like a fascinating picture puzzle in which the pieces stubbornly refuse to fall into place. But when they do and things go right, the story can be written at a breathless gallop and with great pleasure. THE WITCH OF WOONSAPUCKET was one of these.

THE WITCH OF WOONSAPUCKET

Do you believe in witches, keep away from black cats, worry if you bust a mirror, and stay home in bed on Friday the thirteenth? I am only asking, because personally I am not superstitious myself, though I must confess that I am more than a little partial to a small ivory lucky elephant about the size of a walnut that Freddy McRae brought back for me from a golfing tour he made through India one winter and that I carry in my left pants pocket just in case. And, boy, if I hadn't had it along with me that time the Professional Golfers' Association Championship got itself h'anted, I hate to think what would have happened to poor Elmer Brown, who was just a big dumb kid, but sweet and decent, and that swell Mary Summers he was so struck on.

I mean, when it comes to that stuff about witches riding on broomsticks and Old Ned moving into a guy's golf bag and telling him what stick to use and where to place the ball to turn a tough par-five hole into a drive, a pitch, and a putt, your Uncle William Fowler, Esq., just gives it the broad 'haw.' But there's something cute about that little elephant and it doesn't take up much space anyway; and to think I almost forgot it when I changed suits before I went up to Woonsapucket for the P.G.A. Championship last year because I was so sore at old A. R. spoiling the party for me.

Being the assistant advertising manager of A. R. Mallow & Co., in charge of promotion, means that I do all the dirty work. And that was just what I was called upon to do when, the day before I was to leave for Massachusetts, I went in to see A. R. in response to his buzzer. Any time I am yanked in to the boss's office and he is sitting there with his glasses on the end of his nose and a paper in his hand, I know that there is going to be some trouble for William.

'Ha! Ahmmm! Hrrrrmph! Fowler. I have here a memo compiled for me by Mr Gudgins of the business department. It is a list of the professionals under contract to us and their – ah – accomplishments. Top-heavy! Carrying some deadwood. Uncertain times, Fowler. Business unsteady. Everyone nervous. Good time to retrench. Must cut down, eh? This fellow Brown – hrrrmph! – Elmer Brown from – ah – Osceola, Iowa. What has he done to earn his pay?'

Well, he had me there, because Elmer hadn't exactly set any fairways on fire since I had signed him up three years before when it had looked as though he might be going to win the Open. But he was such a decent, earnest guy that I thought I'd at least have one crack at saving him, so I said:

'Gee whiz, A. R., he's just a kid. He placed seventh in the Open in '36, and had it won if he hadn't folded on the last three holes, and——'

'Ha! Exactly, Fowler. There is no room on the Mallow & Co. payroll for professionals who fold. This young man has done nothing since then, according to my memo, but place ninth in the Los Angeles Open, and twelfth at the Masters Tournament in Augusta. His contract has expired. I do not wish it renewed. He has brought no credit to A. R. Mallow products. Ha! Hum!' With the last 'Ha! Hum!' he pushed his glasses back up on the bridge of his nose, which was always the signal that A. R. meant what he said and there was no use arguing.

Of course they would hold the P.G.A. in a place by the name of Woonsapucket, Mass., five miles from Salem, but to the boys who cover for the papers, a thousand miles from anywhere. As far as our business is concerned, the lines are all pretty well laid out in that tournament, which is just for the pros, and there's no scrambling or chiselling or gambling to be done as there is around an Open, beyond a little polite needling. We always like it when one of our pros wins, and advertise it, but it doesn't count with the public like the Open. So for me it's just an annual week's vacation where I can relax, follow the boys around, and have myself some laughs. But it's a bad way to start a good time to have to give a nice kid the heave-oh. I guess maybe I'm just too tender-hearted.

There wasn't even a hotel at Woonsapucket and there was no room to stay at the Woonsapucket Golf Club, which was eight miles outside of Salem, so they had the boys quartered around in private houses, the citizens chipping in with room and board as a matter of civic pride. I found I was sharing a room in a fine old house with our Freddy McRae, who had as good a chance as anyone to win the tournament. I told him that I was going to have to give Elmer Brown the axe. He shrugged his shoulders and said: 'That's a shame. He's a good kid, even though he is an awful hick. That's all that's the matter with him. He hasn't got that hay out of his hair yet. He's shy and scared. Every time he steps on to a tee with someone who's got a name, he's licked.'

I went out to the club Saturday morning, the day before the tournament started. It was a pretty course, long, and winding through woods every inch of the way. I had been wondering whether I would break the news to Elmer before or after the tournament. I suppose it would have been kinder to wait until it was all over and keep that load off his mind, but I thought that maybe if I told him right away it would make him just mad enough to go out there and play some golf. And if he could make any kind of a showing in the tournament, maybe I might risk giving A. R. another argument.

I found him putting on the practice green. Not that he was hard to find, because he had a build like a heavyweight's. He was grain-fed, big, husky, with corn-tassel hair and blue eyes and a broad mouth. He'd been brought up on a farm out in Iowa.

I didn't waste much time after the handshake and the usual about how his game was going. I came right out with it and said: 'Look here, Elmer. I'm sorry to have to be the one to tell you this, but you're on the spot.'

He straightened up from a putt he was going to make. Gloom was smeared as thick as butter all over his big, good-natured pan. And he looked scared too. He said: 'Oh gee. Do you mean——?'

I started to give him a lot of stuff right out of A. R.'s book – retrenchment, unsettled conditions, nothing personal, economy wave, things ought to be better next year – when he cut in with:

'Aw, gee, Mr Fowler. I know. You don't have to let me down easy. I know I ain't been winning enough to clean the rust off a mashie. If it hadn't been for you folks I'd a had to go back to the farm long ago. I guess I knew it was coming.'

There was a sort of silence in which I felt rotten, and he leaned over and banged a nine-footer into the cup. Then he straightened up and said:

'Mr Fowler, would it do any good if I won the P.G.A.?'

I looked at him. 'It would help, kid. It would give me an argument with A. R. Even if the P.G.A. doesn't count a hell of a lot selling merchandise, A. R. is smart enough to know that the man who wins it is also capable of winning the Open, or one of those other big publicity tournaments like the Masters.'

He said: 'Gee, Mr Fowler, I just gotta win, then. I just gotta.' It was pipe-lined straight from his heart. And before I could speak the question I had written on my face, he said:

'I got a girl, Mr Fowler. Gee, she's sweet.'

I said, 'Oh-oh!' The last time one of our pros got himself a girl, it came so close to costing us the Open I didn't even want to think about it. But he hadn't heard me. That far-away look of men in love and fighters who have been popped on the chin came into his eyes, and he was off. 'Gee, Mr Fowler, she's the most wonderful person I ever met.'

So I got the whole story from him. He had been assigned to
the Wellbye cottage, kept by a spinster, Miss Sarah Wellbye,
and the house had been in the family for more than two hundred
and fifty years. Miss Wellbye's niece, Mary Summers, was staying
there with her for her vacation. Mary was a college girl, a
stenographer in Boston, and had black hair and blue eyes and
wasn't any bigger than a milking stool, but gee, she was sweet
and smart as a buggy whip, and he had fallen in love with her
the first day he saw her, a week ago, when he arrived there to
practise, and he couldn't understand why, but she liked him too,
and they were going to be married when the tournament was
over; the thousand dollars' prize money would get them started.

Well, the more he rattled on, the glummer I got. There he
was, all full of young love and wanting to get married to a nice
girl, and I had just fired him. And I knew just how tough it was
for a young pro who wasn't winning anything to keep himself
fed, let alone marry.

And as for winning the P.G.A.! I didn't have the heart to
tell him. As McRae said, he was a shy, hero-worshipping type
who got the meemies every time he played anybody with a
name like MacDonough, or Crabby Wilson, or Craig, or Steubner.
All they had to do was throw a ball on to the tee and he was
licked. And the P.G.A. was match play against the toughest,
coldest, most hardboiled, goat-getting crew in the racket. He
didn't stand any more chance with them than I would of breaking 80 at Pinehurst with a croquet mallet and a butterfly net.

But I gave him a little pep talk and wished him luck and then
beat it off to the locker room to have myself a little snort. It
certainly was a swell introduction to a lousy time.

They really give a golfer a workout the way they play that
P.G.A. It stretches out over a week. The first two days they play
eighteen holes, each of qualifying medal play, starting Sunday.
The low sixty-three qualify, along with last year's champion, who
qualifies automatically, making sixty-four in all. On Tuesday they
play two eighteen-hole matches, which knocks the field down to
sixteen by nightfall, and from then on, it's thirty-six holes a day
to the end.

Outside of Elmer's troubles there wasn't a thing to worry
about. All of our boys, and we had four in the tournament,
qualified nicely, and, for that matter, so did Elmer, but that didn't
surprise me, because the guy wasn't so bad at medal play. He
could cock a ball a mile when he really let out and wasn't under
pressure. He was so big and powerful that he never used more
than a three-quarter swing. But that didn't mean anything,

because by Tuesday night Elmer would have departed for
Osceola, Iowa. The poor sucker had managed to get himself into
the tough side of the draw. And, brother, that upper bracket read
just like the Social Register of golf. It was loaded for bear. At
least a dozen of them were champions or former champions.
Angus MacDonough, the Fairgreen pro who had won the Open
that year, was in the lower half, and had a cinch. Also I met
Elmer's girl, Mary Summers.

There's something sweet, right away, about the name Mary,
and she lived up to all of it. She had that quiet sincerity that
seems to go with dark hair and blue eyes. She wore her hair
very smooth and glossy so that you wanted to touch it with your
hand, but, for all her tiny figure – she came just about up to
Elmer's shoulder – she had a good, strong, firm chin and a mouth
that looked as if its owner might mean business sometimes. And
was she stuck on big Elmer! She didn't seem to mind that he
wasn't the brightest guy on earth. All she cared was that he was
sweet and kind, and could break her in two, maybe, if he ever
took a full backswing before he hugged her. Why do all those
cute tricks go for guys like that when here is your Uncle Fowler
around just dying for someone soft and agreeable who will soothe
his feverish head when he brings it home at night, hot and throbbing from the daily effort of thinking up ways to make more dubs
buy more A. R. Mallow products?

We met on the clubhouse porch after the qualifying round.
Elmer was drinking himself a glass of milk and kidding with the
guys, because they all liked him, he was so modest and decent
and unspoiled; and he called out: 'Mr Fowler, I want you to
meet Mary Summers. Mary, this is Mr Fowler of the A. R. Mallow
Company. That's the company that – that – I have been working
for. He thinks I have a chance to win.'

Mary gave me one of those deep, kind, welcoming smiles as
though, by thinking that, I belonged, and shook my hand and
said: 'This is the first golf match I ever saw, Mr Fowler, but
surely Elmer will win because he plays so beautifully. And of
course you know why it is so important to us. Elmer told me
that – that you know,' and she suddenly gave Elmer's arm a little
hug with such a natural, tender gesture that I thought I'd got
one of our Tuff-Hide balls stuck in my throat because all the
time I was looking right over her shoulder at what amounted to
Elmer's walking papers. It was the draw-sheet on the club bulletin
board, and Elmer was down to play old Archie Crobb in the first
round. Uhuh. You got the name right away. It was just like
taking a kid out of the amateur ranks for his first professional

prizefight and saying: 'Come on in here, son, and meet your opponent. His name is Joe Louis.'

Archie was a crochety old Scotchman, but he had been around for years and had the smoothest swing of the pack. And how he loved to take those youngsters apart in match play!

'Do come and take dinner with us at Wellbye Cottage, Mr Fowler,' Mary was saying.

'Gee, yes,' Elmer added. 'It's the most interesting house you ever saw. It's full of things, just like a museum, from before the Revolution even . . .'

But I was hardly listening to them. All I could think of was that poor kid trying to tell his girl that he was out of the tournament, out of a job, and flat broke. I mumbled something about thanks and congratulations and, sure, Elmer would come through, and got away. I even had half a notion of going to Archie and asking him not to pour it into the kid too badly, though a lot of difference it made whether he went out three and two or nine and eight. But Arch was too mean, anyway. He loved to rub their noses in it. So I just went into the locker room down to the crying corner where the guys who had failed to qualify were gathered. I felt at home there, it was so nice and gloomy.

Were you ever around a golf tournament on the day when they play those two eighteen-hole sudden-death matches? Brother, it's a shambles, and you know it. The corpses of the famous dead lie piled eight high in the locker room, the grillroom is made hideous with the groans of the wounded and dying, and those that survive come off the course with a look of madness in their eyes. The word 'Upset' falls with a monotonous and sickly thud upon the eardrums. I lost Whitey Brompton, one of our best men, to an unknown pro from Alabama who hit the ball as though he had a twitch, and Reggie Ring, another of our topnotchers, had the tough luck to meet Crabby Wilson, the Sweetwood pro, when Crabby was red-hot. That made two. And I just did pull Freddy McRae through in extra holes in the afternoon. Excitement? Plenty of it, with stars dumped right and left.

Oh yes, and Elmer was still in the tournament when the day was over. He beat Archie Crobb on the nineteenth hole, and in the afternoon took over Nelson Rohm, the crack Midwest pro, one up on the eighteenth. I didn't see it happen; nobody did, for that matter, but the scorer who went with them, because they had no gallery. But from what the scorers told me afterwards, Elmer just had all the luck that can happen to one guy at a time. Crobb had him dormy on the fifteenth. On the sixteenth they were both on in two, but off the pin. Elmer had to make a birdie to have a chance to stay in the show, so he jumped at the putt and rolled four feet past the hole. He sank the one coming back, but it was too late then, because Crobb shoved his putt to within eight inches of the hole for a sure half. The old guy waited for Elmer to knock the ball away and concede the victory. Elmer didn't say anything, so Crobb took his time studying the putt, while the kid stood off to one side with a funny expression on his face, staring at Archie. Crobb putted carefully and surely so that he couldn't miss, and then, by gum, the ball shot off in the funniest way and finished eight inches to one side of the hole. Archie glared as though he couldn't believe it and took a five to Elmer's four. Elmer squared the match on the eighteenth and won it on the nineteenth with a great birdie.

In the afternoon round, against Nelson Rohm, he was cooked again. They were all square on the eighteenth tee. Elmer topped his drive, took an extra one in the rough, and lay four on the edge of the green. Nelson hit a screamer, his best drive of the day, and had the easiest kind of a niblick pitch to the pin for a sure four or a possible three. The scorer said Elmer must have been thinking of that train ride back to Iowa from the horrified way he stared at Nelson while the Midwest pro measured the distance, niblick in hand and got ready to give him the axe. And then, apparently for no reason at all, Rohm hit his niblick shot right up on to the clubhouse porch, nearly killing an eightball who was carrying a tray of drinks. He had to play it off flagstone from behind a pillar and bounced it into some shrubbery and from there into a bunker. He took a nice juicy seven. Elmer won the hole and the match with a six. Funny, huh?

I went to look up Elmer to congratulate him and give him another pep talk. That girl, and luck, were sure working wonders for him. I found Mary, but she hadn't seen him since he had come off the course. She was a little troubled because, she said, he had walked right past without looking at her, but I smoothed that out by explaining that when a guy comes off the green after winning a tough match he sometimes doesn't know his own mother.

Do you know where I finally found Elmer, and it was late too, and the locker room practically deserted? In the washroom, staring at himself in the mirror with the wildest, scaredest, funniest expression I ever saw on any human face. Funny, too, that he didn't seem to see me come up behind him, because when I clouted him on the shoulder with a 'Good work, kid!' he jumped as though he had seen the Devil and let out a yell. He came down on his feet, but his knees were shaking.

He said: 'Ow! I – uh – er – th-th-thanks, Mr F-F-Fowler,' and turned and ran right out of the washroom and out of the building too.

I put it down as a case of unstrung golf nerves after a couple of harrowing matches.

Which just goes to show you how wrong Mr Fowler can be.

And one after another, my guys got themselves kicked out of the tournament. You remember who met in the finals, don't you? That's right, Elmer Brown and Angus MacDonough. Elmer had walked right through Alex Gliddy, Crabby Wilson, and Chubby Craig, three of the best and toughest golfers in the business. I didn't see the matches because I was busy trying to root our stars through, but they said those three played the worst golf in their lives. Gliddy got an attack of hooking and parked five tee shots in a row out of bounds. Crabby Wilson couldn't putt for sour apples. He three-putted seven greens. And Chubby Craig, the greatest iron player in the game, actually got to shanking. Elmer, on the other hand, apparently couldn't do anything wrong. He holed out from bunkers. His ball took all the right kicks. If he got into trouble with his tee shot, he'd blast the next one so close to the cup he could blow it in. It was the talk of the tournament.

Yes, and there was some other kind of talk going on too, and I couldn't run it down. It was more a feeling that was in the air that you couldn't get hold of. The pros were off Elmer. They were giving him funny looks, and not speaking to him or kidding with him any more. And they used to love him. But the strangest thing I heard late Friday, when the semi-finals were finished, was that when Elmer's match with Chubby was over – he beat Chubby 8 and 7 – Craig refused to shake hands with him. Instead, they said, he waved one fist in front of Elmer's face in a queer way and snarled some word at him, and then turned and walked off the green. I thought maybe I'd better find Elmer and see what this was all about. But I couldn't locate him anywhere around the clubhouse. It was beginning to bother me, so I went into the locker room and had a couple of snorts. All right, maybe I had four, then. Anyway, when I got into my car parked behind the clubhouse I thought perhaps I wouldn't drive it just yet, but would sit there awhile and try to figure things out. I guess I must have fallen asleep, because when I woke up it was dark. It was nine o'clock by my wristwatch. I was just going to drive myself home when I saw a figure sneaking out the back door of the clubhouse. By its size and a flash of light on yellow hair, I knew it was Elmer. At the same time another figure suddenly came up the path. I knew that one too, dark as it was. She said:

'Elmer dear, I've been looking for you. What – what is wrong?'

The boy stood there in the dark for a moment. 'N-nothing, M-Mary.'

There was a long silence. Then Mary began to speak again, in a low, clear, steady voice.

'Elmer, this afternoon after the match was over, I was going through the woods to the car. Two of the golfers were walking just in front of me. I don't know their names, but they were two who played and had been put out. They were talking about you. They were saying that you had cheated.'

There was another long silence in which I could hear my heart going 'bonk – bonk – bonk . . .'

'I went up to them, told them who I was. One of them said: "Ma'm, we're sorry, because it's true. He admitted it. If you don't believe it, why don't you ask him?" and then they both walked away. Elmer – I am asking you now. Is it true?'

Did I listen for Elmer's answer? Yes, brother, you bet I did. It was a long time coming. At last he stammered: 'M-M-Mary – gee, Mary – I – I – I can't say anything – I can't – I can't . . .'

So there it was. It seemed like hours before Mary said in a sort of small, hurt voice: 'I – I'm sorry, Elmer. I guess that's all, then. I just can't stand a cheat. If you win that tournament through cheating, why – why, don't ever speak to me again.'

And then she turned and ran off down the path, and a moment later I heard a car starting and driving off. Elmer waited until the last sound had died away. Then he let out an awful groan, turned, and went back into the clubhouse. Me, I wasn't more than six steps behind him.

I found him sitting in a corner of the darkened locker room with his head in his hands. I slid alongside him, put my arm around his shoulder, and said: 'What's the matter, kid? Why don't you tell me and get it off your chest?'

He gave a couple of shudders and finally said: 'Mr Fowler, I want to go home. I want to default tomorrow and get out of here. You can post my default for me. I want to get out tonight, now, right away.'

I tried to jolly him. I said: 'Oh, come on, Elmer, you can't do that. You're going great. You've got to stay in there and fight for old Alma Mallow. You're the only one we've got left. You can't leave now. If you do it'll cost you your job, and what's more, you'll never get another job because you'll be branded a quitter.'

He shook his head and groaned: 'I don't care. I don't want

another job. I just want to get out of here.' Suddenly he stopped,
hesitated, and then blurted out all in a heap: 'Mr Fowler, I've
done something awful. I – I'm a witch.'

I thought it was still those snorts I'd had earlier. 'You're a
what?'

'A – a witch, Mr Fowler. I – I cheated. I put a hex on Mr Crobb,
and Mr Rohm, and Mr Gliddy too, though I didn't mean to,
honestly, Mr Fowler, and I guess it got Mr Craig too, though I
didn't put it on him, but it won't stop. I gotta get out of here,
Mr Fowler, I just gotta. Can't you see?'

He wasn't kidding. He was on the level. He was so much on the
level that there were tears in his eyes.

I said: 'Listen, kid, why don't you tell me what the hell this is
all about? I don't believe you're a cheat, and I don't believe in
witches, and——'

'I didn't mean to do it, Mr Fowler. I didn't believe in it either,
but I was desperate. I had to win. Mr Crobb had a "*gimme*" to
win the match, and I was out of the tournament and my job,
and I couldn't marry Mary. Otherwise I wouldn't have said the
words. Honest I wouldn't, Mr Fowler.'

I saw I had kind of to nurse him along to get anything out of
him, so I said: 'What words?'

'The words in the book.'

'Uhuh. What book?'

'The book I found in Mary's house. I just looked into it. It's
old-like. They have a lot of things there from before the Revolution – pictures, and arrowheads and guns, and books, printed in
the old kind English, and there was this one book I just looked
into, one night.'

'What was the book?'

It was tough getting the story out of him because he was really
unstrung, but it finally developed that he had found a copy of
something called *Of Ye Plague of Wytches in Ye Colonies*, by the
Reverend Hallelujah Snite, printed in Boston in 1699, and had
read the thing out of curiosity and found some sort of words in
it which, according to the Reverend Dr Snite, the witches of old
Salem used to summon Old Nick for a party. It was getting tough
to keep from laughing, because I wanted to badly.

'Just what were the words?'

'Do I have to say them?'

'Go ahead. I'm a Psi Kappa Psi myself. . . .'

He gobbled a little and finally came out with some balderdash
that sounded like 'Abrogath Ahrimanes Abaddon,' and then
looked around him frightened, as though he expected to see Old

Harry snap to attention out of a cloud of sulphur with an 'At your service, sir!'

'So what happened?'

'Well, I was in this jam and was practically out of the tournament, and then I suddenly remembered those words. I didn't really believe in it, but I had to do something, Mr Fowler. Mr Crobb couldn't miss an eight-inch putt. So I said them.'

'Out loud?'

'Oh, gee, no. Just to myself.'

'Could old Archie see you?'

'No, sir. I was standing behind him out of his line so he couldn't see me at all . . .'

'And Archie blew the putt! Wow!' I just couldn't hold it in any longer and had to let go with a dozen guffaws that shook the locker room. 'Kid, it's the discovery of the age. You write 'em down for me. Will I give it to that louse J. Sears Hammett of the Fairgreen Company the next time I play him a five-buck Nassau.'

But the kid wasn't laughing. He said: 'But you don't understand, Mr Fowler. It's no joke. I didn't believe it at first, so when Mr Rohm had me on the hook, I said them again and Mr Rohm put his niblick shot into the clubhouse and took a seven. And when I played Mr Gliddy I guess I must have said them once more without knowing it, and the Devil made him hook five tee shots in a row, and by then I was so scared I swore I'd never use them again, but it's too late now, I've sold myself to Satan. I didn't say anything when I played Mr Wilson, but there he was just the same, keeping Mr Wilson's putts out of the cup, and when I'd pull a six iron out of my bag I'd hear him say: "Wrong club, sucker, it's a seven; play it high and fade it from right to left. Can't you see that wind in the top of the trees?" I've raised him, Mr Fowler, and I can't get rid of him. If I'd only done it once, maybe he wouldn't have charged just for a demonstration. But he must want me awful bad, because he's working overtime. I can't make a bad shot. And I've lost my girl on account of him.'

I said: 'Listen, you big dope, those guys would have blown those shots anyway. Didn't you ever jab at a six-inch putt and see it stay out? Or get an attack of sausage fingers and find your game slipping away? All that stuff is a lot of hooey anyway, but if it'll do you good and make you think you can beat those guys, what the hell! And anyway, they don't know about it, so——'

'That's one of the worst troubles, Mr Fowler; they do!'

'What? How could they find out——?'

'I – I told them, Mr Fowler – yesterday before I played Mr Craig.'

'You what? Why, you sap——'

It seems that the kid was scared and worried and uncertain whether he really had made a spell, or whatever it was, because he knew from his farm upbringing that Beelzebub doesn't do that kind of work for nothing, so he had asked old Crobb whether he had felt anything when he made that putt, and of course the old guy had said: 'Yes, why?' Huh! Show me a golfer who won't grab for an alibi. The poor dope had told him, and of course Crobb had snarled: 'Ay, I feltit something pushit my elbow. I no hae missit a wee putt like that gang on thirrty years.' And Rohm then chimed in and said when he mis-hit that niblick shot it was just as though somebody else was swinging the club, and Gliddy recalled that coming down the seventeenth fairway he had actually said: 'This damned driver of mine must be bewitched.' And Crabby Wilson had said: 'Hah! No wonder I couldn't get a putt down all day.' And then they had all turned on him and accused him of cheating, hexing them, casting the evil eye, and conduct unbecoming a member of the Professional Golfers' Association. The match when Chubby Craig shanked all day had finished it.

'They're in the grillroom right now, holding a meeting over it, Mr Fowler,' concluded Elmer. 'They're going to have me barred anyway. Let me go back to Osceola, Mr Fowler. I can't go on. Satan's moved into my golf bag. I just gotta hang it up.'

I said: 'Listen, kid. You stay here until I get back. I'm going to that meeting. Those sharks aren't going to push one of my guys out of a tournament that way. You do as I say, understand?'

And I went busting into the grillroom. I was just in time too. There was a big crowd of the pros there, and Archie Crobb was saying: 'All those favouring to expel Elmer Brown and bar him frae the final say——' when I walked through the door and finished it for him:

'Say what? Are you guys nuts? What's the matter with Brown? Can't you birds take a licking without crying?'

Crabby Wilson said: 'We can when it's on the level,' and Nelson Rohm shouted: 'What are you doing in here, Fowler? This is a closed meeting. You don't belong here.'

I said: 'Maybe I don't, but I'm not going to let you railroad one of my guys out of this tournament for nothing.'

'For nothing!' shouted Crabby Wilson. 'He put the whammie on me! Every time I'd go to putt, my eyes would water so I couldn't see the ball.'

'He admittit himself he called on the De'il,' said Crobb. 'The mon's a witch. I haven't misstit a wee put like thot in thirrr——'

I said: 'You're a fool, Crobb. There aren't any male witches.'

'Aweel, then, callit him a wizard, it's a' the same.'

'I'll say he's a wizard, the way he plastered you three straight holes after you lost your nerve and blew a kick-in.'

'What about his telling me he put a spell on me before I hit that shot to the eighteenth? The ball went up into the clubhouse, didn't it?' said Nelson Rohm.

'Yeah,' I said. 'He told you afterwards. I suppose you never missed a green in your life before. Sure, the kid's a little screwy like all you birds, but——'

Angus MacDonough chimed in here: 'A mon has no richt to do wi' bogles in a gowf match. I'll no have to do wi' him. The De'il's in his bag.'

I said: 'O.K., boys. You do what you like, but I'm going out and dig up a couple of golf writers and give them the story of how a lot of grown men who got licked by a green kid had to work up an alibi for themselves.'

I thought that would do it. It did, too. There were a lot of sensible guys there and they talked it over and finally agreed to do nothing and go ahead with the tournament.

'But you tell that young mon I'll no be bewitched,' warned Angus. 'The fairst spell I feel, I'll magic him wi' a niblick.'

I went back into the locker room and got Elmer and said: 'Son, you'd better get all that nonsense out of your head. They were holding a meeting to consider the course for next year's tournament. You come on home with me and get a night's sleep and tomorrow you'll pin Angus's ears back for good old Mallow.'

He shook his head. 'Aw, what's the use, Mr Fowler? I don't want the job any more. I've lost Mary. She thinks I'm a cheat like the rest of them do.'

So I piled into him about quitting and gave him a ten-minute speech that any football coach would have paid me for, winding up with: 'You can't let this thing lick you this way. Go on out there and prove that you can whip——'

He interrupted me suddenly. A change seemed to have come over him. He jumped up and said: 'I will, Mr Fowler. By crickey, I will. I can make good. I will. *I know how.*'

I took him home with me. Boy, I was tickled to death. Mallow was going to collect another championship. I wouldn't have been so pleased if I'd known what he really meant . . .

So the next morning we went out to play the final match against Angus MacDonough, with me carrying Elmer's bag.

That's right. I had to caddie for him. Elmer's regular boy, a big African from Mobile by the name of Four Toes, met me down by the caddie pen, and he was on his way out, headed south. He said: 'You gotta excuse me, Mistuh Fowler. Ah ain' gonna carry dat bag no mo'. De Debbil's done got in it. Ebbrybody say so. Ebbry time Ah give a club to Mistuh Brown de Debbil he say to him to take another. Ah heerd de voice an' seen de smoke commin' outen de bag. No *suh*! Ah ain' touchin' it no mo'.' All the other caddies had disappeared. I picked up Elmer's clubs and went to the first tee. Elmer didn't even notice that I was carrying for him. He was like a guy all wrapped up in something. Angus turned his back on him and so did Angus's caddie, who was none other than Dutch Steubner, another Fairgreen pro. That witchcraft story had got all the caddies so scared they wouldn't go anywhere near Elmer. It was a good thing there weren't any of the top-flight golf writers around that tournament or they would have been asking plenty of questions. As it was, some of those smart guys from Boston were nosing around trying to track down some of the rumours they'd heard, and I had to tell plenty of lies. There was nothing unusual in Angus MacDonough refusing to look at an opponent, or speak to him, because he had the reputation of being a mean, goat-getting grouch in match play, but I wondered whether the reporters would catch on to the surreptitious signs he and Dutch and all the other golfers who were in the gallery made every time that Elmer would look at them – you know, fist doubled up with thumb and little finger sticking out, and X's and circles in the air.

I was glad when we got started. I wanted to get it over with. There were about a thousand or so in the gallery, and they must have felt there was something in the air, because they were sort of hushed when they moved off after us, following two nice drives that split the fairway, Elmer's some forty yards past Angus's. Angus knocked a four iron on to the green, about fourteen feet from the pin. Elmer pulled a number seven out of the bag. I said: 'It's a six, kid. There's an upslope in front of the green. If you don't reach, it'll stop the ball dead.'

Do you know what that fool kid did? He put his hands over his ears. Then he said: 'Stand behind me, caddie.' I got it, all right. He meant: 'Get thee behind me, Satan.' Then he hit a perfect seven iron. Only, as I said, it was a six-iron shot. The ball hit in front of the green, hesitated, and then rolled back down the slope. And his chip hit the bank and stopped outside of Angus's ball. Elmer had to putt first and rolled to within a foot of the cup for a fairly sure five. It was Angus's turn to putt.

He took a long time over it and then hit one that certainly was a dilly. I never saw a worse shot on a green. He must have lunged at it. It wound up seven feet past the hole to one side. Angus stared at it as though he couldn't believe it. Then he turned angrily on Elmer, but before he could say anything, Elmer went over to Angus's ball, knocked it away with a 'That's good,' and walked off the green. There was a murmur of astonishment from the crowd.

I said: 'What the devil did you do that for, you sap? He was a sure thing to miss that putt coming back and you'd have halved the whole. Now you're one down.'

'No, I ain't,' said Elmer softly, 'no, I ain't. I'm one up. On that feller you just mentioned. And I'm going to whip him all the way.'

So that's how it was going to be. Yes, and that's how it was, too. When I brought him in to the clubhouse at the end of the first eighteen holes, he was exactly fourteen down. He under-clubbed, he overclubbed, he conceded putts, he took penalties. The people in the gallery were sore as pups, grumbling and threatening to demand their money back or complain to the officials, but Angus was tickled to death, and so were the other pros. They acted just as though they had it coming to them. The newspaper boys kept barging up to me, asking: 'What's he doing, throwing the match? What's the idea?' and I'd yell: 'Oh, leave us alone. Didn't you ever see a guy in a slump before? He'll be all right after lunch.' But of course that last was hooey. It was all over. I could have killed Elmer, except that for the first time since it all started he seemed halfway happy and some of the fear was gone from his face. I left him alone in a corner of the grill drinking milk and went out by myself. I was too sick to eat. I passed a group of officials conferring in front of the club-house and heard they were going to call a meeting before the tee-off again after lunch. They had to, because everybody was squawking. I went into the woods bordering the sixth fairway to cool off. I didn't even want a drink. I had my hands stuffed down into my pockets and was kicking at things.

So that was how I came to haul that lucky elephant out of my pocket, because after a while I got to feeling it there, sort of hard and funny-shaped. I said: 'You're a fine damn mascot, you are! You're supposed to be lucky, eh? You're nothing but a Jonah, and here you go,' and with that I took a baseball pitcher's wind-up and heaved it as hard and as far as I could into a clump of bushes.

There was a gasp, and somebody said: 'Ow!' I ran around to the other side of them to apologise to whoever I had beaned.

You guessed it. It was Mary Summers. She was sitting on a log.
There were tear-stains on her face where she had been crying.
The elephant was lying at her feet.

I said: 'Gee, Mary, I'm sorry. Where have you been? I've
wanted to see you. Elmer——'

She began to cry again. 'Oh, Bill, I'm so miserable. I accused
Elmer of cheating, and left him without giving him a real chance
to explain. I don't care what he's done, I love him. He isn't a
cheat. And I saw what he was doing this morning. And instead
of helping him, I – Oh, Bill——'

So then I told her the whole story, right from the beginning.
And sometimes she laughed, but with tears and tenderness behind
it, and sometimes she cried and made little gestures with her
arms as though she were taking the absent Elmer into them. I
wound up: 'The poor kid is off his nut. He thinks he sinned saying those words, and has to atone for it by throwing the match
to that old sour-puss Angus and beat the Devil that way, even
though it costs him his job and the chance to marry you; and
Angus, the old goat, behaves as though he had it coming to him,
with the other pros egging him on, because by blaming it all on
Elmer it gives them an alibi for their lousy golf. The reporters
are hot on the trail of the story, though they haven't got it yet,
but if it gets out, the kid'll be ruined. The officials are going to
call a meeting in the clubhouse private office before the afternoon. Maybe they'll disqualify him right there. I don't know. It's
an awful mess.'

The girl took a deep breath and straightened up. Gee, she was
a sweet sight with her blue eyes shining. She said: 'Bill – Bill –
we've got to do something. Right away.'

'I know, but what? Maybe it's too late.'

She was staring down at my elephant suddenly. She said: 'Bill,
what is that?'

I said: 'That's my elephant. I carry it around in my pocket.'
'What for?'

'For luck. But the luck was all bad, so I heaved it.'

She picked it up, gazed at it for a moment, and then handed
it to me. There was a strange look on her face.

'Put it back in your pocket, Bill. Maybe it will turn out to be
the best friend you or I ever had.' She glanced at her watch and
gave a little gasp. 'Oh! There isn't much time. Hurry, Bill! Go
to that meeting. Don't let them leave. Do anything to hold them.
I'll be there at two o'clock,' and she was streaking off through
the woods like a young deer.

I went back to the clubhouse, but quick. The afternoon tee-off time was two-fifteen. At ten minutes to two the meeting was called by the officials. It was attended by Elmer and myself and Angus and Dutch, and all the pros that Elmer had beaten, and half a dozen others. Old Bill Wattley, the chief referee, didn't waste any time. He was boiling mad. He lit into poor Elmer and said that what he had done that morning was a disgrace to professional golfing, that people had paid good money to see a fair match. He lit into old Angus too, and the other pros, and said that he had heard a lot of silly stories, and there and now meant to get at the truth of the matter before he decided what action he would take.

Nobody wanted to say anything at first because, now that it was going to be dragged out in open meeting, they were a little ashamed, I guess; but finally old Archie Crobb spoke up and said: 'Meester Wattley, 'tis ony richt he should gi' back to us what he tookit by foul means. He's admittit he has to do wi' bogles and Beelzebub and the sperrits o' the pit. I no hae missit a wee putt like that in thirrrty——'

Elmer suddenly got up, big, lanky, and miserable, and interrupted. 'Aw, gee, Mr Wattley, let me default and get out of here. I don't care what they say about me. Mr Crobb is right. I didn't deserve to win. I——'

'Oh yes you did, Elmer,' said Mary Summers. She had opened the door and come in very quietly. It was just two o'clock. She had a book under her arm, and she threw it down on the table. It was old and yellow, and from where I sat I could see it was the treatise by the Reverend Hallelujah Snite. Everybody stared at it as though it were a snake, including Elmer.

'Oh yes, you deserve to win, Elmer,' Mary repeated, and then looked the whole crowd over coolly and a little as though they were insects. 'I know the whole silly story. All you gentlemen who are so righteous, did you ever hear this: "Let him who is without sin cast the first stone"?'

A fly buzzing on the windowpane sounded just like a dive-bomber, it was that quiet.

'Mr Crobb,' said Mary Summers, 'turn out your pockets!'

Nobody moved. 'Wha – what did ye say, lass?' said old Crobb.

'I said turn out your pockets, Mr Crobb. Put whatever you have here on the table. At once.'

By jeepers, old Crobb did. He was hypnotised. His hands came up from his pockets full of junk which he laid on the table – some bills, coins, a little roll of tape, pocket-knife, half a dozen tees, and a little rabbit's-foot set in silver.

'Now you, Mr Wilson,' her voice rising, 'and you . . . and you . . . and you . . . all of you. Out with them.'

By jeepers, they were *all* hypnotised. Even I turned mine out before I knew it. And then Mary was at the table, picking out objects from each pile and sweeping them towards the centre, the rabbit's-foot, punched coins, cat's-eyes, a piece of heather in a locket, framed four-leaf clovers, miniature horseshoes, little worsted Aucassins and Nicolettes, a curiously shaped stone or two, chunks of carved wood, a little silver devil on a ring, pairs of dice, medals, carved elephants, a piece of jade, and a silver pig.

She pointed to the pile. 'What do you call these?' she said.

They all grinned sheepishly, and Archie Crobb said: 'Eh, lass, what's wrang wi' a mascot?'

'Wrong? Do you know where the word "mascot" comes from?' asked Mary Summers. 'In old French the word "masco" meant a sorceress or witch. You're all in it, every one of you. There isn't one of you who doesn't carry a talisman that you think gives you something on the other fellow, an edge, a spell, a lucky charm, something supernatural. And you dare to pick on Elmer? You ought to be ashamed of yourselves, all of you. That book there, that you're all so afraid of,' – she flipped it open – 'do you know what it is? It was written by a half-crazy, superstitious ninny about a pack of harmless, innocent old women who were drowned and stoned and hanged not more than five miles from here in Salem, to the everlasting shame of that city and a monument to ignorance and stupidity. Do you know what that spell is that terrified all you big brave men so that you couldn't hit a little golf ball? There it is. It was used by a lot of poor, ignorant, self-deluded wretches to curdle milk. And it never curdled anything but your dispositions. There, read it and see if it is any worse than that collection of ridiculous junk you carry around with you this year of 1942 to ward off bogies. Grown men, all of you. Very well. You're all even now. Put your nasty things back into your pockets and try to act like men and not a lot of frightened old women. Elmer Brown, you go right out and play that man golf, out in the woods there where everything is fresh and sweet and clean. And – and' – she hesitated suddenly and her lower lip began to tremble – 'and – I don't care whether you win or lose, I'll marry you because I love you, and I don't care if we s-s-s-starve . . . Oh, Elllllmer——'

And she was in his arms, crying, and all the pros were around her, patting her on the shoulder and apologising and trying to make up to Elmer, and Mary kissed Elmer as though nobody was there, and Elmer suddenly raised up his arms with his fists clenched and shouted: 'I've won! I've won! I've licked it. And now I'll lick you too, Angus MacDonough. Come on out on the course and take it . . .'

Whew! I'm glad I don't have to describe that last eighteen holes for you. You read about it. The greatest comeback in the history of golf, they called it. And that Angus was playing too. You don't catch him giving anything away. But nobody ever saw golf like that kid played. He'd never really hit a ball before as hard as he could because of his size and strength, which might rob him of control. But now he had the control too. When they set par for that course it wasn't for the kind of golf Elmer shot. He simply made threes out of the fours, and fours out of the fives.

There weren't more than fifty people on the tee when we started, but by the time we reached the ninth, there were two thousand galloping on our heels, and Elmer, who had turned in thirty, was only seven down. Even the cooks and waiters came out of the kitchen to see the miracle. As I toted Elmer's bag past the clubhouse from the ninth green to the tenth tee, a Western Union boy handed me a telegram. It was from A. R. Mallow, who must have been listening in to the match on the radio. It said:

TRUST YOU HAVE NOT MADE MISTAKE OF LETTING BROWN GET AWAY FROM US STOP IF HE WINS RAISE SALARY TWELVE HUNDRED A YEAR STOP A. R.

Me make the mistake! Wasn't that just like A. R.?

You read how Elmer squared the match on the seventeeth to the greatest frenzy of cheering I ever heard, and then slipped up on the eighteenth to let Angus halve him. Then Angus got into trouble on the nineteenth and was only on the edge of the green in three, while Elmer was on in two, but with a nasty, curling, downhill ten-foot putt. Angus chipped into the cup from off the edge for his four, and the crowd gave him a great hand. A careful, certain four would keep the match open for Elmer another hole. A three would win it. But the putt was downhill, and if it missed the can, the ball would roll on and cost him the match and the championship if he missed coming back.

Elmer knelt down and studied the line. He studied it from every angle, inspected each blade of grass in the path to the hole. Everybody knew that he was going to go for the cup and the match.

He bent over his putt and waited to steady his nerves. And then I saw old Angus MacDonough do a funny thing. He fished into his pocket and hauled forth a little scrap of paper, studied it, glared at Elmer's back, and his lips moved; then he looked back at the paper again. Somehow, out of the corner of his eye, Elmer must have seen him too, for he straightened up all of a sudden, grinning.

Then he said: 'The words, Mr MacDonough, are: "Abrogath Ahrimanes Abaddon," but they don't mean a damn thing if you haven't got the golf to go with them. Watch this.'

He leaned over and stroked the ball and I shut my eyes. Then I heard a gentle 'Bonk!' as it fell into the cup, and everybody was yelling and screaming and dancing, and Mary Summers was in the centre of it all, with her arms around big stupid Elmer's neck . . .

Boy, did I kiss that little old good-luck elephant of mine. Wouldn't it have been hell if I'd left it at home?

Penntifer's Plan

••

*This novelette was written in the fall of 1937. It is at once a
prophecy, a romantic adventure and a love story. The prophecy
is that of the Battle of Britain and the destruction of the city of
Plymouth. The romantic adventure is the form and content, and
the love story is my own – a writer falling in love with England.*

*Actually there are so many ingredients in this story, personal
as well as impersonal, that I hardly know in what order to present
them. In point of fact there probably is no order of presentation,
for once a story has begun to germinate, ideas for it, notions,
characters, etc., bubble up from all kinds of hidden recesses of
the mind.*

*For instance that summer of 1937 I had again rented my
cottage in Salcombe, Devon and I remember that there was a
small aero club that flourished there, drawing its membership
from the people of the village, shopowners, tradesmen, the garage
man, the chap who ran the electrical shop and fixed one's radio
and so on.*

*Once a week when the weather was fine an ex-R.A.F. flier, a
hedge-hopping barn-stormer, left over from the last war, would
drop his Moth on to a farmer's field atop of Bolt Head, hang a
wind sock from a pole and open for business. Members of the
aero club would then go over and practise flying. Occasionally in
the company of a friend of mine, the late Joe Payne who owned
the electrical appliances shop at Salcombe, I would go over to
the field myself and air out as the saying goes. I had taken out a
private pilot's licence some five years before and this gave me a
chance to keep my hand in. My friend Payne, incidentally, joined
the R.A.F. when war broke out and did become an R.A.F. flyer
and took part in the Battle of Britain. After the war he was acci-
dentally drowned in Salcombe harbour. Something of Joe Payne
is in this story.*

*Something, or even a good deal, of many of the people I learned
to know at that time from the village and the farms, their staunch-*

*ness and simplicity and their shy patriotism and feeling for
England, is likewise a part of this story as well as my own, for
in those days living close to them and on a Devonshire hillside
overlooking the sea, I was learning to love England and its people
myself. And that affection too, I think, is manifest in this tale.*

*I cannot remember whether the feeling was general – I only
know that in the summer of 1937 I myself had no doubt that
Germany was bent upon world domination and that before long
the non-Fascist world would be at war with the Nazis, or rather
the Nazis would be warring upon us. I had been to Germany
both in 1936 and 1937, felt the rising heat of war and conquest
fever, looked at and listened to the Nazis and Hitler in action.
Actually it was no great trick at the time to know that war was
coming. Everyone in Europe apparently did.*

*If the germ of this story began with the little aero club at
Salcombe it received impetus from the Walter Mitty in me.*

*Surely you have read Mr James Thurber's character Walter
Mitty, whose fantasy life was led as a hero in many fields. The
Mitty stories come as a great relief to me for up to that time I
was unaware that anyone else shared this kind of infantile madness.*

*I should really be ashamed to confess these puerile fantasies
which began in boyhood, but for the fact that time and again
they have swum into my consciousness when I have needed them
and I have been able to adapt them commercially.*

*I have, in imagination, rescued enough beautiful maidens from
villains to staff a beauty chorus; I have been the boy wonder
who disarms the bandit chief in the great train robbery, earning
the undying gratitude of the passengers; the young lieutenant
who holds the salient and saves the day; the sea captain, grim-
lipped, who brings his ship through the tempest; Robin Hood,
Ivanhoe, and d'Artagnan all rolled into one.*

*What is embarrassing to report is that some of these daydreams
persisted into adult life. And this is where I welcomed the advent
of Thurber's Mr Mitty to save my face, for during the early days
of sports writing when I made frequent use of air transport in
hurrying from city to city to cover major sports events, the flying
hero daydream went something like this:*

*I am sitting in a transport plane minding my own business
when suddenly I look up into the pilot's cockpit and see that both
pilots have slumped unconscious in their seats and the plane is
unguided and may crash at any moment. Or as a more attractive
variation there was the sudden appearance of the pretty hostess
of the aeroplane – and they were always prime beauts on those*

airlines – looking pale and frightened, yet trying to be calm as she inquires: 'Is there anyone among the passengers who can fly an aeroplane? There has been an accident. Both pilot and co-pilot are unconscious. Oh, who will save us?'

Casually I hold up my hand. 'Don't fear, miss. I can fly a ship. I'll get us down.' To the murmurs of admiration from the other passengers, I go forward to the pilot's cabin, remove the body of the unconscious pilot (don't ask me how the two men got unconscious at the same time, because I never bothered to work that one out) with the aid of the beautiful hostess, who by now is hopelessly in love with me. A few moments of experimenting to familiarise myself with the gadgets on the dashboard and I am in full control, heading for the nearest airport. I cut the throttles, I glide, I approach. Thump! We land and roll safely to a stop. I have done it!

Now the relieved and grateful passengers crowd around. 'Hurrah for Gallico, who saved us all!' Reporters dash up and the dramatic tale is quickly told. The officials of the airlines reward me with a cash bonus which I modestly turn aside while the headlines roll from the presses:

'HEROIC SPORTS WRITER LANDS TRANSPORT PLANE SAFELY AFTER PILOTS PASS OUT IN MID-AIR; *Amateur Flier Saves Lives of All Aboard.*' Also '*Photo shows courageous writer with pretty hostess, surrounded by cheering passengers.*'

I do not insist that a person needs to be quite that idiotic to write and sell fiction stories, but it helps.

There was one serious catch to my full enjoyment of this childish daydream, and that was that I couldn't fly an aeroplane. And just imagining that I could didn't seem to be enough. The dream world and the world of reality seemed to merge here and drive me to action. Suppose some day something like that really should happen . . .

What actually moved me to take up the art, however, were the practical considerations. I thought that every modern man ought to be able to fly an aeroplane just as he was able to drive a car. I thought it would be good to write about in my sports column. I also had a notion that some day I would be able to cover certain sports events from the air, and which indeed later came to pass when I took up my own plane over Newport to cover the American Cup Yacht race and over Detroit the speedboat matches between Gar Wood and Kaye Don.

Leland Hayward the producer, then an agent, was himself taking flying lessons at the time. He put me on to his instructor

Swanee Taylor and I began my training on a Kittyhawk, soloed in due time and took my licence.

The pangs and joys of learning were duly reported in my daily sports column. Flying in those days was still supposed to be 'dangerous.' With my helmet and goggles I thought of myself as the very devil of a fellow. The kite that I flew could achieve a speed of circa 75 miles an hour with an enormous amount of fuss and bother and clatter and nearly shaking itself to pieces. In those days war planes were flying at 200 and 300 miles an hour and the prototype of the Hawker Hurricane was to crack the 400 miles an hour barrier. I knew an American navy flyer by the name of Al Williams who took me up on one of those speed flights in a navy war plane. This experience was packed away in my mental attic. When the idea for 'Penntifer's Plan' came to me there it was ready to be used, my own personal experience in the difference in the speeds of aircraft and what might well be the result of such a difference.

PENNTIFER'S PLAN *is not the story of a little boy who rescues grown-ups from danger in mid-air. It is the story of an English butcher of Plympsmore, South Devon, who loved the soil to which he was born and bred. But it's there all right, the daydream, and you will not have to look hard to recognise it in its present guise.*

I used to drive to Plymouth once a week to do my shopping. The great port and the surrounding countryside were drenched in sentiment and romance for me. I loved to wander along the Hoe or walk the older alleys and streets of the grey city. And I remember one day, when I was in the big market, thinking of the war that was coming and what it would do to this quiet town and its people, the butchers' stalls, and the greengrocers in their long white coats, the old women with their shopping bags, and how it would look when the bombs began to fall.

In 1944 when I went abroad as war correspondent and European editor of 'Cosmopolitan' magazine I visited Plymouth and looked in vain for any of the old landmarks I had known. Woolworths had gone, the market-stalls, Spooners, Great Department Store of the West, my old butcher shop where I used to trade, everything had been wiped out and I thought again of the story I had written called PENNTIFER'S PLAN. *A cut version of it had appeared in 'Cosmopolitan' magazine in 1938, but recently rummaging through my effects I came across a carbon copy of the original story and this I would be pleased to have you read.*

I do not think the truth or fallacy of the mechanics of the final battle in the tale are important. It was still a curiously accurate forecast of the Battle of Britain, which saved England as surely

*as the little wooden sailing ships of Drake and the men who
manned them saved her in the days of Elizabeth I. It has to do
with men more than aeroplanes, for we know today that the lads
who took the Spits and Hurricanes into the sky to challenge and
beat the Luftwaffe were the same kind of people as the men and
boys of Penntifer's crazy, patchwork Armada. They performed
miracles of gallantry and tenacity far transcending their machines.
They were stubborn, liberty-loving Britishers. Which is what this
story is about.*

PENNTIFER'S PLAN

The tragic disaster that overtook England in the early autumn of
1938 came to the attention of John Penntifer, butcher, of Plympsmore in Devon, chiefly through the neatly clipped sentences and
impersonal voice of the British Broadcasting Corporation announcer, except for one important episode where he happened
to be an eye-witness. But this exception and its important consequences will be dealt with later. It was from the interior of
the box of his seven-guinea wireless set that Penntifer learned
of the thing that had happened to England, and of the new
method of making war, which was not war at all in the old
accepted sense, but rather a more convenient form of international piracy and blackmail, nicely glossed over with a diplomatic language and phrases that made Penntifer snort.

Even when he told of the practically total destruction of the
British air pursuit and combat fleet, sent up in a mad scramble
to intercept the combined bombing fleet of the two powers that
had appeared at five o'clock one Friday afternoon over London,
and with no warning had simply up-ended hell's cauldron out of
the sky, the announcer never permitted itself more than the
respectable tincture of apprehension and regret worked out for
the phrase: 'Is dangerously ill . . .' And used for the S O S
messages that always preceded the late news, copyright reserved.
'Will Mary Blagdon, last heard of at 347 Clacton Road, Walton-
on-Thames, go to 19 Tinsley Road, Manchester, where her mother,
Mrs Albert J. Blagdon, is dangerously ill? . . .'

The same quiet, even phrasing and polite regret – 'It was some
time before a sufficient force of British combat planes could

be mustered and sent aloft to engage the obviously' (precious word) 'hostile bombers, and when this was finally done, they found themselves set upon, outnumbered, and outdistanced by a new type of fighting plane apparently lurking on a higher level than the bombers.'

The announcer (he was talking from the Regional Station in Surrey, because the B.B.C. building in London had been blown to rubble) found time to comment on an unfortunate oversight of the Air Ministry that became evident when the British fighters went aloft. It developed that the English machines, thought to be the fastest and most modern in the world, were fifteen miles an hour behind the aircraft of the two powers, yards slower on the climb, and not so powerfully armed. The result of this was that of the machines answering the belated alarm and leaving their aerodromes, not one quarter returned, and of these not more than a third were undamaged and fit to fly. In the meantime the lazy, circling bombers were reducing five London areas to powder, twisted metal, and junk, while pieces of the dead lay strewn in the pitted streets, or hung from chunks of blasted mortar, or were shredded against whatever walls were left standing. The first estimates placed the civilian dead at more than one hundred thousand. The loss in R.A.F. planes and pilots was appalling.

The announcer continued: 'Late yesterday evening the Ambassadors of the two powers called upon Leslie Spanka-Winwold and denied that their countries were at war with Great Britain or that the outrageous attack upon London was intended as an act of war. In a statement prepared jointly by the two Ambassadors and handed to Mr Spanka-Winwold they said: 'The unfortunate liquidation of certain portions of London, and other cities that are to follow, does not of necessity indicate an abandonment of the principles of world peace to which the two undersigned powers have always been dedicated, but instead may be regarded as a token of their sincerity in their effort to obtain what they consider a necessary re-balance of power throughout western Europe. The immediate abandonment of the English position with regard to the recent developments in Russia, France, and Spain as well as Brazil and the Argentine would see a resumption of the cordial and friendly relations that have always existed between the British peoples and those of the two powers. Nevertheless, in order to assist the British public in demanding that the Government reshape its policy, further minor demonstrations of two-power solidarity are planned at key points of the British Isles.'

'Gaw,' said Penntifer. 'What cheek!'

He listened to a partial estimate of the disaster due to bombing and fires, and the plans of a badly shaken Government for immediate defence of the country, a defence that even the carefully worded broadcast could not conceal was badly broken by the loss of half its aircraft and pilots.

'Gaw,' said John Penntifer again, and for no particular reason consulted his watch. It had gone ten-thirty. He went downstairs into his shop and checked over his lists. Five areas in London were blackened, blood-drenched smudges, but that did not alter the fact that he would have to drive into Plymouth in the morning. The wholesalers wanted a ticking off. The beef had definitely been inferior. And there was also that matter of business for the Aero Club, of which he was the most enthusiastic member. Come rack or ruin, it all wanted doing, just the same.

He was a big, grave, placid man, was John Penntifer, butcher of Plympsmore, and not easily disturbed, but in him that night was a stirring anger that it should have happened, a feeling as though he had been cheated and let down. He was living, he had thought, under a system where that sort of thing was properly looked after. It was, he understood, a democracy, but a democracy that somehow always seemed to favour the rich and the titled so that they got into the seats of power and thereby managed to perpetuate their riches and their titles. This never bothered Penntifer so long as they ran things comfortably and smartly and left him enough shillings in the pound wherewith to taste and pursue the joys of leaving the ground on Sunday afternoon and propelling himself carefully around the airport, in grave, methodical circles, and plunking himself back on the field again with sweetness and precision. His taxes, he knew, went for Government, and rearmament, and defence. But the message of terror and disaster that he had absorbed that evening reached through the staid placidity that was part of him and told him that he hadn't got his money's worth. The people who were supposed to be looking out for him, and whose business it was to stop the sort of thing that had happened, hadn't.

Before locking up, Penntifer went out into the narrow street where the grey stone houses had their doorsteps flush with the macadam road that was Fore Street while it ran through the little Devon village, but which, when it emerged, simply became Route B3212 from Exeter to Plymouth again.

It was a soft, glorious night, and the narrow band of sky that he could see across the slanting, slated roof-tops was milky white and shimmery with stars. The street was deserted. The inhabi-

tants of the village were indoors at their wireless sets. He looked
up into the sky and listened intently. He thought that from far
off and from no quarter that he could place he heard the thrumming of distant engines, and knew there were wings in the
sky.

He stood there in the street, this large, solid man, coatless, in
his collarless shirt and vest, and wearing his house slippers. A
heavy gold watch-chain crossed from one pocket of his vest to
another. His brownish hair, with just a touch of iron in it, was
thick, and cut so that it lay across his brow, almost to his bushy
eyebrows, in a sort of bang, and he had a short, drooping
moustache that followed the complete curve of his upper lip. His
eyes were large, placid, soft, and deep blue, and his complexion
high and florid. He was as firm and big and solid as the beeves
he quartered and carved and sold, but he was reaching to the
stars. He was wishing that he could fly that night and join with
the distant thrumming. He wondered how long it would be
before he would be permitted to attempt night flying. Flight
Lieutenant Handwie had been very encouraging about it. Lieutenant Handwie was his instructor, and the absolute czar, over-
lord, and god of the Plympsmore Aero Club. A sense of depression
overwhelmed him as he remembered what had happened that day.
Somewhere Handwie must be flying to the defence of England.
He might never come back. One of the objects of driving into
Plymouth and the next morning was to see about getting a room
at a hotel where the Aero Club, in conjunction with the larger
and more powerful Plymouth Aero Club, was to give a little
surprise dinner to the lieutenant.

It was curious, but characteristic of Penntifer, that in his mind
he never made any connection between the swift battle above
the earth that had destroyed what remained of England's chivalry
and aristocracy, the real flower of her youth, and paralysed her
air power and defence, and his own flying. Air fights and steel
machines that dove and wheeled and snarled and buzzed like
furious wasps, that could go up like lifts, hanging from their
airscrews, and thundered in to land at over a hundred miles an
hour, were as completely beyond his ken as is the multi-
cylindered, underslung, supercharged, and long-hooded racing
automobile to the man who methodically drives his car about
the highways, for work or pleasure.

John Penntifer, the Devon butcher, quite by accident had come
upon a passion in middle life, and that passion was flying. It
had begun when his friend Harry Pryne, the local radio engineer,
had persuaded him to go for a hop in Plymouth one Sunday

afternoon. Then John Penntifer had discovered that it was beyond neither his means nor his capabilities to learn to fly. He took his licence. And what was more, he founded and sat permanently in the chair of the Plympsmore Aero Club, which boasted sixteen members and one aircraft.

Penntifer's flying was as careful and placid and staid as his demeanour, and, in fact, as his appearance. No one would ever have taken him for a qualified and licensed pilot except for his eyes, which were those of men who look into far spaces. Many of John Penntifer's ancestors had been to sea in the way of Devon men. But he flew by sheer determination and love of it, and almost constantly by the book. He was heavy-footed on the rudder pedals and heavy-handed on the control stick – so much so that he had nearly driven Lieutenant Handwie to tears during the early instruction period, but even in his heavy way he had managed to pick up some of the rhythm of flying. He couldn't etch a sweeping circle with his wing, but he could edge around it and get there eventually, and he was always terrifically precise about his work. Handwie often wondered where Penntifer got his pleasure out of the sport because he was always so busy doing something with the plane – trimming a wing, or eyeing the gauges, or wiggling the stick. But Penntifer was quite in heaven from the moment that he climbed into the cockpit and put his big, thick fingers on the throttle and settled his feet heavily on the rudder pedals.

He flew a little Loddwell Gull. She was a tiny grey biplane with a nice respectable wingspread. She cruised at seventy-five miles an hour and had a top speed of eighty-five, and she was his love and his life, his dear lamb and his worship. There were other planes which were the individual property of wealthier members, but the little grey Gull was owned by the club and therefore he had a share in her.

You can see now why, at that time, there could not have possibly been any connection between John Penntifer on a Sunday afternoon, wearing his second-best suit of clothes, a black and grey stripe, with a leather jacket over his coat, and brown helmet and goggles, picking the Gull up off the field at Plymouth, where the club had its hangar, wheeling it twice around the airport, and setting it down again, or executing slightly squared figure eights, or spiralling down from two thousand feet in little jerks that bristled the nape hairs of real flyers, but which nevertheless brought him in to land without sideslipping or gunning over the wires – between that Penntifer and the war drums that throbbed in the upper skies. John Penntifer had never in his life, which comprised ninety-seven flying hours, been higher than five thousand feet.

Once, just once, on a bright-starred and unforgettable day, he had been for a few minutes at the controls of a transport plane that had settled into Plymouth on charter, piloted by a friend of Lieutenant Handwie. The pilot had taken up Handwie and Penntifer and, on Handwie's recommendation, had permitted Penntifer to sit in the co-pilot's seat and take the controls. Penntifer handled the wheel as though it were the Chalice of Antioch, but when he laid his huge feet on the rudder pedals, he made a three-mile error, in spite of trying to pretend the rudder controls were made of eggshells. He was quite fascinated with the speed of the contraption; it was one of the first of the new English Douglases, which could gallop smoothly at two hundred and ten. They fly like angels, but must be gentled at all times. When the pilot told him to raise the nose a little, he raised her a thousand feet before he realised it, and a smile curled his lip in spite of himself as he thought of the long struggle to hoist the Gull a thousand feet by climbing turns, his eyes glued to an apparently immovable altimeter needle.

The throbbing in the distance had died away. Penntifer went back inside. He gathered up his slips, locked the shop doors, and went upstairs where his wife was standing white-faced with her hands folded over her stomach under her apron, gazing at the wireless with a puzzled, doubtful look on her face. She was a Devon woman, thin and dark-haired, with the inevitable moustache that seems to come to middle-aged English women in the country. But she had fine eyes. She had been a good wife to John Penntifer, and a good mother to their two girls and three boys. She disapproved in a negative way of her husband's flying, but merely from a normal reaction to the woman's instinct for self-protection, a sort of 'what-will-become-of-us-if-something-happens-to-you?' business. Secretly she was quite proud of her husband's ability to fly and his chairmanship of the Plympsmore Aero Club.

'He said everyone's to put out their lights because of the air-raiders,' she told him.

'Hum,' said Penntifer. 'Well, then, out with them. Though there'll be no danger here.'

They extinguished all the lights, and in the darkness Penntifer called up his friend Major Charterod, the land agent. Ordinarily, under the system in which Penntifer lived and was happy, he and the major would never have progressed beyond nodding acquaintance. The major was Indian Army, retired, though still

F

this side of fifty, a pukka major, D.S.O. and all, and far removed from Penntifer by caste, even though he was working for a living now, selling houses and taking inventory. But the flying had broken through that barrier. Flyers are a race and people apart, somehow. They recognise and respect something in common with one another. The major, who was a little dried-up chap with a semi-bald head, and Penntifer were very fond of each other. Their wives of course never met, because neither one of the women cared to shock the system to that extent, but the two men frequently sat together in the lounge of the Devon Arms and drank their pints of lukewarm bitter and discussed flying and their respective pets. The major was more than a little partial to a low-wing Alpha monoplane that was practically a glider with a motor in it. It would float for hours, coming in to land sometimes clear across the field. It made for good talking.

The two men had much to say to each other over the telephone, news to exchange. The major, an ex-soldier and a more highly bred and sensitive person than Penntifer, was a mass of shock and nerves over the news. He was applying in the morning for return to active service. He had tried to telephone relatives in London, but Trunks reported that all exchanges except the South Kensington one were down. News grew worse and more confused every hour. The Government had not yet declared war on the two powers. It was doubtful whether such a declaration meant anything anyway. The fleet had been ordered home at once, and avoiding the Mediterranean route. It was leaving the Empire wide open, but this was one time when the Empire must shift for itself.

There was no precedent for what had happened. England had been assaulted with a brutality and a ferocity that she had not experienced since the days of the Norman invasion. Now she was like a prizefighter who had been away from the ring for a long time and who upon returning receives a frightful bash in the face at the first crack of the bell and finds himself sitting on the floor, sick, bleeding, and thoroughly addled.

It was obvious that war must be declared, but equally obvious that an invasion of the land of the two powers was costly and impractical and now, in view of the danger to England, impossible. Bombardment by the fleet might be a punishment, but the fleet could not be spared. In times of stress England, drawing on the skeins that stretched over the world, pulled her fleet about her like an old lady settling her shawl about her neck to keep out the damp. More obvious still was reprisal by air. One of the two-power capitals was three hours away by fast bomber. But

two thirds of the British combat fleet had been smashed in the
first surprise attack from the air, rent, split and shattered earthwards, by hordes of silver wings that simply cascaded out of
the higher levels, like hot steel out of a furnace, crackling and
spitting and blasting. And a hundred and thirty-eight of the
largest and fastest bombers had been destroyed in their hangars
near Swindon.

England was as vulnerable as one of those fragile, long-legged
spiders with no sting. For this was neither war nor ordinary
piracy. It was gangsterism, raised to the nth, or international,
degree. The two powers had simply expanded their internal
policies and methods and applied them on a large scale. They
had in effect used the technique of the American gangster's
version of the half-strength black powder bomb tossed over the
transom to wreck the room inside without too much damaging
the inhabitants thereof, and accompanied by a note: 'This is to
let you know what we want. If we don't get it, the next one will
be filled with dynamite.' This was blackmail on a magnificent
scale, with the price as yet concealed by diplomatic verbiage, but
with the victim to be put in the mood to yield, no matter what
the price. By the time anyone could come to her assistance it
would be too late. England at that moment needed a breather
and a chance to recover. That was exactly what the Intelligence
of the two powers intended she should not have. She was a tough
old muscle and, once she had staggered through the first round,
might last out the fight.

Penntifer told the major he was driving in to Plymouth in the
morning, but that he would see him when he returned if the
major had not already gone up to London. Under the circumstances the little dinner to Lieutenant Handwie would probably
not take place, but at any rate he ought to talk it over with the
chairman of the Plymouth Aero Club.

The broadcasting stopped promptly at twelve. Not that there
was not still news and horror aplenty to retail to the shocked
ears of Englishmen. But the broadcasting always stopped at midnight, with the tolling of Big Ben. And so because it always had
stopped before, it did on that night too. England was something
like that. Only there was no chiming of twelve strokes by Big
Ben that evening, because the two powers' Intelligence had struck
at tradition as well as depots, and Big Ben was a tangle of
crumpled steel and wheels and spindles, a clotted mass of
wreckage that somehow hung, a little obscenely by two or three
still unsevered cables, from the naked front of the split and
shattered tower.

John Penntifer and his wife went to bed together as they always had for many years, but Penntifer did not sleep well that night. His stolid nerves were as steady as ever, but his soul was uneasy. He could not have put it that way, exactly, but he had been hurt because England had been hurt. There were not many countries left where you could get at the hearts of its people through rocks and soil, where men were rooted like the mandrake.

In the morning Penntifer did the chores of opening his shop, saw that his apprentice clerk was capable of dealing with requirements of the day, backed his little Morris out of the garage, and drove the seven miles to Plymouth, through Plympton, Yealmpton, over the bridge where the grey town sprawled over its hills in front of him.

The Morris was old and rattly and carried its own commotion along the street with it so that Penntifer never heard the high-up drumming in the heavens, the high, throbbing drumming that was spreading like a canopy over the upper levels, the unseen levels of the upper sky. He was driving down Tavistock Street, on his way to the meat market, his attention focused on his driving and the traffic in the grey street.

But at Old Town Street, which he had to cross, the traffic was against him and he had to stop in moody contemplation of the back of the bobby turned to him, arms outstretched like a scarecrow, his white-gloved hands sticking out of the end of his sleeves. His motor was only idling, and so, in common with the people on the street, he now heard the bombs thudding and blasting into Devonport, straight ahead, and the shriek and whine of the anti-aircraft shells as the batteries opened their hopeless fire.

All the people on the street stopped stock-still and listened and froze, looking skyward, and it was just as though a film had been suddenly stopped and all the busily moving objects on the screen had become an inanimate magic-lantern slide. When the policeman turned to permit traffic to cross Old Town Street, nothing moved except at the very end – John Penntifer, who crossed and continued on to the meat market, where he had to tick a man off because he had been sending inferior meats. In his ears was the sharp 'spang-spang-spang' of anti-aircraft rifle fire, and the grandiose, periodic 'ka-ta-KLUNG!' of heavy air bombs slamming home. His mind played with the phrasing that had come slipping so smoothly out of his wireless set: '. . . further minor demonstrations of two-power solidarity are planned at key points of the British Isles . . .'

Penntifer parked his car just outside the wholesale meat district and entered the half circle of the meat market, a street lined on both sides with open shops in which hung whole bullocks and sheep, halves and quarters of pork, and lambs, still unskinned, and the butchers in their bloody white aprons moved about with knives in their hands, past counters heaped with tripe or dark-red livers. But the knives were out of their hands, and the butchers were running, seizing one another by the arm and shoulder, and pointing skywards; and all chins were pointing out at right-angles, and necks were stretched until one saw the stubble hairs against the red skin.

John Penntifer looked up too, and in the small patch visible above their heads he saw little white cotton-wool puff balls and then, later, black and yellow bursts, and shivering lines of smoke that spread falling fingers from the coronas of the explosions in the air. Too, he saw something streak earthwards in a comet of smoke, and another of the same, and disappear, and the high drumming was in his ears, but he began to have a queer sense of confusion and instability as though things were no longer very greatly to be relied upon, and that which he knew for reality took on a much more dreamlike quality than ever before.

The butchers should have been standing behind their counters, or running their knives down the halves or sides of beef, or fishing down in vats for pickled tongues, or weighing honeycomb tripe, instead of running about their half circle of a street, craning their necks skywards and reaching for one another.

The butchers should have been standing behind their counters, weighing out ribs or rumps of beef, instead of rolling in the stained and bloody gutters, holding their heads, rolling over and over; and the long sides of beef and mutton should have been suspended from their large, sharp hooks instead of lying in the gutter with the rolling butchers and the two old women dressed in black with their skirts over their heads and their white underwear showing.

John Penntifer too was rolling in the gutter, with his bowler hat crushed down over his eyes. The big, stained cobblestones were very close to his eyes sometimes, and then again they were distant, and the houses and the butcher stalls were spinning around as though they were all nailed to cardboard and had a pin through them.

Because of the pain and the singing in his head, John Penntifer could remember little how he had come to be in the gutter with the meat and the butchers when a moment before he had been standing looking skywards at the little white puff balls and the sulphurous yellow and black shoots and wavy fingers of smoke, but as his head cleared a little, he did remember or rather was dimly conscious of there having been an abysmal and cataclysmic noise, as though a panel of sheet iron, a mile square, had been struck a violent blow with a hammer the size of a battleship.

He picked himself up on his feet, and although he could manage to stand, when he tried to walk he teetered and swayed as though he were dead drunk. But he set off in the direction that an instinct told him had been the origin of the great sound.

He was walking along East Street behind Old Town and all the shops and Woolworth's. There were no windows at all anywhere any more, and he could look right into Woolworth's and see the welter of women lying on the floor, and those who were standing, fingering their faces with puzzled looks, puzzled because the fingers came away so red.

Penntifer walked on without knowing why or where, turning left at the corner, and so coming back into Old Town Street, close to the corner of Bedford Street where had stood the five-storey building of Spooner & Company, known as the Department Store of the West. The big demolition bomb had scored a direct hit in the centre of the department store crowded with women and children at their morning shopping, which was why it was no longer there except for one fractured wall that had not toppled into the street and a pyre of dust and powdered plaster that was rising out of the horrible bubbling cauldron that had been the centre of the store and that was now a hole in which weltered living and dead human beings and fragments thereof, stone, plaster, glass, beams, and merchandise.

One wall had been blown right into Old Town Street, where Penntifer now picked his way, flattening out small cars and people as though they had passed beneath a steam roller, wrecked two buses that were passing, killing everyone in them, and smashed the windows and façades of the shops on the opposite side of the street. Old Town Street was knee-deep in broken glass, rubble, twisted steel, and bodies. A picric acid stench hung heavily in the air with the settling dust, and after the appalling blast of the bomb the silence was even more dreadful, because there were no longer any noises of heavy buses and motor cars and clanging trams, and the shuffle of many shod feet on pavements or bells of bicycle-riders. The only sounds in the streets were soft dripping sounds and the moans and cries of people who were not yet dead.

Penntifer was a butcher by trade, and therefore used to blood and bone and meat, but the dead and the dying in the streets, among their own fragments, made him sick, and he turned away retching and fled as quickly as he could up Old Town Street, leaving the sights and the sounds behind him, until by a slightly roundabout way he came back to where he had parked his car. It was intact except that the rear window was blown in. When he got in and pressed the starter button, it came to life. Another explosion shook the earth, but it was farther away. Nevertheless, Penntifer's system could stand no more shocks. He was as close to panic and nervous disintegration as such a solid, stolid unimaginative man could come. He jammed the car into gear, turned it around, headed north along Notte Street to avoid any piled-up traffic on the road he had come, turned down Hoegate Street, and thence east and back into Tavistock Street, out over the ten-mile-an-hour bridge, and up the long hill into the open country, where for the first time he could even make an attempt to marshal his thoughts. The gunfire had died away, and the explosions too. When he reached the top of the hill, he turned around and looked back before driving around the bend that would from then on hide the sprawling red-roofed town of Plymouth. He counted nine columns of smoke rising from different sections of the city, and in one spot he could see shoots of orange flame through the black smoke. He looked back no more, but sent the car around the corner and over the brow of the hill, and inside of a minute he was driving through the soothing greens and greys and terracotta reds of the Devon countryside.

His eyes were on the cool green of the fields divided by their grey walls, a soft old grey, the same as that in the houses and the roofs of the houses, and on cows that grazed and switched their tails, on the high green hedges that bordered the road, and on an occasional thick, whitewashed cottage with an old thatched roof. Sometimes he drove past a farmer ploughing up the red earth or turning under the remains of a crop, with white gulls walking stiff-legged behind him in the furrows, white gulls, and black rooks, mingling for the leavings. He passed through little wooded spots, where the boles of the old beeches were smooth and ancient and glistening, grey-green in colour, moss-patched, and all the branches intertwined overhead, and one knew that those trees had been there a long, long time.

He was thinking at that moment of another line in the statement of the Ambassadors: 'The unfortunate liquidation of certain portions of London and other cities in Great Britain that is to follow . . .'

The world 'liquidation' brought a literal picture to his literal mind: 'to make liquid . . .' He thought with deep distress of the drip-dripping he had heard on Old Town Street after the explosion. Men and women had been made liquid. He pressed the accelerator harder and the little car complained and clanked. But he was again close to panic to get home. He was not a demonstrative man, but he wanted to see his wife and his children and lay his hands on them and feel their skins whole and solid and know that they had not been made into liquid.

But the road, and the fields and orchards, and little wooded spots, and patchwork countryside of corn and grain, and greens were all solid and peaceful, and a powerful anodyne to his shocked and battered nerves. There they were. There they were as he had always seen and remembered them. With a sinking pang he thought of them blowing up as Spooner's, the Department Store of the West, had blown up, trees cracked, and splintered walls, torn and broken, and the pleasant fields blackened and erupted.

No two men's patriotism is the same, or hinges upon the same images. To John Penntifer, this was England, the meadows, the hillsides, the warm, terracotta-coloured earth, the remnant of olden forests with their trees that had been young when men in armour were old, the solid houses, and the winding roads sunk low beneath the parallel walls of green hedgerows that in the spring were dotted yellow with primrose, and in the summer crimson with poppy.

It was neither London nor Plymouth nor particularly his own grey house, except for the multicoloured garden kept up by his wife, that was England to John Penntifer. It was this land. Cities rose and fell, and came and went, but the land stayed as it was, the hills and the hedges and the grass and the trees, and he could feel so old, so one with their antiquity. Sometimes he felt as though he wanted to stand in that soil, rooted like a tree, with his legs buried to his knees, so that he could feel a part of it. He passed a grey lichen-covered wall that ran along the side of the road and ended in an old tollhouse, nearly hidden by climbing ivy. When Simon Penntyfer, the boatswain on the *Silver Blade*, one of Drake's ships that had fought against the Spanish Armada, had come ashore at Plymouth after the battle and had walked up this road, he had seen the same old tollhouse and the same hills. All this ground had been lived over, walked over, and bled over for so long. He was English by absorption from the soil. As his name had grown from the Norman Pontefiere to English Penntifer, so had he grown out of that land. So that land, as he drove through it, filled his heart with love and a deep yearning to shield and protect it.

No one would have known those things were going on inside

John Penntifer because, being middle-aged and married and respectable and, above all, the butcher of Plympsmore, he was not supposed to have things going on inside of him beyond a knowledge of the quotation of beef and mutton and a neighbourly interest in the customers who came into his shop. But then nobody ever knew for certain what went on inside of people. Certainly no one, not even a very profound man, could have managed to correlate the hash of vagrant thoughts and isolated ideas, and stray wisps of imagination, and little unrelated bits of stubbornness, plus a number of vague ideas about aerodynamics, that eventually gave rise to what in conception and later in execution became known simply as Penntifer's Plan.

The plan was already buzzing around the inside of John Penntifer's head, the head with its droopy thatch that was so like in colour and conformation to the thatch on the roof of the Devon cottage as he drove home that terrible morning, through Yealmpton and Plympton, towards Plympsmore. Or rather pieces of it were like parts of a picture puzzle that one knows belongs to other parts, or suspects might fit, and so lays aside until they shall be wanted. Some of the pieces were just sentences that he planned to use in his address to the Aero Club when he called the meeting, such as: 'General Joffre used taxicabs to save Verdun.' He was not sure either of General Joffre or the Verdun part, but he was certain about the taxicabs. Or: 'The Spanish Armada appeared off the coast of England exactly three hundred and fifty years ago, in 1588, and Simon Penntyfer sailed out of Plymouth aboard the *Silver Blade,* Captain, Sir Hector Dowson.'

The butcher drove slowly down the one street of Plympsmore where the doorsteps of the grey houses reached to the edge of the road, and turned his car down the little alley into the garage behind the store. He went upstairs to his home over the shop, where he found his dark-haired wife sitting in the living-room with the children about her, the two girls and the three boys. They all looked grave and puzzled. They were listening to their wireless set, as Penntifer and his wife had listened to it the night before. The daily programme had been suspended. Only news came out of the polished and fluted little box. And all the news was appalling.

What Penntifer had managed to live through at Plymouth, was the practical extermination of the surviving parts of Great Britain's air fleet. The two English naval bases – Portsmouth and Devonport – had been attacked simultaneously and the naval air arm wiped out. The *Queen Mary* had been sunk at her dock.

Again the technique had been the same as had been used in the opening raid on London. The bombers blasted the open towns. When the British flyers took the air, the two-power fighters that had been in ambush above the bombers dived on them and wiped them out. They had speed and numbers on the English. Three thousand died in Southampton, three thousand seven hundred in Plymouth. Then the two attacking wings, one in the west, the other in the east of England, headed north and began to converge. They left destruction and carnage at Bristol, Birmingham, Liverpool, Manchester, Hull, and Leeds before they turned eastwards again and flew out to sea and vanished. And by that time there was nothing left on wings in all England capable of pursuing them.

The announcer said in his well-modulated voice, still tinged with accents of regret: '. . . the Air Ministry neither wishes nor is able to conceal from the British people that it has suffered a disaster of the first magnitude, in the failure of the remaining war craft to render any opposition to the raiders, and in the eventual destruction of nearly all the British planes participating in the defence of the nation. Other plans for the defence and safety of those living in danger zones are maturing and will be revealed as soon as they have reached the practical stage.'

A later bulletin said: 'His Majesty the King has been in conference with his Ministers since late last night. His Majesty shed tears unashamedly when apprised of the toll of dead and dying among his subjects.'

At this point John Penntifer wept a little too. He loved and felt a little ashamed of his helpless King, who sat with his Ministers and cried when they told him what was happening to the human beings who were technically his subjects and for whose welfare he was equally technically responsible.

The tears shed for him by his King touched Penntifer, but they did nothing to assuage the uneasiness in his soul. A king who wept for his people was a good and kind king who inspired love and picture-postcard loyalty. Somehow, those drops of salty water dripped from glands in the skull that the year before had been anointed as royal and holy symbolised to Penntifer the things that had gone out of British leadership, the toughness and the swiftness and the ruthlessness of the barons and lords and royalties of the days of his ancestors, the seagoing and land-roving Simons and Abels and Peters and Harrys, Penntyfers all, who followed leaders and whose leaders took them to where there was trouble and then did something trenchant about it.

From what Penntifer could make of the death lists, a lot of

the shoots from the old family trees had been nipped in the disaster to the air fleet. He shook his head. The old ones were soft. Many of the young ones were dead. His plan came rushing back to him and swirled around inside his head, where it burned and buzzed and made his heart beat faster and his breath come quicker. The impossibility or impracticability of it never dawned upon him, but that was mainly because he never quite saw it very far towards fruition, even in his own mind. That is, he could not quite see what would happen *after* the plan was once in operation. All his thoughts were occupied in getting it into operation, and what finally crystallised him into steady, stubborn, accumulative action that was undeniable and unstoppable because of the fundamental simplicity and strength of the man's person and character was a bulletin read into the microphone by the B.B.C. announcer, which issued forth to fall upon the ears of John Penntifer, butcher of Plympsmore, England, and his wife and his dearly beloved five children.

In sum and substance it was this: The two powers' Ambassadors had again paid a visit to Whitehall – the bulletin neglected to describe the fact that they wore morning coats and silk hats, carried umbrellas in approved English style, and smiled broadly. At Whitehall they left another note from their governments, in which demands were crystallised. And even to one as ill-versed in international diplomacy as John Penntifer, the scope of the débâcle of the English air arm was made all the plainer by the tenor and nature of the demands. In addition to certain political changes on Great Britain's influence in western Europe, the two powers made the demand that quite evidently was what had really inspired the raids. Briefly, it was that Great Britain retire bag and baggage, wholly and completely, from her Empire in the East.

Her holdings were to be divided between the two powers.

Had one been anywhere off the coast of England at that moment, one might almost have heard the gasp that arose, house by house, from the shocked nation gathered around its loudspeakers.

The diplomatic language of the note maundered on: '. . . more equitable distribution of latitude for expansion . . . a redistribution of territories more in line with the new nationalism and the rights of rejuvenated nations and peoples . . . three-day period permitted for ingestation and dissemination . . . no further liquidations or demonstrations deemed necessary during that period . . . However, at the close of the seventy-two hours, unless the Government shows a willingness to comply with the

demand of the English people to accede to the wishes of the
two-power Governments, then a further period of liquidation of
the English people may be expected to ensue immediately, this
time untempered by mercy and the purely demonstrative nature
of the earlier manifestations, and in its effects such that the
Government would not be able to avoid a popular uprising
designed to install a government more favourable to the peaceful
and forward-looking aims of the two powers.'

'Coo,' said Mrs Nancy Penntifer. 'What's it all mean?'

John Penntifer had learned a lot since the night before. 'It
means we have three days to get out of Africa, India, and
Australia. If we don't agree, they'll come back and blow us all
to pieces. City by city. County by county. They can do it now.
We have no more defence from the air.'

He stopped and thought for a moment. And then he suddenly
contradicted himself: 'No, by God, they cannot. They cannot.'

He went to the telephone and rang up Major Charterod's office
and inquired of his assistant who answered: 'Has the major gone
up to London yet? This is Penntifer speaking.'

'No. He's here. I'll put him on.'

The major came on the telephone. 'Ah. Are you all right, old
man? I heard you'd got back from Plymouth. We heard the explosions. It's terrible. They're completely disorganised up in
London.'

John Penntifer said: 'Yes. Yes. Thank you. Look here, Major.
I want you to call a meeting of the Aero Club at once.' The major
was the honorary secretary.

'Eh? What? Oh, look here, John. This is no time for Aero Club
meetings. Those matters before the committee will simply have
to wait until such time as . . .'

'No, no,' said Penntifer. 'I want – as chairman, I must insist
upon a full membership meeting at once. If you will get some of
the members on the telephone, I will ring the rest. Let us have
it in your office. Let us not delay an instant. There is so little
time. Seventy-two hours. Hurry up, Major, I beg of you.'

'You are in earnest, John? You have something of importance
to say to us?'

'Of the greatest importance. Call the meeting, Major. If you
will notify the upper half of the list, I will do so for the bottom
half. Everyone must attend. Let us say at two o'clock.'

The Plympsmore Aero Club, Mr John Penntifer, chairman,
Major Wesley Charterod, honorary secretary, Mr Frank Good-
hue, honorary treasurer, met at Major Charterod's office at two
o'clock that afternoon. There was a full attendance with the

exception of Mr Prindy, the stationer, who was off on holiday. They all came from their work, in the costumes of their trades. Art Derry had come over from Cooper's garage in his greasy overalls, his face grease-stained. There were Harry Pryne, the young radio engineer who had introduced Penntifer to flying, and Mr Ambrose Abbott, the surgeon. Frank Adams, who owned the little sweet shop in Fore Street, and the shy, unobtrusive Alvin Hamby, the local solicitor and commissioner of oaths. There were Colonel Atkey, retired, who owned the fast little cabin ship, a Turnley Eaglet, Peter Ellis, who owned the boat-builder's and was therefore the wealthiest man in the village and who had added to the club's roster of ships the Atcherly Rook, the low-winged two-seater monoplane, the one that Major Charterod so liked to fly, and Arnold Attray, one of the big laundry people, who owned the remaining plane, a fairly fast Collidine Linnet, a sports model.

They all sat around solemnly on camp chairs provided by the major, all fifteen of them. And John Penntifer sat in the centre, at the head of a long table, in his going-to-Plymouth clothes, just as he had returned that morning.

Penntifer rapped on the table with the gavel that was his beloved badge of office and cleared his throat. He then said: 'I pronounce this meeting open,' and cleared his throat again. Mr Hamby very softly said: 'Hear, hear!' as though he were just practising, in a manner warming it up for later use.

'With your permission,' said Penntifer, 'we will dispense with the reading of the minutes of the last meeting.' He looked around him and took note of the affirmative nods. The little company was waiting and electric with anticipation. All of them showed signs of the strain they had been under since the attacks on the country had begun, and particularly the terrible disaster at Plymouth, so close to home. Penntifer could feel that they were looking to him to explain the reason for calling a meeting of an amateur flying society, organised for sport and pleasure, at a time when each felt that his shrift might be very short. He wanted to rise up and blurt out his plan, the idea that had been buzzing and burning inside his head, tell them all, ask them what they thought, force them into seeing it as he did, compel them to take action, so that the plan might have a chance to work before it was too late.

But that was not the English way of doing it, and John Penntifer, for all the absurd, impossible, impractical romanticism of his plan, was essentially British. Had he been French he would have been a firebrand, kindling his associates to his own

temper, rallying them, pleading, exhorting. But as it was, he sat
with his hands on the table before him, gazed at the tense men
out of his light-blue eyes, and nibbled for a moment at a strand
of his moustache before he said: 'Unfinished business. Ah – with
reference to the committee's report. It has been suggested by the
honorary secretary that this be tabled at the present moment,
due to the urgency of the measures it is proposed to put before
you.'

Mr Hamby said: 'Hear, hear,' and Mr Adams, who always
seconded any proposals, said: 'Second?'

Colonel Atkey, who was inclined to be testy, said: 'Yes, yes,
yes. Come, come, get on with it, man. What is it you have
brought us here to propose?'

All of the members looked shocked, and Mr Hamby said
severely: 'Order.'

With a calm that he did not feel, John Penntifer said im-
perturbably:

'Ah. Then – new business. I have asked the honorary secretary
to call this special meeting——' he paused. All his resolve and
courage fled. His plan to save England was an utter imbecility.
All of the jargon that had whirled through his head on the trip
home – Spanish Armada, taxicabs to Verdun . . . five-mile error
. . . hare and tortoise – recurred to him, and he wondered if he
had gone mad, whether the shock of the bursting bomb close
by in Plymouth had not deranged him. Now that the moment
had come, his carefully rehearsed speech left him and in its place
remained only terror. He wished desperately that he had talked
his plan over with Major Charterod before calling the meeting.
But he hadn't. His mind groped for some subterfuge, something
else he could tell them. But he could think of none.

And then, as suddenly as it had come, his panic was gone. His
plan was clear and simple to his eyes. Only his method of telling
about it changed somewhat. He cleared his throat and said: 'Ah
– gentlemen, the recent events have shocked you all deeply. They
have shocked me beyond words. The things that I have seen,
this vurry day. And now, as you have no doubt 'eard, we are
asked to give up what we 'old in to the east, a part of the Empire,
as the price for being let off further attacks.' He paused again,
and then said very simply and directly, so that it seemed as
though he had asked the question individually of each man: 'Is
there any here among you who would not willingly die for
what's right?'

Harry Pryne laughed a bitter little laugh and said: 'Looks like
a lot of us might be goin' to whether we liked it or not. If friend

Penntifer has any quicker way than sittin' around waiting to be
blown to pieces, I'm for it.'

Mr Hamby said: 'Hear, hear!'

Penntifer continued: 'Our air force upon which we depended
for protection has been destroyed. There's neither ships nor men
to fly them. The best machines and the best pilots are gone, I
'eard it over the wireless. So now, between shame, or the death
of England, and maybe the death of us all, and our families,
stands only – us.'

All the men looked up. 'Eh?' said old Colonel Atkey – 'us? Who
is us? What are you driving at, man?'

Penntifer turned his light eyes on him. 'Why, just us,' he
replied, 'us as is 'ere, and in Plymouth and Bristol and Leeds and
Manchester, us as is wherever there's a landing field and a wind
sock and a machine to fly. Us is the private, amatchoor pilots
of Great Britain. There's eighty-seven hundred of us. I've seen
the register. There's fifty-four hundred odd machines private-
owned, not countin' them as belongs to the commercial lines.
Now, I have a plan. And here it is . . .'

All the men in the room scraped their chairs forward a little
closer and leaned towards the table. John Penntifer began to
speak again.

When he had done, Colonel Atkey sniffed and said: 'Impossible.
I never listened to such utter rot in all my days.' Mr Hamby
started to say: 'Hear, hear,' but checked himself out of loyalty
to Penntifer.

The other men were silent, looking now at the butcher of
Plymsmore, who had risen to his feet from the very earnestness
of his speech and who stood before them now solid, respectable,
everyday, with his heavy gold watch-chain crossing the dark
expanse of his broadcloth vest like a harbour chain. His moustache
drooped and his half-grizzled hair fell across his brow. He was
their solid, undemonstrative chairman. It seemed incredible that
this fantastic idea had issued from his lips.

There he stood, sweating a little, stolid, uninspiring. The things
he had said, the plan he had advanced, had not imbued his
listeners with either belief or confidence. Colonel Atkey thought
that he read the temper of the meeting and said: 'Pah! Twaddle!
I didn't come here to be made a fool of.'

John Penntifer spoke again, and it was as though a voice had
been given to an oak tree and was issuing forth from its gnarled
depths. And as he spoke, he made probably the first and only
gesture he had ever made when talking to a group of men. Not
at all knowing that he was doing it, he took one hand from his

pocket and held it out before him, open, curled a little, palm upward.

'But there's only us left,' he said. He said it with a deep, wonderful simplicity as though in his ears was the cracking of all doom and still he wished to interpose his body as a shield and take first the brunt of what was to come. 'There's only us left as can get up off the ground and fight. Who'll take up a plane with me?'

The power of leadership fell like a red, swirling cape over his broad, black-clad shoulders. The aura of leadership began to leap from his body like hertzian waves from a great broadcast unit. All the heads of the men sitting around the table came up with a jerk and a snap as though they had suddenly heard the call of distant trumpets. Harry Pryne, the radio engineer, answered him. He had a thin, nervous, sulky face. 'I don't give a damn. I'll take up a ruddy plane and fly the wings off of her. I'd just as soon go that way as get picked off like a sitting bird.'

'Hear, hear,' said Mr Hamby, and John Penntifer warmed to it. 'The others,' he said, 'we must tell the others. Get 'em on the telephone. There's not much time. Who'll ring Fred Bereo of the Plymouth Club? Perhaps the lines are down.'

It was Major Charterod who reached back over his shoulder, took his telephone off his desk, and rang the number of the Plymouth Aero Club. When he was put through, he told Fred Bereo, the secretary, of John Penntifer's plan.

There was a queer excitement in the secretary's voice. He said: 'Several of us are dead. I'll call a meeting of those I can get, at once. We'll telephone you.'

The plan was quite clear and simple to the major now. He asked: 'Who do you correspond with?'

'Corryge in Cardiff, and a man named Allen in Bristol. They're both good clubs.'

'Get through to them, old man, and start them on this. Time is so short.'

'Right-ho, old man.'

Penntifer's Plan was already seeping, spreading out over England when John Penntifer, suddenly shocked by his parliamentary impropriety in the face of a great crisis, was putting it to a vote before the members of the Plympsmore Aero Club.

'All in favour, say aye.'

Chorus of ayes!

'All against, vote no.'

'No,' said Colonel Atkey loudly, and he added: 'But dammitall, since it's passed, you may have my plane.'

Penntifer's Plan whipsawed across England, went up and down and across, slipped across the borders of Scotland and Wales, and even nipped over into Ireland.

A clerk in an office in Whitehall in London leaned over to another at a neighbouring desk and said: 'I say, have you heard anything about this thing called "Penntifer's Plan"? There was a fellow on the bus this morning, talking. . . .'

'Can't say I have except that you hear that there's some sort of a do on. My wife was talking to her sister, who lives in Birmingham, last night. She said they were quite excited in Birmingham over something that was known as Penntifer's Plan, but that was all she knew. There's supposed to be a meeting over it at the Air Ministry at twelve.'

At Nottingham, a group of men, some thirty, sat in the living-room of the Coach and Horses Hotel, waiting. They were in type similar to the band that had met at Plympsmore. Some of them nursed pewter jugs of warmish beer. Others sat with their hands idle. Their leader, a tall, sandy-haired man with a stoop, would go anxiously to the door every so often and look out towards the hall and the reception desk and the porter's booth. Then he would return and sit down and play with his watch-chain. From far down the hall came the thin tinkle of the telephone bell. Everyone in the room stiffened. Then the porter, in his green linen jacket and striped apron, came shuffling down the hall. The stoop-shouldered man was at the door waiting. 'It's for you, sir,' said the porter. 'Personal call for Mr Lester Cridmore. A Mr Penntifer from Plympsmore is calling you.'

'By Jove! It's come. It's Penntifer himself.'

Cridmore rushed down the hall and into the telephone box next the porter's booth. His hands were trembling as he shut the door and picked up the receiver. The group of men had followed him down the hall, and he could see their flushed and excited faces pressed against the glass door as he said: 'Yes . . . Yes . . . Hello. Are you there, Mr Penntifer? This is Cridmore speaking, Midlands Aero Club . . .'

Sir Fraser Woolmer, the Air Minister, sat with his head bowed in his hands in his enormous office in the Air Ministry. He had aged twenty years in one week. His cheeks had sunken shockingly and his eyes had a feverish, glassy sheen, deep in their sockets. With him were three men. They were Mr Aaron Waldo, the

Prime Minister, Mr Leslie Spanka-Winwold, the Foreign Minister, and Lord Haldare, First Lord of the Admiralty.

They were the big men, the strong men of the Empire, but they were little frightened children contemplating the wreck of their possessions, things that had been trampled on and shattered by the ruthless foot of an adult bully. They were so close to panic that their dignity lay over them no thicker or stronger than the white skin inside an eggshell.

'There's a man named Penntifer supposed to have a plan,' said the Prime Minister. He was dark-haired, dark-eyed, translucently pale.

Sir Fraser raised his head. 'Who is he? Where is he?' He was ready to grasp at anything, even an unknown name, a name that meant nothing to him.

The Prime Minister lit a cigarette, and a close observer would have seen that his hand was shaking.

'We don't know entirely. It's got around somehow. Supposed to be a chap somewhere in Devon. What is the use? Another day and a half and our time will be up. Have you anything left that can put up a fight, Fraser?'

The Air Ministry jerked his shoulders. 'Penntifer – Penntifer . . .' he said as though the name were hypnotising him. He was feeling the strange mysterious surge that Penntifer's Plan was sending about England even though none but a very few knew what it was. 'Penntifer . . . Why doesn't someone send for him – bring him up here? . . .'

It was the Prime Minister's turn to shrug. 'He is supposed to be coming to London to lay his plan before us – according to the latest news. Probably some crank.'

The First Lord of the Admiralty said: 'For God's sake, Waldo, let me send the fleet and at least blow up as much of their coast-line as we can get at from the water.'

Sir Fraser Woolmer was like a man under a spell. But then he was already entering the illness that carried him off two weeks later. He half whispered: 'But what *is* Penntifer's Plan?'

The door opened quietly, but all the men looked up. It was Sir Fraser's personal secretary. He said: 'I beg your pardon. I would not have disturbed you. There are some men here who will not go away. They insist upon seeing you, Sir Fraser. A Major Charterod, India, retired. And a Mr Penntifer, stoutish chap. If it hadn't been I'd heard the name——'

'By God!' said Sir Fraser Woolmer. 'He's come!'

A man and a girl stood in a deserted street outside the White Unicorn in Wells. It was midnight. There were clouds scudding across a half moon. It was cold. There was the faint scent of the coke that the English always burn in their small towns, pungent, vital, and nostalgic. People who have smelled it once never forget it. The name of the man was Edward Stokes. He was the mechanic of a Wells garage. He was thirty, with light hair and light-blue eyes and a small frame, but his face was thin and pinched as though when he was young he had not had enough food, physically and psychically. The name of the girl was Ellen Snivers. She worked behind the kitchenware counter of the Woolworth's in Wells. Her teeth and mouth were too small, but she had rich, thick brown hair and large, dark eyes. She was bundled in a cloth coat and wore no hat.

'Yer goin'?' she asked. They stood on such an old street that the houses above them leaned wearily against one another. They stood against the leaning houses.

'Mornin'. Dawn.'

'Like as not ye'll not be comin' back?'

'Like as not.'

The girl sucked her breath in between her teeth. 'Oo's 'e?' the girl said fiercely, and swiftly, hotly jealous and frightened withal. 'Oo's 'e, that you should follow 'im? Gorn flyin' off to get killed. Oo's John Penntifer?'

The man scratched his head. He did not know who John Penntifer was. He just knew that he had been called and that he was following him. ' 'E's got a plan,' he said. 'All of us is going. If we don't it'll be the end of everything.' He looked up at the crooked gables of the houses outlined for a moment against the clear moon, the crooked angled gables, and the black chimney-pots, and the houses that had leaned for so long. It seemed to him worth while to go. The girl's fingers were cold in his warm hands.

She clutched him suddenly. The half wail, half cry that was torn from her was old. The old streets and the old houses had heard it before down through the stone-bound centuries. 'Don't go! Don't go! You'll not come back. You'll be killed. Then wot shall I do? Wot shall I do? Oh, don't go . . .' She ended in a sobbing, with her face pressed to his coat at the neck, and her fists pounding at his breast.

'I'll come back,' said Edward Stokes, though he had no great conviction that he would. Suddenly he felt the thing that was flowing so deeply out of the girl, out of her deep, hidden springs. It caught him up, and he clutched at her and they held to each other, and in his nostrils was the bitter scent of coke smoke, and the little of perfume that she had in her hair.

He tried to say: 'I got to go. I got to be up at four.'

She was still fierce, wild, and breathless. 'No – not tonight. You can go when you got to. But not now. No. No. Come.'

She had him by the hand and was pulling him slowly through the doorway of the house next the White Unicorn in Wells, where she lived in a single tiny room – slowly through the doorway and up the stairs. He was joyously and wonderfully glad and excited . . .

That morning an identical scene was enacted the length and breadth of England. On the stone aprons of the large aerodromes or on tiny farmers' fields distinguished only by a pole surmounted by a wind sock, the little planes stood, biplane and monoplane, low-wing and high-wing, single-seaters and two-seaters, open and cabin planes, their motors coughing and chaffering, their props idling. The men who were going to fly in them moved about them dressed in warm, bulky clothing, in flying overalls, or just in what they had, trousers and leather jackets, their helmets on their heads, the flaps turned up and away from their ears. Mechanics were filling the planes with oil and petrol and testing the controls. Many other men stood by, watching. On some fields there were two dozen planes drawn up on the line. At others but two, and sometimes only one. At five o'clock the muffled pilots strapped their helmets under their chins and climbed into their cockpits. There were last handshakes before they cried: 'Stand clear!' One by one they moved away into the wind, into the dark, grey morning. They left the earth, circled, and vanished. But London was a lodestone. All their spinning noses were pointed towards London. That morning the air over England was alive with wings and humming and throbbing. In some homes men and women cowered again because they thought that the terror had returned. But in many, men said: 'There go Penntifer's men. God speed . . . God bless!'

They came from Nottingham and Oldham and Sheffield, from Leeds and Manchester and Liverpool, Newcastle and Gateshead. Hull and Grimsby, Bolton and Blackburn, Norwich and Peterborough, Birmingham and Coventry, Glasgow, Edinburgh, Kirkcaldy and Dundee, Perth, and Greenock and Kilmarnock, and as far north as Wick, all flying southwards, pointing for Croydon. They flew north from Southampton and Folkestone and Tunbridge Wells, and east out of Winchester, Salisbury, Taunton, and Exeter. They were flying eastwards over the Channel of St George, from Dublin and Carlow and Kilkenny and Tipperary. Their instructions were simple: 'Take off at five. Fly to London. Land at Croydon. If there is no more room there, land at Brooklands, or Shepherd's Bush or Upper Marley, or Heston. But come without fail!' They came. Out of Hampshire and Surrey, Sussex and Essex they flew, from Norfolk and Suffolk, Lincoln and Nottingham and Cheshire, from Land's End, Devon and Dorset. The mountains of Wales heard the beat of their motors. They poured out of York and fairly buzzed and swarmed out of Lancashire. There was fog over Kent, so they hedgehopped. The men of Gloucester all had a rendezvous over Gloucester Cathedral, and they flew to London at six thousand feet, in the shape of a cross. It was a ragged cross because no two planes were of the same speed and power, but a cross nevertheless.

The first Ambassador of the two powers called upon his colleague, the second Ambassador, not at his Embassy, but at his home in Berkeley Square. They were grim men, the two, because they were living under sentence of sudden death. He said when they were alone: 'I am glad that you telephoned. You have information about this man Penntifer. It is difficult to understand. His name is suddenly on every tongue . . .'

The second Ambassador produced a small dossier, a stiff red cardboard envelope, from which he removed a sheet of paper. He licked his lips and read: 'John Penntifer. Aged forty-three. Lives in Plympsmore, South Devon, where he is by trade a butcher. Holds an amateur pilot's licence and is chairman of the Plympsmore Aero Club, a small local flying club. Is married and has five children. During the war, served with the Third Devonshire Rifles. Was wounded and decorated at Mons. Has no connection whatsoever with the Government. Has been flying only three years. Holds Class B licence. Inherited butcher's shop from his father, Martin Penntifer, who died in 1923. Church of England. Not regular in attendance. Well spoken of by villagers of Plympsmore. Tends to his business, which is solvent. Only hobby, amateur flying.' Then followed a description of John Penntifer. There was also a small photograph of John Penntifer. The two Ambassadors put their heads together and looked long at the square, dark figure, with the fringe of hair over his brow, and the drooping moustache.

The first Ambassador said: 'This is the man who has brought three thousand aeroplanes to London. And there are more arriving all the time. I cannot believe it.'

'He is evidently a fanatic of some sort. I have heard of such things before. The English are in a state of extremity. When a people reaches such a condition, it will sometimes blindly follow any leader.'

'These planes——' began the first Ambassador.

His colleague smiled and shook his head. 'They have been carefully checked upon arrival. There is not a single craft there that has a speed greater than a hundred and twenty miles an hour, and most of them are powered under a hundred. Not one of them is armed. No Englishman ever carries arms. They have not so much as a pistol among them. So——'

'So——' echoed the first Ambassador. 'What can come of this? What have we to fear?'

'Nothing. It is a forlorn and hopeless gesture. They will never leave the ground. They have no power, no guns, no radio. Our ultimatum expires in thirty-six hours. The Prime Minister is ready to yield now. If not——' He made a gesture of dropping something.

John Penntifer, Major Charterod, and Mr Harry Pryne sat closeted with the Prime Minister Waldo, Foreign Minister Spanka-Winwold, Lord Haldare, First Lord of the Admiralty, and Sir Fraser Woolmer, Secretary of State for Air. Sir Richard Clapperby, the Home Secretary, hastily summoned, had joined the group. Only Major Charterod was acutely conscious that he was sitting with the Government of England – what there was left of it – and because he was an old Army officer he was embarrassed and frightened. Harry Pryne was still looking sulky and a little contemptuous. So these were the bigwigs. Well, they didn't impress *him*. They were as frightened as anyone, and all they could do was to ask a lot of silly questions, and get up and walk around, and sit down again, and raise objections, and look at one another.

Penntifer was neither impressed nor frightened, nor embarrassed. He was very glad that he could talk to these men about his plan, which suddenly was no longer something leaping about and burning inside his head, but something that was happening. There were more than four thousand private planes landed around London. Their pilots were stolidly standing by them waiting for him, John Penntifer, to tell them what to do. He had not expected this, but now that it had happened, it seemed all right, and he was prepared to do so. First, however, he must convince these men that they need not give in, that there were still men in England who could and would fly and fight. And then he must get them armed.

John Penntifer had no quixotic idea of mass suicide of his

pilots to save England. He was for a stand-up fight on as even
terms as he could get. But he was determined to have his way
on both points, because they seemed to him the right ones.
Everything that had been done previously was quite obviously
wrong. It was time that something right was tried before it was
too late. He tried to make all this clear to the five men who sat
around the long, shiny table: the shrunken, sunken Woolmer,
the pale, dark, ascetic-looking Waldo, Spanka-Winwold, who
looked like a cartoon with his oversized head and Kipling
moustache, the neat and frosty Clapperby, all clipped and smart
and finely, too finely, bred, and the old diehard Haldare, who
wanted to take his fleet out and fight and to whom the new ways
of war and international gangsterism were inexplicable. To him
John Penntifer was like a being from another planet, and his
colleagues much worse even, for listening to him. A butcher
from Plymouth taking up the time of the Government in the
deepest crisis it had ever been called to face – shocking!

The Prime Minister said: 'These are all private machines,
privately owned and flown, Mr Penntifer?'

Penntifer nodded. He wondered why they kept asking him
obvious questions.

'How were you able to persuade them to fly to London?' Mr
Waldo was primarily a politician and curious about any kind
of mass movement. But Penntifer did not know that, so he
replied by telling him the truth.

'We telephoned them,' he said. Lord Haldare snorted in disgust, as much at the utter impossibility of the reply as the broad
Devon accent of Mr Penntifer. He had no experience with the
efficiency of the pyramided telephone call.

Sir Richard Clapperby asked: 'What exactly is it you want?'
He was another career man who had weltered in intrigues. The
arrival of four thousand men by air under a leader who was a
stolid butcher from a place called Plympsmore meant only one
thing to him – a *Putsch*.

Mr Aaron Waldo shook his head angrily. Sometimes his
colleagues depressed him. Mr Penntifer looked puzzled. 'Want?'
he echoed. 'Want? We want nothing. We came to fight. There's
only us left, now that you 'uns have botched the job.'

Waldo grinned. Good for old Penntifer. Then there was a kick
in him. He did have something. He enjoyed the look on the faces
of the Ministers for Navy and Foreign Affairs. Spanka-Winwold
was more Waldo's type. He said: 'Let us stay close to facts.
There are now over four thousand private planes with private
pilots around London. How many more are coming?'

Mr Penntifer drew a crumpled piece of paper from inside his bowler hat, which he had never relinquished, and consulted it; then he replied: 'Six thousand and eighteen, if they all get through.'

'How do you propose to fight without arms?'

'Arm us,' replied Penntifer with a direct simplicity that shocked even Lord Haldare into momentary approval.

'Hm,' said Spanka-Winwold. 'The time is insufficient. We could not possibly adapt those planes for direct gunfire. It would take a month.'

'Give us a man in the back with a machine gun,' John Penntifer said. This was, after all, no different from addressing the members of the Plympsmore Aero Club, except that, by and large, some of these men seemed to have less common sense and understanding. 'We can all fly front cockpit sor. Put a man in back with a gun. If you 'aven't' (Lord Haldare winced at the ' 'aven't') 'got enough machine guns, rifles will do. Anything that shoots, sor. There was a chap came into our aerodrome once. Pilot. Had been in the naval air service. 'E brought down a 'Un with a pop from 'is service pistol. It was in the early days. I mind him tellin' of it.'

Lord Haldare, looking at Sir Fraser Woolmer, made a circular motion with his finger around his forehead, but Woolmer shook his head and said to Haldare: 'But you can't get around the fact that the planes are here, devil take it. That's been done, hasn't it?' He turned his sunken feverish eyes on Penntifer. 'Granted that we could do that – what then? None of you are trained to fight in the air. You have no means of communication. Some of your planes – most of them – will be outspeeded a hundred and fifty miles an hour . . .'

Penntifer leaned forward on the edge of his chair with his bowler hat held firmly between his thick, stubby fingers. His plan was so beautifully clear and simple now. Not like it had first been when it was buzzing inside his head like a wasp trapped on a windowpane. Everything could be answered.

'Give us all the flying men you've got left to work the guns. We'll fly the planes. The speed? The difference in speed? Why, sor, that's a part of the plan, sor . . .'

At the word 'plan' the heads of all the men in the room came up sharply. They were all succumbing to the hypnosis of the sound of the phrase, something solid and reliable – 'Penntifer's Plan!'

'It is then your wish' – it was Sir Clapperby speaking; he was psychically unable to get the idea of the *Putsch* out of his head –

'your wish that we reply to the powers refusing their demands?'

Harry Pryne interposed sullenly: 'It ain't our wish. It's what we damn well want.' Major Charterod looked shocked and started to say something, when Penntifer, waving his hat for emphasis, interposed: 'We don't want to give up the Empire like that, sor. We're not used to it. It's not been our way. When the Spanish Armada was on its way 'ere' – he consulted the paper again – 'three hundred and fifty years ago, an ancestor of mine sailed from Plymouth to stop 'em. Let us go up an' fight, sor. We've stopped 'em before. We'll do it again, sor.' He had addressed his last pleas, somehow, to the Prime Minister. Sir Fraser had sunk together again.

Lord Haldare suddenly barked angrily: 'Rot! Nonsense!' For a moment, Penntifer thought it was old Colonel Atkey speaking again. 'The whole thing is absurd. War cannot be conducted by civilians. Send these madmen home, Waldo. We're in a bad enough spot as it is. This undisciplined mob will only make it worse.'

'Is this your advice, Lord Haldare?'

'It is.'

'What is your opinion, Spanka-Winwold – Sir Richard – Fraser?'

Clapperby snapped: 'Get rid of them. They'll bring a worse bombing than ever down on us.'

Sir Fraser Woolmer said nothing. Spanka-Winwold fingered his chin and made a mouth. 'Mmmm . . . What do you think, Aaron?'

The Prime Minister's eyes were snapping darkly, and for the first time there was a flush on his almost translucently white cheeks. He was a Jew, and had a Jew's sensitivity and feeling for humanity behind history. He said:

'Turn them loose, I say. They're England. You chaps aren't. You used to be, but you aren't any more. You've forgotten how to fight. You've bred it right out of your line. I say send them up. They'll rip the sky loose from its mooring before they let those murderers through. Send them up. Let them try Penntifer's Plan.'

They were all on their feet, and John Penntifer was standing, too, with his rusty bowler hat between his fingers, and his low collar tight around his neck. They were going to try his plan, the thing that had come out of his head; it was all coming curiously to life like the incredible throbbing flight of the amateur pilots to London. For a moment, as he stared into the famous faces around him, the whole thing took on the quality of a dream, but John Penntifer knew that this time it wasn't.

*   *   *

It was no dream when he sat at the stick of the little grey Loddwell Gull, at eleven thousand feet, forty miles due east of London, over a little town called Tilbury. Beneath him was the yellow, widening River Thames. And in the rear cockpit sat an R.A.F. lieutenant, an observer by the name of Postgate. Postgate sat with a five-gallon tin of petrol between his knees and one of the new Bren machine guns in his hands. He was connected to John Penntifer, Pilot Penntifer, by a speaking tube. Three hundred yards to his left floated Major Charterod in the golden Alpha low-wing monoplane. The major had a gunnery sergeant in his rear cockpit, likewise equipped with a machine gun. The major was very happy. Off to the right was Harry Pryne flying old Colonel Atkey's Turnley Eaglet. They had done a nice rush job on the Eaglet – nailed boxes to the floor, loaded up the cabin with spare petrol and ammunition drums, punched a hole through the roof. She had a hump back, did the Eaglet, and so when Private Catwright of the Fusiliers climbed on to his boxes and stuck his head and shoulders through the hole in the roof, he was quite above the backwash of the propeller. Also he was glad to see that he could fire his machine gun in all directions. It was understood that once he took his position through the roof, Pryne would strap him into place.

They were all in the sky, Penntifer's band. They formed a curving curtain at eleven to twelve thousand feet that spread around south, south-east, east, and north-east of London. They draped their wings over the nest that was London. All that night they had been tuned and fitted up, and prepared, and fuelled and armed. What flying men there were left went in the rear as gunners, and, in accordance with John Penntifer's wish, the amateurs sat at the stick. It was a part of his plan. He could not say why, but the Devon butcher had felt from the first that he wanted men at the controls who would do instinctive things when the time came, men who knew their little fluttery planes.

Penntifer's Plan was in operation. At nine o'clock in the morning the time limit of the ultimatum of the two powers had expired. At five minutes past nine the Prime Minister made the brief, simple speech that thrilled the world, in which he invited the two powers to come and take what no Englishman ever surrenders. At fifteen minutes after nine the first plane whipped around, faced into the wind, roared its tiny engine, and rolled off the apron at Croydon and into the air. This was John Penntifer in his Loddwell Gull. From then on they poured into the sky as fast as they could be wheeled into line and sent off, one behind another. They rose from Croydon, from Heston, and from Hatfield, from Gatwick and Hendon, and Brooklands and Abridge. In some places they went off one to the minute, and in some aerodromes, where there was more room, even faster. At ten o'clock there were more than thirty-five hundred in the air, climbing, climbing, climbing, reaching for their ceiling as quickly as they could pull themselves up by their labouring little props. At half past ten the last one was off the ground. Their instructions, written out laboriously by Penntifer, were broadcast to them at the aerodromes. They were to fight as long as they were able. They were particularly to adapt themselves to the *difference* in speed between themselves and the attacking fighters, by using the simplest of manœuvres such as the wing-over or stall turn, the Immelmann, which was the same thing done at speed, and the sideslip. They were to remember to begin all of these manœuvres long before they deemed it necessary in point of time. They were specifically to avoid trying to get into any battle plan or formation, but were to fight and fire whenever and wherever a suitable target presented itself. When the Army's mechanical ears on the ground gave warning that the enemy was approaching, fast R.A.F. machines, the few remainders of the British air fleet, would take the sky, seek the level of the defenders, and fire smoke bombs of warning, the colour, black, white, green, or red, to determine the general direction from which they might be expected. And that was all.

And so John Penntifer sat at the controls in the front cockpit of the grey Loddwell Gull and tried to keep his feet from being too heavy on the rudder bars. His air-speed indicator showed that he was cruising at seventy-five miles an hour. It was a clear, bright day. Four thousand feet below, there were a few small patches of broken clouds, but not enough to offer cover. He looked over the side and saw a steamer slowly moving down Thames and out towards the Channel, which lay blue and shimmering to his right. He could see the irregular streets and red dots of houses of Gravesend and Barking. He felt nervous, but happy. He was flying. The hollowed and stained butcher blocks with the red slabs of meat and the tubs of tripe and the pinkish strings of sausages were very far away. The country below him was flat and criss-crossed by straight roads, unlike his hilly Devon. He looked out at the canvas stretched taut over the struts of his wing tips and wondered what would happen when bullets began to rip and tear. He was not wondering whether he would get back or whether he would die. He did not expect to die. He saw no reason why he should. He believed that his plan was sound and that if he was killed it would be merely a piece of bad luck. No, he was worrying over whether he would carry out his manœuvres successfully. He felt oddly embarrassed because Flying Officer Postgate of the R.A.F. was in his plane. He felt that he must fly well and do honour to his beloved instructor, Lieutenant Handwie. He wondered whether Handwie was alive or dead. Probably dead. Four-fifths of the British fliers had succumbed in the two attacks. But Postgate was no doubt a connoisseur of good flying. Hence Penntifer's nervousness. It was the same way he always felt when Lieutenant Handwie turned him over to a brother officer, or a friend, or an inspector from another county, for a check flight. In his mind he rehearsed the things he had to do to complete the simple manœuvres of which he hoped to make use. It was definitely stuck in his mind that the simpler they were, the more effective they would be. He had had the feeling all along that it would be *their* type of flying, his and the other amateurs', that would in the end prevail . . .

Postgate spoke into his ear through the speaking tube, and Penntifer jumped. He always did at first when talked to through the tube. He heard Postgate say: 'One of our buses coming up. Just under your left wing. The do must be going to get under way. Watch him.'

Penntifer strained his eyes – it is very difficult to see a plane beneath you when you are in the air – and suddenly made out the craft with the two coloured circles painted on the upper wings. It was climbing steeply. Penntifer kept it in sight by making wide, careful circles. As it came up to their level, both Penntifer and Postgate could see that there was something painted on the side of the plane, large white numbers. They read: '15,000.' Then from the plane burst little black puffs of smoke that widened out into balls and drifted backwards from her tail.

'The east,' Postgate said. 'Due east, probably. They're just plain barging over out of the east. No attempt at surprise.'

'What's the number mean?' asked Penntifer.

'Their altitude, probably. They're coming over at fifteen thousand feet. That doesn't give Archie much to shoot at. Head east.'

Penntifer dropped a wing and gentled the rudder bar with his right foot – he had been flying due north at the moment – and saw the compass swing around until the large white *E* showed on the black compass ball. He looked and saw planes all about him heading towards the east, the mouth of the Thames and the open Channel. He could see and counted thirty, and there were more converging all the time into the area of the Thames basin, all shapes and sizes and colours, bright, gay oranges and shining reds, deep blues and light blues, green ones and white and a few in sombre black, tiny things, a tatterdemalion armada that made Penntifer draw in deeply with pride the mixture of clear, cold air and fumes. Yes, they could not lose. Three hundred and fifty years ago, the foreign Armada had threatened the little island, and Englishmen had gone forth in little ships, and they too had turned their faces towards the east, looking for the enemy to harry and harass and beat him . . .

Penntifer spoke through the tube to the officer. 'How can we make them come down to our level? We can't climb any higher.'

'They'll come down,' said Postgate. 'They must.'

As a matter of fact, as it turned out later, Penntifer's Plan was attended by extraordinary luck and circumstances that he could not know of or foresee. Bombing at twenty thousand-odd feet, or even fifteen, is a haphazard business. It is valuable only as a terrorising agency. Accuracy is entirely problematic. But this was a punitive expedition, one that was intended to do serious and lasting damage. And it was only the wiping out of the English defences that had made it possible at all. The bombers were planning to come down to five thousand feet over London and possibly lower. The two-power armada knew of the pitiful amateur air fleet that might lie between them and London. But what they didn't know was the extent to which they had been armed overnight. For Mr Spanka-Winwold had crowned a night of glorious achievement – supplying men and guns to the tiny planes was no mean task – by a neat *tour de force* that gave him great satisfaction. When the two Ambassadors called at Downing Street he arrested them immediately, gave them the opportunity of telephoning to their Embassies news of the English decision to fight, and then sent them to the Tower and had them shot without further fuss or bother, for piracy. Mr Spanka-Winwold was feeling the stirrings of things that had sent a band of English amateurs into the morning sky against hopeless odds. There was something about Penntifer's Plan that was catching. The Foreign Minister grinned to himself when the news of the execution was telephoned him. But that was the reason why the enemy did not know more about Penntifer's air fleet, except that it was to be brushed aside by the fighting planes in another general slaughter, while the bombers went on about their appointed business. The mechanical ears had picked up the invading air armada ninety miles off the English coast, at fifteen thousand feet. But by the time the first advance scouting flights caught sight of the ridiculous motley crowd of coloured specks in the air, awaiting them, they were down to ten thousand feet.

That was how John Penntifer first saw them from the air. They came in waves, in formation, just a thousand feet below him, all silvered and metallic, with the sun splintering on their metal skins. Some of them were stubby and kiwi-winged, some had little metal pants where their landing wheels ought to have been, and some of them had no wheels at all. The fighters were flying at ten thousand feet. Two thousand feet below them were the huge bombers with their great silver, triangular wings with the little bumps on them made by their three and four engines. Some of them flew in line and some in V's, and some in a new formation that Postgate had never seen before, a half-circle with the open end to the rear. Penntifer thought he had never seen such a glorious sight in his life.

Then, to his surprise, he found the air to the right and the left of him, and above as well as below, thick with tiny canvas, coloured planes. He saw that they extended as far as his eye could reach on either side of him. In a moment the two lines would meet and cross over one another. The time had come to do something, to fight. He wondered whether he would know how.

Then he saw a plane to the right of him suddenly stick its nose down and dive, and another and a third, and simultaneously the tiny silver planes below nosed upwards and began to hang on their props. The first of the English planes that had dived sprouted a bright orange flame at the engine and then, as it plunged, poured forth ribbons of smoke. But it fell on a giant four-motored bomber beneath it and carried it down, spinning like a lazily falling leaf, quite out of control.

Penntifer heard Postgate say: 'One! I say, what luck! They've got to come up to us. Steady, old man. Let them. When they reach us, fall away and flatten out and I can give them a burst from beneath. We want them on our tails, but they don't know that. I'll tell you when to drop.'

A tiny steel machine suddenly rose at their side as though it were being hauled up with ropes. Penntifer saw a helmeted figure at a gun. 'Now,' said Postgate. Penntifer pressed the stick hard over to the left and jammed top rudder and heard the wind scream through his wires until Postgate coolly commanded: 'Flatten her out.' Then above the roar of his engine he heard the first chaffering of Postgate's machine gun and then heard his muffled 'Got him, I think. It's against all the rules. Mind the fellow diving.'

In a quick glance over his shoulder Penntifer saw a bright plane

pouring on to him and immediately pulled the stick back, and
when he had the nose raised, eased on the throttle and kicked
right rudder in a wing-over or stall turn. For an instant his plane
was a grey cross against the sky, and a target, and bullets zipped
through it, but Penntifer didn't know it. He let the Gull dive into
the finish of the turn and saw the little all-metal fighter whip up
into a similar manœuvre, but at the high speed of the Immelmann. When it came out, it was ahead of them and a mile and a
half away. Two planes were attacking it, one from above and one
from below, and then a third picked up the fight, and the three
chivvied it until it blew up.

'Oh, well done!' said Postgate into Penntifer's ears. 'Well done.
Fine flying.'

It made Penntifer happier than anything ever had in his life
before, not excepting the day that he had passed his flight test
and received his licence, or even his first solo flight. He looked
about him. He wanted to do some more fine flying. The drop had
brought them into the path of the second line of bombers coming
over. Penntifer could see the machine gunners in the jutted-out
front cockpits of the four-motored planes, and could see that they
were working. The air was now full of roar and crackle, and
another of his little light sports fleet caught fire and began to fall.
The line of bombers came on like a gigantic steel scythe sweeping across the sky. To give Postgate a shot at them, Penntifer
simply flew at right-angles across their line of flight. By rights
Penntifer should have been riddled. But the gunners in shooting
were calculating for their own speed and equal speed from the
target. It was just that it was too simple a shot. A man highly
trained in tricks and gunnery angles, and modern battle technique
can sometimes be relied upon to go completely to pieces in the
face of a simple problem such as knocking a sitting hare off a
rock. This essentially was a great part of Penntifer's Plan. Postgate
shot two of the oncoming gunners and then Penntifer, who was
beginning to catch the rhythm of the battle, sideslipped under
them and then flattened out in time to let Postgate get in half a
dozen bursts. Two of the bombers began to throw smoke and
limp. They fell off in flying speed. A dozen of Penntifer's planes
fell away, dove them out of the upper sky, and finished them off,
and in turn were attacked by a flight of the enemy fighters from
above. The amateurs rolled and swooped and scattered with the
the fighters on their tails, shooting them to ribbons. Beneath him
Penntifer saw chunks fly from his planes and watched them fall,
out of control. He felt himself tapped on the back of the helmet.
He turned and looked. It was Postgate. He was gesticulating. He

showed Penntifer the severed piece of their speaking tube. It had been shot away. Then he pointed down at the scattering planes and made a swooping motion with his hand. Penntifer understood, closed the throttle, and dived. Others of his fleet were diving too. He saw Harry Pryne's Eaglet pass him like a plummet and drop on the tail of a beetle-bright fighter. Private Catwright ecstatically loosed a burst almost at point-blank range. The fighter rose in a desperate climb and for a moment exposed its silver belly to Postgate's fire, and Postgate blew it to pieces. It fell, tumbling cartwheel fashion, end over end.

The attacking planes began to get rattled. Instead of going on, they turned to fight, bombers as well as pursuit planes. It closed up the gap in the one weakness in Penntifer's Plan. Penntifer's planes could never catch the big two-hundred-mile-an-hour bombers. They could have crashed through, taken their losses, and flown on to their destination and unloaded most of the bombs before the defending fleet could have caught up. But flights that have been trained to fight in formation and hold the formation above all are at a disadvantage when the formations are broken, and the two-power formations were being broken by two things – preponderance of numbers and difference in speed. They were so much faster than Penntifer's planes that they were continually overshooting their mark. Before a flight could turn and manœuvre back, two or three of the little sports planes had nipped off a straggler and crumpled him. Too, the Penntifer planes were all fighting singly without rhyme or rhythm. A flight of two-power pursuit planes would waste itself on a single defender, shoot it down, and return to find bombers trying to fight off swarms. The bomber is not a mobile fighting unit. He can defend himself up to a certain point, but when he loses his screen of pursuit planes and fighters, he begins to work into a bit of a panic. Also unorthodoxy makes him nervous. The fast, brilliant boxer is always in more danger of being hurt and beaten when he stacks up against a slow, awkward, unorthodox novice than when he meets a man of his own skill, but a trifle slower. Penntifer had filled the sky with just such slow, sticky, unpredictable, individual fighters who had no idea but to put themselves in a position to do damage, who did nothing according to the accepted rules of air fighting, and who simply nullified the speed advantage of the two-power ships by having no speed at all. It was the lesson that John Penntifer had learned the day that he had had the controls of the fast transport plane for a few minutes and had made a five-mile error with the bare pressure of a finger. A good fast man can sometimes beat a slow man at his own game, by slowing down to his speed and then just keeping ahead of him. But the two-power planes couldn't slow down without their controls going mushy. They dived on the tails of Penntifer's planes and that's where the English wanted them, because only then could the men in the rear cockpits shoot. The two-power battle fleet outnumbered and outspeeded the English Air Force by two to one. Penntifer's amateur fleet outnumbered the attackers.

The bombers, instead of going on, wheeled and began to fight.

Edward Stokes, the mechanic of a Wells garage, was flying a Pudney Sportwing. In the rear cockpit sat Corporal Smivver. The corporal had a rifle in his hands and a couple of hundred rounds of ammunition because there had not been enough machine guns to go round. They had been over West Ham when the storm broke. Stokes looked out over the nose of his little machine through the spinning prop at the grim, knifelike silver line that was sweeping out of the east.

'Gaw,' said Edward Stokes to himself, 'I'd like to know wot I'm doin' 'ere. I'm no blinkin' 'ero.'

Corporal Smivver brought a cartridge up out of the magazine of his rifle into the breach and wiped a fleck of dust off the sights. The Sportwing had a ceiling of nine thousand feet, so that Edward Stokes was below the first flight. Three enemy fighters dived at him, spitting fire. Edward Stokes did not know what to do, so he turned his ship broadside with a sickening little skid. It improved the target for the two-power single-seater fighters, but it also gave Corporal Smivvers what he very much wanted – a shot. The attacker was pouring himself right down Corporal Smivver's sights so that when he pulled the trigger he quite naturally shot the pilot through the head. The single-seater never changed its angle. It missed the Sportwing by six feet and flew on into the ground. A few seconds later Pilot Edward Stokes sighed and leaned backwards against the rear of the cockpit, his head on his chest. Corporal Smivvers already had slumped quietly to the side of his cockpit. His rifle, with one shell exploded, was twisting over and over again on its way to earth.

The little Sportwing then did a curious thing. It neither fell, nor burst into flame, nor spun. It went into a long, sweet, gentle glide for earth. Its engine had stopped because most of it had been shot away. All by itself the little craft came winging down out of the fight that was raging in the upper sky, its nose pointed towards London town, as though in its last extremity it was going home. It was heading into the wind too. It sailed over a clump

G

of trees, cleared a low wooden fence, and landed in a field, where it bumped and bounced twice and then dropped its tail with a thud and rolled on for some fifty yards until it came to a stop. When the people ran up to it they found the two dead men who had come home.

The first group of prisoners reached Whitehall a little after eleven o'clock. There were seven of them, the crew of a four-motored bomber that had been forced down with three engines disabled. They were ushered into the office of Mr Leslie Spanka-Winwold. With him were Sir Fraser Woolmer and Mr Aaron Waldo. The leader, a major in a light-green whipcord uniform, recognised them and saluted. Mr Spanka-Winwold inclined his head courteously. The major drew himself up and said: 'We do not understand why we have been brought here. We beg to claim the rights of prisoners of war. We are all commissioned officers.'

Mr Waldo was looking at them mockingly but said nothing. Mr Spanka-Winwold said: 'Hmmm. Yes. Unfortunately for your cases and the cases of all others who happen to fall into our hands, war has not been declared. You have been brought here to enable you to communicate with your Government for a few minutes by telephone if you wish to do so. Afterwards – ' He paused and his look took in the seven men with no emotion whatsoever – 'afterwards you will be taken to the Tower and hanged for piracy . . .'

Major Philip Charterod, D.S.O., Indian Army, retired, put his light, floaty Alpha monoplane into a right-hand sideslip, a thoroughly wrong manœuvre to get away from the snarling, whining dive of the seven-plane patrol that had aimed its V at him like a stickless arrow. But it was so wrong that it accomplished its purpose. It got him away on the underside of the attacking dive. He wondered why he did not hear the clatter of Captain Ledyard's machine gun. The captain had a broken leg, which was in a cast. He was the gunner assigned to the Alpha monoplane. He had shot down two pursuit planes, a single-seater and a two-seater. The bellies of the fighters all flashed silver in the sunlight as they whipped up and over in a perfect half-loop, half-roll in unison. Captain Ledyard should have been ripping the underside of those silver bellies with his gun. Major Charterod flattened out and turned around to look, and then understood better. The captain was dead.

'Blast!' said the major. 'Damn and blast!' His eyes yielded

tears that blurred his goggles for a moment. He remembered the
happy grin on the young captain's face when they carried him
out and loaded him into the cockpit and put the gun into his
hands. He had been shot down in the first attack.

Suddenly the major no longer had any desire to live. He had
the most curious longing and love for the man who had been behind him. He wanted to be where he was. A black and grey twin-
motored bomber was zooming towards him. The major altered his
course so as to bring him head on into the bomber's path.

'Coming, old chap,' he said, and flew himself and what was left
of the man in the back into the face of the bomber, and lived
long enough thereafter to know that he had taken the bomber
with him before the all-engulfing crash of the tangled planes ripping into the green earth, blotted all into the never lifting darkness.

The weather dispatcher at Margate reported to the big wireless
weather station at Droitwich: 'There's a devil of a fog rolled in
here. It's closed right down.'

The fight blazed along a twenty-five-mile air front. The sky was
free from artillery bursts because Archie had been warned to
keep out of it. But it was filled with the rolling, snarling whine of
the high-powered fighters, the low, steady, humming drone of the
bombers, and the sharp crackling and rattling of gunfire. The
fight was working down lower too, and every so often one of the
little specks circling and spinning and wheeling in the heavens
would plunge to earth trailing a long, feathery tail of smoke.
Sometimes it would be one of the gaily coloured wood and canvas
planes, but more often a silver fighter; and once a bomb on the
bomb rack beneath one of the grim, huge bombers was exploded,
the bomber flew into silver pieces, and five aircraft within range
of the explosion crumpled their wings and fell to earth, four of
them enemy planes.

The two-power planes were out of formation. They were fighting and shooting hard, and the white lines of their tracer bullets
criss-crossed against the blue. But the amateurs were above and
below them. It was Indian warfare in the air, guerrilla sniping,
the big hunt. Sometimes one of Penntifer's men would fly deliber-
ately as bait, fall away, and watch the too fast fighter hunted
and harried from three angles. In the final analysis, the formation-
drilled fighters were no match psychologically for the antics of
the individual defending airmen.

At a quarter past twelve the fight was over. The enemy

machines turned their noses to the east and ran. What was left of Penntifer's fleet circled and circled and watched them run because there was no use pursuing them. They didn't have the speed. A little over six thousand private planes had taken the air. Just under four thousand remained flying. Hardly one but was pockmarked with bullet holes. They remained in the air until some of the surviving R.A.F. machines went up and flew signs past them: 'FOG – LAND AT ONCE.'

The remnants of the two-power air fleet flew into the white mist that rolled in from the sea and, for the most part, never flew out of it again. It was the strange, yellow-grey blanket of fog that for three days covered all western Europe.

'The Armada became distressed through lack of fresh water and soon encountered violent storms which added to its troubles as it attempted to sail home around Scotland and the West Coast of Ireland. Many ships were wrecked, and in Ireland their crews were massacred; many more sank in the open sea. Only half the ships that left the Tagus returned to Spain, and in those death and sickness were appalling. The complete failure of the invasion project was due to the English plan of keeping to windward and fighting at long range, which was followed throughout . . .' (From the STORY OF THE SPANISH ARMADA.)

When the R.A.F. bomber flying the landing sign passed him, John Penntifer turned around to see what Lieutenant Postgate had to say, but the lieutenant was unconscious, with three bullets in his body. Penntifer felt lonely. The fight was apparently over. He thought he would go home. He wondered how much petrol he had left. He knew it couldn't be much . . . Ahead of him he could see the rolling white bank of the approaching fog, and he turned tail and fled for Croydon. He hoped that Lieutenant Postgate was not dead. He knew that many had died that day, but of the completeness of his victory he knew nothing. He had done the thing that had been in him to do – to take up a plane and fight with it as long as there was anyone or anything to fight. He looked back again and saw that Postgate had shifted his position and that his eyes were open, and he was glad. The lieutenant had a ghost of a smile for him, and Penntifer nodded and motioned towards the ground to show that he was going to take him quickly where he could have help. Penntifer wondered why he himself was untouched. He was desperately tired, but he had not a scratch on him. Then he bethought himself of his ancestor Simon Penntyfer,

who had come roaring and rolling up the Hoe at Plymouth in the
Silver Blade after the battle with the Armada. He was no meta-
physician, this plain British butcher, but in the way he had of
wondering about things, deep inside, so that no one ever suspected, he did wonder whether old Simon had been looking after
him. He was thirsty, was John Penntifer, and he thought that the
thing he wanted most just then was a pint of bitter.

Croydon was in sight in the distance. There were many planes
around him now. Curiously, Penntifer did not look upon them as
his fleet, but just as other planes flying back home as he was. He
did not think that many of them were carrying home their dead,
and that many were still to crumple and crash with haven in
sight. He was thinking about his wife and his five children, who
would perhaps now be safe from being blown up, shredded . . .
he groped inside his head for a word, found it – liquidated – made
into a liquid. They would not be liquid. They would be there for
him, safe, whole, solid, comfortable . . . He, John Penntifer, their
husband and father, had seen to that. He thought of sitting in
the lounge of the Devon Arms, arguing with Major Charterod (it
nearly killed him when they told him later of the major's gallant
death), and of the joy of the Sunday flights from the Plymouth
airport.

He had been right about his plan too. That pleased him. It
pleased him almost as much as thinking back over Lieutenant
Postgate's saying to him: 'Oh, well done, fine flying.' Supposing
he had just not said anything to anyone about this idea of his
that the super-fast planes would be handicapped when they came
up against the slow ones. Well, John Penntifer thought it just
showed that a man ought to speak what was on his mind – always.

His engine suddenly went 'Pop-pop! Pop!' uttered a loud sigh,
and quit. But it didn't matter. Penntifer was already over Croydon airport, at three thousand feet. It just meant being that much
more careful coming in. He must make no mistakes. He had never
made a real dead-stick landing before. The prospect excited him
and he wondered whether he would do well.

So . . . begin with a tight spiral after heading into the wind.
Well, the wind must be due east where that fog bank was coming
from. Tight spiral first, and keep the eye on the point of landing.
never take the eye from it. He was listening to instructor Flight
Lieutenant Handwie again. The wind was singing in his wires.
He had wrapped her too tightly. He came out with a lurch and a
skid that would have drawn a frown from his instructor and that
made him shake his head from side to side in distress. He *always*
did that. He regulated the speed of his glide and began to circle.

He supposed they'd make a fuss when he got back. He was a modest man, but sensible withal, and after all it *had* been his plan. Medals and speeches . . . they might offer him a knighthood. Well, he wouldn't take it. Sir John Penntifer. Bah! Lot of good the 'Sirs' and 'Your Lordships' had been to the country.

He remembered what the Prime Minister had said: 'You've bred all the fight out of your lines.' They wouldn't make him or his children like that. It didn't pay to become soft. Good chap, that Prime Minister. *He* had understood that a man could love the place where he had been born, love it so much he would rather die than give it up or have it liquidated.

He made his final turn and levelled off to land. He was gliding over the rows of low red brick houses fringing the airport and he saw the long runways stretching out before him. Those were homes below him, the dwelling-places of plain people like himself, complete with kitchen and big bed and missus and children, and his heart swelled with new joy that they were still standing intact and whole.

His heart swelled and filled for the land beneath him, rising to meet his wheels. He pulled back on the stick, touched, and rolled. Men were running out to meet him, waving, shouting, gesticulating. But he did not see them quite because for the moment his eyes were blinded by the sudden welling of tears to his eyes from the love of the soil that he had touched once more.

Oh, Them Golden Mittens

••

Oh, them Golden Mittens might seem an odd kind of story to offer British readers, but it is for this very reason I have included it in this book. Although it is as American as chewing gum and Coca-Cola it might very well have happened in England, say at Wandsworth or Wormwood Scrubs. And the tough boy is no longer exclusively an American problem.

The background is that of the Golden Gloves amateur boxing tournament of which I was the originator and promoter in the days when I was Sports Editor of the 'Daily News.' It is a tournament with which the British are not wholly unfamiliar since several times in the past you have sent teams to compete against the Americans in international Golden Gloves matches.

In New York the popularity of this tournament produced extraordinary production problems. An entry list of between three and four thousand boys was nothing unusual and in order to cope with the task of winnowing this field down to thirty-six, for the finals staged in the Madison Square Garden before capacity crowds, month long series of elimination bouts in all classes had to be conducted. Sets of these bouts were awarded to the various amateur boxing clubs which flourished in greater New York. Many of these elimination bouts were conducted for charity.

On the banks of the Hudson River, at Ossining, New York, stands the forbidding, grey pile of Sing Sing Prison, to the underworld known as the Big House. It is here that major criminals sentenced in the State of New York are sent for punishment, confinement and likewise execution. Here is found that horrid little chamber which houses the electric chair, into which condemned murderers are strapped and shocked to death. New

199

York City probably supplies the greater part of the eighteen hundred prisoners incarcerated there. New York is very much aware of Ossining and Sing Sing up the river and if someone refers tactfully to the fact that 'So and so has been away, up the river' one knows what is meant.

If any good can be claimed for the Golden Gloves tournaments it is that perhaps we saved some boys from making that fearful journey in that we took tough specimens, many of whom had seen the inside of reform schools, and channelled their uncontrollable truculence into more civilised outlets, of honest competition, sportsmanship and fair play. We gave them a goal that they could achieve only by mastering themselves as well as their opponents, and at tournaments' end by forming the victors into a team for inter-city and international competition we gave them for the first time a sense of belonging. I know for a fact that in this manner we snatched many a brand from the burning.

But to return for a moment to Sing Sing Prison it was at the turn of the century, the tough, hard place where caged men were treated no better than animals. In the early 'twenties the prison was fortunate to receive in Warden Lawes, an enlightened man who insisted upon bettering the lot of the inmates, in conformity with modern penology as well as civilised thought. One of the reforms he instituted was from time to time to invite entertainers to visit the prison and give a show for the inmates. The prisoners were also allowed to form their own baseball team and occasionally play against visitors from outside the walls. However, there had never been a set of boxing bouts staged within the prison walls and when I suggested to Warden Lawes that I could bring up one of my Golden Gloves elimination tournaments, a set of sixteen bouts in different weight divisions, he accepted. And thus one February 22nd, the national holiday celebrating Washington's birthday, we journeyed up the river with some thirty-two contestants plus doctors, trainers, handlers, referees and myself as chronicler of this innovation.

The bouts were staged in the great assembly hall of the prison with the ring set up on the stage and the prisoners seated in long grey-clad silent rows. This silence was to come to us all as the grisly shock of the experiment for the first five matches, thrilling and bristling encounters as I remember them, were conducted in a deathly quiet because as we later found out under the eyes of the K.P.s, or keepers, the convicts were afraid to cheer or shout cries of encouragement to the boxers.

It was the first time we had ever heard a fight, the scuffing of agile feet on canvas, the whistling of breath and the soft thup-

*thup of blows intermingled with coughs of pain as they landed.
Heretofore all these sounds had been covered over by the crowd
noises, individual cries, running murmurs and rolling roars of
cheering. It was the first time too that I had ever heard the
silence of fearful men caged by the law. There they sat, 1,800
men convicted of crime, from robbery to murder, with their
emotions pent-up within them just as their bodies were imprisoned in their cells. The effect was sinister, chilling and
thoroughly frightening.*

*I remember feeling that to go through the whole programme
of bouts thus would be simply unbearable and we asked the
Principal Keeper whether the spirits of the men might not be
released for this one afternoon. I think he was impressed by the
silence too, for this was a situation no one yet had come up
against since the whole show was an experiment, and he too was
disturbed by the horrid contrast between the torrid exchanges of
blows in the ring and the silent, stony faces of the men in the
audience. He went down and spoke to some of the keepers and
then to a few of the prisoners who were apparently leaders
amongst them or trustees.*

*When the next bout took place there were at first one or two
tentative, isolated cries of encouragement. They kindled others.
The fire spread and before the fight was a minute old the auditorium was ablaze with shouting and cheering men who for that
moment had become human again.*

*I remember too that upon that occasion one of our boxers
suffered a mild concussion and our tournament doctor, for safety's
sake, ordered him kept in the prison hospital overnight for
observation. The following morning, however, he was right as
rain when the doctor picked him up with a car and brought him
back to New York.*

*These then are the ingredients. This story was written in
October 1940 aboard the S.S. 'Santa Elena' of the Grace Line en
route to South America on a research assignment for a magazine.
Shipboard is a wonderful place to write. There are no disturbances, no telephone calls, and one is bored. I had left the
news and sports writing behind me four years ago, but walking
the decks, suddenly that day at Sing Sing came into my head,
those awful sounds of fighting and silence of the grim, grey rows
of prisoners, and I thought too of some of the boys we might
have saved from that same fate, and thinking, OH, THEM GOLDEN
MITTENS began to take shape in my head. As always there was
a portable typewriter in my cabin, I retired thither for four days.
I hope you will enjoy the result.*

OH, THEM GOLDEN MITTENS

The long line of naked boys was passing in review before the doctor and the sports editor and their staffs. The *Daily Blade* was conducting the physical examination of the candidates for the Golden Gloves, the newspaper's annual amateur boxing tournament.

One by one the boys were sent twenty-five yards up the floor, clutching their papers, straight into the scrutiny of the white-haired doctor waiting for them. By the time they came to a halt in front of him, the spare, crusty man with the keen but kindly light-blue eyes knew more about them than they would have dreamed.

Another candidate began the long walk. The doctor nudged the sports editor and said: 'Here's the kid I was telling you about. He'd be a sure winner against Chicago. He's got a sweet-heart of a left. A little skinny for a welter, but he'll fill out. Look at the walk on him. He's a tough kid.'

The boy walked and held his head with truculence. He had a hard face and a trap mouth. He had blue eyes, too, but they were a peculiar off shade that made him look much older than his eighteen years. They were eyes that had the curious trick of going pale. There were times when they imparted to his flat young face a curiously deadly quality.

'All right, boy. What's your name?'

'John O'Connell.'

'John O'Connell? How much do you weigh?'

'Hundred an' forty-two.'

'You're down too fine. Better get some meat on you before the tournament starts.'

That cold, hard little knot of anger that he knew so well formed down inside John O'Connell. It was easy for the doc to talk. Get some meat on him! On what he was eating? But they said if you made the Golden Gloves team that fought against Chicago, you got to eat at a training table, with steaks every day.

'Got your letter from your father? Give me your card.'

O'Connell handed over his card and a letter in a grimy envelope. The doctor noted that his hand trembled slightly. He kept the card and studied it, handing the letter to the sports editor, who read the brief scrawl: *I give my son permission to join in the Golden Gloves. Dan O'Connell.*

The sports editor handed the letter back to the doctor, who read it and said: 'Who signed that, boy – your father?'

'Yeah.'

'Oh, yeah?'

The doctor's blue eyes were boring through O'Connell. The knot of anger inside the boy was growing again and he was afraid they might find out that Sol Lefkowitz, who ran the stationery store, had written the letter for him. There had been that line on the entry blank: 'Entrants below the age of twenty-one must bring a letter from their parents permitting them to enter the tournament.'

Parents! What if you didn't have any? O'Connell had never known his mother. His pop had left him when he was six. He had got into some kind of trouble. Bad trouble. He guessed he was dead now. Old lady Slattery, who had looked after him until – until he had gone away – was always saying: 'You hang out with them hoodlums and you'll come to a bad end just like your old man.'

A bad end! His pop, and a bad end, and himself. It was all a part of it, the dreams at night, the sweating fear, and the cold knot inside that would want to grow and grow until it exploded in a blinding clouding flash of red. If they found out about that letter, maybe they wouldn't let him in the Golden Gloves. He had to get in. It was always better when he was fighting. When the knot began to grow like that, he always wanted to swing on someone. His chin came up. His eyes seemed to show more white. 'You heard me,' he said.

The doctor grinned a little and said: 'We take your word for it. I saw you dish it out a couple of weeks ago. Can you take it?'

'Yeah. I can take it.'

'Well, you're gonna get a chance to find out. This is a tough tournament. Where you been boxing before, boy? Upstate? You're not from the Metropolitan district.'

The boy said nothing. His mouth was closed in a tight line. The doctor ignored his failure to reply, studied his body and examined his teeth briefly. He said: 'I see you're unattached. A kid like you ought to be fighting for Holy Name, or Ascension Parish House. They're up around your neighbourhood. I could get you in.'

The boy was staring at the doctor now out of his pale eyes. He said in a flat voice, his thin mouth barely moving: I don't want no part of them. I wanna fight. You gonna trow me out or ya gonna let me fight? I ain't afraid of fightin' nobody.'

'Oh, a tough guy, eh?' said the doctor cheerfully. 'Save that for the ring, boy. Read the letters on that card over there. . . . You've got good eyes.' He paused and then snapped suddenly: 'You ever been away, boy?'

The knot inside O'Connell wasn't cold any more. It was beginning to burn. Burn and swell. What did the doc have to pry for? Everybody was always prying. Did he know about the stretch in the reform school, and that his name wasn't John O'Connell, but Jimmy Conners? Couldn't he ever get a break? The blazing, ballooning thing grew inside him. If he swung on the doc now, they'd put him away again. He hated the tall man with the white hair and the searching blue eyes the way he hated everything and everyone, only worse. So bad that he wasn't going to be able to hold it.

O'Connell's face was paper-white. His fists were clenched. He said, without opening his teeth: 'What's it to you?'

Searching blue eyes met pale and deadly ones. The old man was looking through him, coolly, appraisingly, probing every corner of him, weighing, judging. O'Connell lowered his head slowly. He was trembling.

The doctor said in a matter-of-fact voice: 'Nothing. We don't care who you are or where you've been as long as you're a registered amateur, obey the rules, fight clean, and behave yourself. Get it? Take this card over to that doctor over there and he'll examine you. Good luck, boy.'

The older doctor turned to the sports editor and said: 'He's a killer. He'll kill somebody yet. He's been away to reform school. Probably fought around the bootleg amateur circuit upstate when he came out. He got somebody to write that letter for him. He's tough, isn't he? And scared to death of something or other too. Somebody ought to get hold of that kid and straighten him out. He's just in the spot now like a lot of them. They can go one way or the other. If somebody gets hold of them and gives them a hand, they turn out all right. They're just as apt to end in the electric chair. Next boy!'

The familiar letter in the envelope of the *Daily Blade* was waiting for John O'Connell when he stopped in at Lefkowitz's store to get his mail. He had already fought and won two bouts in the long round of Golden Gloves preliminaries that led through the grimy, stuffy, outlying social centres and amateur boxing clubs to the glamour of the finals in Madison Square Garden. He had knocked his men out in a round each, and the *Blade* had already devoted a paragraph to him as a puncher to be watched in the tournament. He carried the cutting around with him. That's what you got out of the Golden Gloves –

publicity; and maybe one of the big professional managers would look you over and give you a chance.

O'Connell did not much care when and where he was going to fight next. It was all the same. He would see his opponent across the ring, and the knot of anger and hate would harden. It would grow and begin to burn. The bell would ring. Just before it exploded, the thing rose into his throat, filling it and threatening to choke him. Then there would be the blinding flash of red and the roaring in his ears. Sometimes he would still be punching the air after his opponent had fallen, and the referee would have to drag him away.

He opened the envelope, took out the slip and read it:

John O'Connell, 2987½ Second Avenue, 147-pound Open Class, New York Division, Third Round, Sing Sing Prison, Ossining, Feb. 22, 2.00 p.m. Bus will leave from in front of BLADE *Office at* 10.00 *a.m.*

O'Connell could see only three words: 'Sing Sing Prison.' Sing Sing! He grabbed a copy of the *Blade* from Sol's counter and turned to the sports pages. It was true. There was a story there. It told how on Washington's Birthday, by arrangement with the Mutual Welfare League, the *Blade* was sending a card of Golden Gloves elimination bouts up to Ossining for the entertainment of the inmates. It would be the first time that amateur bouts had ever been staged there. O'Connell read his own name in the list of contestants.

The great grey prison that filled his waking and sleeping hours with sweating fear! Were they nuts? Did they think he was going up there to fight? Did they think they were going to get him inside those stone and steel corridors where they said the lights dimmed and the men yelled and howled like wild animals when they fried somebody? O'Connell dropped the paper on the floor and stepped on it as he went out the door blindly. He'd go and tell 'em. They could put him into some other elimination.

The Big House! He had been afraid of it ever since he could remember. It had been drawing him, tugging at him, pulling him, closing in upon him.

He was bad. His pop had been bad too. He didn't remember his pop as being bad. He recalled a big man who, once when he had been sick, had come to his bed in the night and placed his hand on his head and stayed there with him. The hand had been cool and strong and felt good. If he had had his pop he might not be so afraid. He would have been able to trust his pop. He did not trust anyone else. Everyone was against him. When the knot

formed and the rage began to grow, he did not know what he
would do. In the end he would kill someone and they would take
him away to the Big House.

Like the time when he had been caught pilfering with the
corner gang and had slugged a cop and they had sent him away
to the reformatory. There he had learned a number of things that
it is not good for a young boy to know. The Big House would be
like that, only a hundred times worse. And in the end, he knew,
the Big House would get him. It held him in horrible fascination.
Sometimes he would lie awake at nights and plan escapes.

He had always been a tough little street scrapper. In the
reformatory he had learned to box. When he came out, he fought
in the bootleg amateur bouts upstate where you got ten dollars a
fight and were tossed in with a guy twenty pounds heavier. Sometimes he made a little money, sometimes he starved. Once or
twice when he was very hungry he stole and got away with it.
He didn't want to be bad. But he knew that he was, that it was
in his blood.

When he entered the Golden Gloves office of the *Daily Blade*,
it was still early in the morning, and there was nobody there but
the old doctor sitting with his feet up on a desk, smoking a pipe.

He said: 'Aren't you O'Connell? Is there anything I can do for
you?'

'Yeah. Get a hold of that guy that runs the tournament. I ain't
goin' up the river to fight. Let him put me in some other elimination.'

'No? Why? What's the matter?'

'Nuthin's the matter. I didn't sign up to fight in the prison. I
ain't goin'.'

'Don't you want to win the Golden Gloves?'

'Yeah, I'll win it all right.'

'Not if you don't show up for that bus. The tournament's
drawn. We can't put you in any other division. What's wrong
about going up to Sing Sing? What's the matter? You got somebody up there?'

'No. I ain't got anybody up there. An' I ain't going either.'

'Don't you want to do something for those guys up there?
They're your own people. What are you afraid of?'

The cold knot of rage was beginning to form again. Why did
this old fool always have to ask him if he was afraid?

'I ain't afraid of nuthin'.'

The doctor took his pipe out of his mouth and looked at him
steadily. 'Oh, yes, you are,' he said quietly. 'Why don't you admit
it? Come on, what's on your mind?'

For one split moment John O'Connell was on the point of telling him. But that would have been going soft. He had been on
the verge of being a panty-waist.

He was silent for a moment and then said sullenly: 'If I don't
go, does that mean I'm out?'

'Yeah, you're out. You know the rules.'

O'Connell called the doctor a name. The doctor sat looking at
him quietly, tamping his pipe with a long forefinger. He said:
'Why don't you get wise to yourself, O'Connell? You can't get
anywhere being tough. That don't get you anything. We want to
help you if we can. We always look after our boys.'

'I don't want no help from anybody.'

He turned and started to go, but a rustling of papers in the
doctor's hand made him pause for a moment to see what he was
going to do or say. The old man seemed to be looking through
some printed lists. When he found what he was searching for, he
looked up and said, 'Tony Agostino, the Metropolitan champ, is
in your class. He'll be going up. He's a tough little boy with a
mean right-hand punch. You might draw him. Maybe you're not
so dumb. I think you can lick him, but maybe you don't'

John O'Connell banged the door of the office so hard that the
wire baskets on the desks jumped and rattled. The doctor smiled
to himself, relit his pipe.

The ring was pitched on the chapel stage of the prison. With
all the sliding doors rolled back, the room became a large, fan-
shaped auditorium in which were eighteen hundred prisoners in
grey trousers and grey shirts open at the neck. They sat in long
rows, on benches. The lights over the ring made the faces of
those sitting nearest even whiter than they were, and reflected
from their eyeballs. Heavy, stalwart keepers, bulging in blue
uniforms, stood on both sides. The P.K., the principal keeper,
menacing, watched from the platform.

The bell at the side of the ring began to sound insistently, and
the enclosure was cleared. A pair of boxers and their handlers
took their opposite corners. The referee crawled through the
ropes. The Mutual Welfare man, a stocky, muscular chap in grey
trousers and white shirt, stepped to the front of the stage and
announced, reading from a slip:

'Opening bout, hundred-and-forty-seven-pound open class,
third-round elimination, winner to go to the quarter finals. In
this corner, Tony Agostino, Our Lady of Refuge A.A. His
opponent, in this corner, John O'Connell, unattached.'

The two boys rose to their feet and held their arms above their heads to acknowledge the introduction and the expected patter of applause. But there was no applause, nor hum, nor rustle, nor any single sound.

Johnny O'Connell was frightened again.

He had come, he did not know why. Something had pulled him, something that he had not been able to resist. He thought at first it might have been the taunt of the doctor that he was afraid of Agostino. He told himself that that was why he had come, but he knew that it was not so.

The voice of the referee called him to the centre of the ring. In the silence of the vast, crowded hall it sounded unnaturally loud. O'Connell did not listen to the instructions. He was looking out into the faces and eyeballs of the convicts.

They sat as though they were painted there. They seemed to be staring at him as though they were wondering why he was not sitting down there with them.

He was rubbing his feet in the rosin. When the bell rang he came up off his stool to face his opponent, but not with his usual blazing rush. The burning knot that swelled to help him blast his man to the canvas was not there. For the first time.

That made him uneasy. He was afraid, not of his opponent, but of something that seemed to be in the heavy, sullen atmosphere.

Agostino circled, his shoes scuffing around the ring, his left extended. He was short, tawny, powerful, with wavy black hair, square chin, and exceptionally shiny black eyes that glistened like jet buttons under the ring lights.

O'Connell followed him to mid-ring, dropped his left in a feint for the body, shifted, and smashed an overhand right squarely on the side of the Italian's jaw. It landed with a soft 'plock' and sent Agostino staggering across the ring into the ropes.

It was a sneak punch, perfectly executed, and the boy was out, glassy-eyed. Only the rope under the back of his neck kept him from falling.

There should have been a roaring shout from out front, the rising cry of excited men urging a winning fighter on to the kill.

Not a sound came from the grey men on the long benches, not a sigh, not a murmur.

It checked O'Connell's following rush and stopped him in his tracks. It halted the referee, too, who had come forward to stop the bout if Agostino should prove helpless. They stared. The great hall and the hundreds of men therein were welded into a dome of silence. The stricken boy on the ropes began to recover.

He came back across the ring, lashed out at O'Connell, hit him on the nose and hurt him. They clinched, broke, struck again, and suddenly slugged toe-to-toe in a furious flurry.

Now surely they would yell and shout and cheer. The fighter who comes back from oblivion and the brink of defeat, crashing blow for blow, has never failed to stir the heart of man.

Terror began to mount in John O'Connell. What was the matter with them? Why weren't they yelling? He was used to fighting against the crashing waves of shouting that curled and billowed up around him and swept him onward.

O'Connell was being hurt by Agostino, who was tough, pugnacious, and an experienced boxer, but he didn't care. He wanted to look out into those hard, stony faces to see what was the matter with them. Fear he had seemed to have known for most of his life, but nothing so horrible or choking as this fighting in utter silence.

Wrestling to the ropes in a clinch, he saw the men over Agostino's shoulder, looked into their staring eyeballs, and felt the grey, heavy presence of them, row upon row. They seemed to him now to be crouching and lurking like some great silent, dangerous beast that follows its prey with its eyes. He was back amid his old terrifying dreams, stone walls, dark passages, things that lurked, blood and a bad end. The only reality was the blows that stung and hurt. The bell rang. He fell on to his stool. He was shaking. His second, one of the Holy Name handlers who was looking after him, poured advice into his ear. He didn't hear him. He did hear the sports editor say to the Mutual Welfare man: 'Why don't they cheer or yell or do something? I can't stand it. Can't you tell 'em that it's all right to yell? Those kids can't go on fighting in that silence. They'll go nuts. Or I will.'

The doctor, who was at the ringside, said: 'They're afraid.'

'Yes,' said the Mutual Welfare man, 'they're afraid of the keepers. The P.K.'s got his eye on them. I'll see what I can do.'

The bell called again, John O'Connell got up, his feet dragging. There was no more fight in him. He fell into a clinch and held on. So that was it. He knew now what his nameless dread had been when he had come out at the start of the bout. It was his own fears and imaginings realised, the smell and the feel and the silence of the place where men had all humanity ironed out of them, where they sat stir-sodden and hopeless.

That was what it would be like. He remembered something the doctor had said: 'They're your own people.' They were calling him, claiming him.

He was boxing listlessly and carelessly. A brown glove flashed before his eyes. And this blow he did not hear. But he felt the black, stunning jar as the back of his head crashed against the canvas.

Then he was floating, drifting, spinning in a dark silence. He knew that he could get up if he wanted to, but he meant to stay down. What was the use of getting up, of going on, of winning, of becoming Golden Gloves champion? In the end it would be the same. Eventually he would be sitting down there among them.

'Git up, Jimmy! Git up!'

The one high-pitched strident voice from somewhere in the grey mass rang like a trumpet call over the battlefield of the dead.

'Git up!'

There was a laugh, and then a windy, rustling, running murmur of sound, a low humming through grey ranks.

It was surprise and something more than surprise that brought Johnny O'Connell to his feet. The Italian was on top of him, rushing and punching. O'Connell lashed back with both hands and stopped him.

'At-a-boy, kid! Use yo' lef'.' Isolated cries drifted upwards: 'Inna body . . . Inna body . . . Stay away from him . . .'

O'Connell moved forward, whipping short hooks for Agostino's head. Two landed and the Italian went down, but was up immediately, fighting for his life. Like the beat of the sea, the roar of the men below rose and broke all about them as they battled back and forth around the ring. The men were standing on the benches now, shouting advice. The grim keepers on the sides were yelling, too, and the handlers. The doctor was pounding the sports editor on the back, shouting: 'That's more like it. What a fight! The kid's got guts, hasn't he?'

They fought like two wildcats, punch for punch, and the sweet, burning rage was back inside John O'Connell again. He felt no punches, only that blazing, choking truculence in his throat that fired his arms into bludgeoning pistons, And then quite unexpectedly he was punching the empty air, and the referee was tugging at him. The hall was rocking to the old, well-remembered tumult of sound, and then the bell was clanging, clanging.

He saw them lift up the Italian boy and carry him to his corner, felt the arms of the Holy Name handler around his shoulders, hugging him, and the doc was pounding him on the back.

Suddenly he felt very sick. When they sat him on his stool, he fell quietly forward on his face into a throbbing, sickish darkness.

Johnny O'Connell lay with icebags at his head in the prison infirmary, too ill to know or care where he was. His head seemed to be splitting with pain, and sometimes he would slip across the line into dizzy shadows.

He did not know of two conversations that had taken place. In the first the doctor spoke to his colleague in charge of the prison hospital. He said: 'I don't think the boy is badly hurt, though he did hit his head an awful crack on the floor. I think he'll be all right in a couple of hours. But I don't like to take a chance. I'd rather leave him here with you tonight for observation. I'll call you in the morning and see how he is.'

The other took place when an elderly convict whose number was 2X475 asked to see the warden. He was a large man with short, curly grey hair and pale blue eyes. He said: 'Warden, I want to ask a favour of you. That kid that was hurt today is pretty sick, I guess. He's a good kid. He come up off the floor. Would you let me sit up with him tonight and kinda look after him? I used to box when I was a kid.'

The warden said not unkindly: 'You know it's against the rules to be out of your cell all night.'

'Yeah. I guess that's so. O.K. I just asked.' He turned to go.

The warden called: 'Wait a minute, Dan. Was it you who yelled this afternoon?'

'Yeah. It was me. I'm sorry, warden. I knew the kid could git up.'

'I'm glad you did,' the warden said quietly. He was studying the man, his face and his light eyes. He said: 'I've changed my mind. You can keep an eye on the boy if you want to. You're a hospital orderly for the night. I'll speak to the P.K.'

It was past one in the morning. John O'Connell half awakened to the dimly lighted prison hospital as a grey-shirted orderly changed the icebag. He was dimly conscious of the bulk of a grey man who sat at his bedside and another in a heavy blue uniform and badged cap who stood at the foot.

He came up on to his elbows with a cry: 'What is it? The Big House? Am I in the Big House?'

The keeper in the blue uniform stepped nearer the bed and said: 'Take it easy now, kid.'

All of the old fears in John O'Connell swept him into panic. 'Lemme out! Lemme out! I ain't done nuthin'! I ain't killed anybody!'

The hospital orderly and the other at the bedside were holding him down. The boy was half delirious. 'I tell ya I ain't done nuthin'. Pop! Pop! Make 'em lemme out. They're gonna burn me! Pop! Pop! I swear I ain't done nuthin'.'

No. 2X475 stared at the keeper in blue and jerked his head. The keeper hesitated a moment and then wandered away. Then No. 2X475 gently placed his hand on the boy's head and forced him back. He let his broad, hard hand remain. 'Take it easy, son. Take it easy, now. You'll be outa here in the morning.'

The hand felt cool and strong just as it had those years ago when he had been sick and his pop had stayed with him.

'Pop! Pop! Is that you?'

'Yes, son, it's me. Take it easy, now.'

'Pop! I'm scared. Stay with me, Pop!'

'I'm here, son. I'll stay with you.'

'I ain't done nuthin', Pop!'

'Sure you ain't done nothing. You came up here to box with the Golden Gloves. You got hurt. You'll be O.K. in the morning.'

'Don't take your hand away, Pop. It feels good.'

After a little, John O'Connell fell asleep again.

When he awoke later the pain had left his head. He was feeling good. He wasn't afraid any more. The other orderly had gone. Only the big man was still sitting at his side. His hands were folded and his head was down on them. O'Connell watched him for a little. Then he stirred, and the man looked up and smiled and said: 'Better now?'

'Yeah,' said O'Connell, 'I'm better. I done a lotta hollerin',' didn't I?'

'Yeah, you hollered.'

'I guess I'm yellow.'

'No, you ain't yellow. You come up off the floor and win.'

'I hollered for my pop, didn' I?'

'Yeah, you hollered for your pop.'

Something such as he had never known before was in the throat of John O'Connell, a different kind of choking. He said: 'You – you made out like you was my pop, didn' you?'

'Yeah,' No. 2X475 said, 'I made out like I was your pop.'

'It made me feel good for a minute. My – my pop's dead, I guess. They told me he died when I was a kid.'

'Yeah? When you was a kid?'

There was silence between them for a moment. Then O'Connell said: 'Say, was that you yelled when I was onna floor?'

'Yeah, that was me.'

'Why?'

'I dunno. I knew you could beat that Italian.'

'I was scared. Nobody yellin' or anything. I wasn't gonna git up. I heard somebody yellin' an' wasn't scared any more.'

'You been hollering like you was scared. What you scared of?'

He could tell this man, who had been kind to him. One could take kindness from one's own people. They weren't trying to get something out of you. This grey man was the first one he could talk to and tell about it.

'I'm scared of the Big House. I always been. I went off my nut when I woke up and saw the screw and the bars on the windows. I thought I done somethin' an' they had me in stir an' was gonna burn me. I'm scared they're gonna get me.'

'What for, Johnny? You ain't done nothing. You said so.'

'I got somethin' inside of me. It's bad. When it starts up I dunno what's gonna happen. It's a sort of a knot, like, an' then it starts to burn. I git sore. It keeps on growin' until it busts, redlike. I dunno what I done, when it's over.'

No. 2X475 nodded his head slowly. 'Yeah. I know. I had it like that too. It goes away. I ain't got it any more.'

'Honest? When does it go away?'

'When you get older. When you find out some guys are on the square not because they have to be but because they want to. Then it ain't so bad any more.'

'Guys like you?'

No. 2X475 looked down at the white face of the boy on the bed, the young face in which there was no hardness now. 'I guess I ain't no one to preach,' he said. 'But you find out a lotta things you wished you'd of knowed when you was a kid. You find out there's nothin' to be scared of.'

He paused. The ward was silent except for the quiet footfall of the orderlies and the breathing of sleeping men. They had been talking in whispers. No. 2X475 said: 'You're Irish, Johnny. You in the Church?'

'Aa-a-a-h,' said O'Connell, 'Christers, and their talk. What's God ever done for me? Or any of these guys in here?'

No. 2X475 nodded quietly. 'Yeah,' he said, 'I know. You get to thinkin' like that a lotta times.' He went on, looking straight in front of him as though he were talking to himself: 'I got a friend here, Father O'Malley. He never talks to me about God. God is something he believes in, but he don't say I got to. He's give me a lotta help. He got me a good job. He don't ask nothing from me. All he cares about is to help you get a break so maybe you can be something and turn out to be a square guy. Maybe if you turn out that way, that's what helps him to believe more in God.'

There was a long silence. Then: 'You got a great left, Johnny. You could be a champion.'

'Ya think I could?'

'Uh-huh! You got what it takes. You got guts. You got up off the floor. That stuff that comes up inside of you, that makes you want to bust, that thing you're afraid of – you could make that work for you.'

'Yeah?' said O'Connell. 'Do ya think I could?'

'You could save it up until you got into the ring. Then it would be workin' for you. It would be right there. It'd bring you up off the floor, when you needed bad to get up. It would be there when you was tired and felt like you couldn't lift a arm and you needed to go three more tough rounds. And when you'd got it workin' for you, you'd never be afraid of it again. After a while you'd get so that you wouldn't want to have the feeling except when you could use it. You'd feel like you wouldn't want to waste it, because some time maybe if you needed it bad, it mightn't be there if you'd wasted it. And when the time would come when you didn't need it anymore, you might find it would be gone – for good. It's a tough road. You'd need a lot of help an' advice. When you find guys that want to help you that don't get nothing out of it, those are the guys to stick to.'

'Would – would you help me?'

'Me?' No. 2X475 worked his fingers so that his knuckles cracked. Grey was beginning to seep in through the windows. Grey, the colour of the Big House. 'There's nothin' I can do for you.'

'Would ya lemme come to see ya? You know, if I was around here. I mean, stop in.'

No. 2X475 looked up into the high windows, and his eyes were very light in his grey face. He said: 'Who, me? What would you want to come and see me for? I can't do you no good. This ain't no place for you to be coming to. Ain't you had enough of this place?'

O'Connell swallowed. He had to get the thing out of his throat. Finally he spoke softly. 'I ain't afraid of this place no more. You done that for me. Nobody ever done no more. I'm gonna be a champeen like you said. Maybe if I was around here, I'd just wanna stop by an' let ya know how I was doin', see?'

Somewhere within the prison a bell rang. Feet began to shuffle on stone floors. No. 2X475's face was greyer than his shirt, greyer than the light of the dark morning peering in through the windows. He said casually: 'Yeah. I guess if you was around here, or passin' by some time, you could drop in and tell me how you was makin' out.'

He got up and dropped his hand carelessly for a moment on O'Connell's arm. 'So long, Johnny,' he said, 'and good luck,' and walked away.

John O'Connell turned his face quickly to the wall in case the orderly or anyone should come by and see him the way he was. . . .

O'Connell stood outside the great iron-barred gate and drew the February air into his lungs. A coupé drove up. In it was the Golden Gloves doctor.

He said: 'Hullo! You're O.K. That's good. I was just passing by.'

'Oh, yeah? Your office is down in New York, ain't it?'

'Well, what of it?'

'You come up here to git me, didn't you?'

'What difference does it make? I'm here. Get in. I'm glad you're all right. That was a sucker punch you ran into. Everybody saw it coming but you.'

John O'Connell got into the car, his head turned away for the second time that day. The doctor was careful to look straight ahead and tend to his driving.

On the road down, O'Connell said: 'Doc, you're a regular guy.'

'What's regular about me?'

The boy ignored the question and sat silent for another long stretch. Then: 'Doc, can you keep your mouth shut?'

'Telling a doctor is the same as telling a priest. Don't you know that?'

'Doc, I gotta tell someone. Doc, my pop's in the Big House. He's a lifer. But he's O.K. He come an' took care of me. He don't know I know who he was. His name is Dan Connors. It was him that yelled. He yelled: "Git up, Jimmy." that's me. I'm Jimmy Connors. I'm just fightin' under the name of O'Connell. I been away too, doc, when I was a kid.'

The bright blue eyes of the doctor were looking straight ahead to the road.

'He didn't let on he was my pop. I guess if he'd wanted me to know he'd 'a' said something. I'll never let on. But I hadda tell someone. He said I could be a champeen. I'm gonna go back an' see him once in a while. Maybe when I'm champ I'll go back an' box an exhibition there. But I'd never let on I knew he was my pop until he said something. I'd croak first. It's funny, ain't it, that I ain't afraid of the Big House any more, since last night?'

Thief is an Ugly Word

This is a propaganda story purely and simply, but I think if I didn't tell you so and let you in on some of its history you would never know it, at least I hope you would not. Its aim is that of all stories I write, to entertain and divert, but this one carries a small load as well under the guise of an adventure thriller. It joins up something a war agency wished to make public during the course of war, the little known fact of Nazi art looting and the efforts being made to counteract this thieving.

During the war there was created at the behest of Washington, the most astonishing propaganda agency which met and sat in New York, called the Writers' War Board. Its chairman was Mr Rex Stout the mystery writer, and its committee embraced some fifteen or twenty American writers of every stamp. I was a member of this board; its purpose and function was simple and easy to understand. When the psychological warfare boffins in Washington needed a writing job of any kind, the problem was dumped into the lap of the War Board in New York which found the right author in the shortest possible time and got the job done. This would be in the guise of short stories, novelettes, magazine and newspaper articles or even circulars and pamphlets. It worked.

I remember that one time the problem handed us was the fact that there were not sufficient young men opting for the job of bombardier in the airforce. They all wanted to be pilots. The shortage of bombardiers was making itself felt in the airforce.

Ways and means of propagandising to make the bombardier's job romantic and attractive were discussed and I was assigned to write a short story in the 'Saturday Evening Post' about an heroic bombardier. This I did, the story was duly sold and published and to my astonishment shortly after its appearance the airforce reported a satisfactory rise in the candidates for the bombardier's job.

One afternoon at a meeting of the Board we were addressed by Mr Francis Taylor, the head of New York's Museum of Art

216

and Chairman of the American Commission for the Salvage and Protection of Art and Historical Monuments in Europe. This somewhat over-titled Commission was engaged in tracking down and cataloguing paintings, sculptures and other art objects looted by the thieving Nazis in their march through Europe so that when the war should be over old masters and other famous paintings might be returned to their original owners, either museums or private individuals. Actually much of this stuff did turn up in Hermann Goering's caves and other hidden hoards uncovered by the advancing Americans. Mr Taylor was asking for our assistance in making the public aware of the existence of such a project so that people might co-operate.

Co-operate how? By reporting any instances of unusual activity in the art market or the under-cover offer of the sale of a well-known canvas.

For among other things revealed by Mr Taylor was the fact that the Nazis were using their Argentine Fascist friends, in Buenos Aires for instance, in order to circulate and market a number of the art objects the Germans had stolen from France, Holland, Belgium and other conquered countries in order to acquire foreign exchange and ready cash. Everyone knew this was going on but there was nothing much that could be done about it. Since it was unofficial, diplomatic representations were unavailing. Would we try somehow to expose the plot by publication and at least let the enemy know we were on to what was happening?

Simultaneously while Mr Taylor was still speaking the plot of THIEF IS AN UGLY WORD *was taking shape in my mind. Early in the war 'Cosmopolitan' magazine had sent me to South America to do research for a series of short stories set in the capitals of the various countries there. As a result of this I had created a new fiction character and hero, an American refrigeration engineer, Augustus A. Swinney whose qualities included the mathematician's ability to face the fact that two and two made four, coupled with a sense of justice and blunt daring. I had, therefore, the character ready-made and likewise the background at my finger-tips. When the meeting turned to the matter of practical help for Mr Taylor's project I volunteered to write a fiction story which would contain some of the elements of the work of the Commission and its problems as well as exposing the Buenos Aires racket.*

The next morning I called on Miss Whiting, editor of 'Cosmopolitan,' and gave her a brief outline of the story and its purpose as far as I had developed it, and came away with an order. The order, I might add, was based on the entertainment value of the story and not its underlying theme or propaganda value. And I must confess, entertainment was my own prior consideration, for while I was listening to Mr Taylor at the meeting, it was the elements of romantic adventure contained in the dry facts that appealed to me primarily.

Propaganda in fiction is useful only when the characters and the story are thoroughly beguiling, interesting, or exciting and entertaining. It all goes back to the dictum of the great 'Saturday Evening Post' editor, George Horace Lorimer, who said: 'Tell me a good story and I don't care what your background is.' This has frequently been called 'sugar-coating the pill' but I think that that is not only a false phrase but a false notion, because if you start out with the so-called 'pill' in a story and try to make it palatable, the result in nine cases out of ten is a mess, and the story doesn't come off. The pill never goes down. On the other hand, if the telling of an exciting story is the first consideration, the yarn can be materially strengthened by interpolation of facts or merely the beliefs of the writer, if these beliefs are sincere.

If this strikes you as a devious way to go about an exposé and if you might be inclined to say that a factual and documented article exposing the traffic in South America might have been more effective, you would be wrong. It is a fact, startling perhaps in its implications, that fiction has a far greater propaganda value and gains far more credence amongst readers than actuality. I need refer you only to UNCLE TOM'S CABIN *and the results it achieved. A truth becomes far more vivid and active and lives in people's minds to a much greater extent when fictionalised than when presented merely as fact. People like to be told a story.*

While all the characters in this one, including Mr Swinney, are completely fictitious, they are based upon my observations during my South American trip. The wicked ones all represented something I thoroughly hated, Nazism or Fascism in one form or another, the representatives of which constituted our legal enemies in World War II, with the odd exceptions of Fascist Spain and Fascist Argentina, and I know that I secured a kind of personal release out of frying them in this story, really a sense of physical satisfaction that comes with using words as bullets.

I enjoyed writing this story and in particular the delineation of the nasty little art expert and critic called Chester Allen Buskirk, one of those bootlicking camp followers of the arts I had encountered in many places of the world. They were just too too far above things. Art was international and knew no bound-

*aries. In this manner some of them managed to give considerable
aid and comfort to the enemy who was waging total war. But as
I remember the most fun of all was writing the resounding, and
of course utterly false, speech that Mr Swinney makes to the
Countess Amalie the beautiful spy when he dismisses her. Amalie
is, of course, an exaggeration, yet I did see her prototype operating all over South America, Europeans like her without visible
means of support, living in Rio, Montevideo, Buenos Aires,
Santiago de Chile, handsome feline creatures with Paris clothes
and plenty of money to spend on entertainment. They were
supposed to be rich refugees from the war-torn Continent, but
everybody semed to know they were reporting regularly to the
yellow-haired Nazi goons one likewise saw operating all over
Latin America. It was a business. And what Swinney said to her
came from my heart, even though his last line, about the kind
of world we hoped to make out of this war, has a hollow ring
today. I guess at the time I wrote it I was actually naïve enough
to believe that perhaps this time it would be different.*

THIEF IS AN UGLY WORD

If one were to take a pencil and upon a stereographic projection
of a world map execute a series of straight lines connecting New
York, Munich, and Buenos Aires, one would find oneself looking
at a large isosceles triangle, the points of which are at such a
distance from one another that they might seem to preclude the
coincidences of a certain day early in January of 1944. However,
since this is not a mathematical treatise, beyond the simple
arithmetic of Mr Augustus A. Swinney, an American refrigeration
engineer whose life's philosophy could be summed up in the
inescapable verity that two and two add up to four, we are less
concerned with a geometric shape than the shape and pattern
of the events that took place at those widely separated points.

For instance, take the functioning of two gentlemen of similar
general titles, one in Munich and the other in New York, Herr
Professor Hildebrand Bressar and Mr Curtis Henry. Mr Curtis
Henry was active on the American Commission for Salvage and
Protection of Art and Historic Monuments in Europe. His
opposite number, Professor Bressar, operated under the beautiful
title of *Kunstverwaltungsrat für arisch-europäische Altertums-*

kultur, which, literally translated, means 'Art-Custodian-Adviser for Aryan-European Ancient Culture.'

Boiling their work down to the very essence of its nature, Curtis Henry might be termed an art detective engaged in ferreting out the hundreds of thousands of objects of art pilfered throughout Europe by the Germans, with the eventual objective of returning them to their original owners. Professor Bressar, for all of his wing-collar dignity and high position as curator of the Pinakothek in Munich, was nothing more than a kind of superfence, engaged in the disposal of same. Being merely a good, Third-Reich German, and lacking, like most such good Germans, the moral and ethical probity of a cherrystone clam, it would have been difficult to make the professor understand that what he was doing was wrong.

But we are interested in Herr Bressar only because of his ill-concealed satisfaction at the dawning of that certain day in January, illuminated as any particular day of international villainy always is to a German by being thought of as *'Der Tag.'*

In fact, that is what Herr Professor Bressar's assistant called it when he greeted him with 'Good morning, Herr Kunstverwaltungsrat. This is the day, is it not?'

'Jawohl, Herr Reinecke, today. I have had a cable from Buenos Aires.'

'Ah. Then it – they arrive. Everything goes well.'

Professor Bressar consulted a cablegram on his desk and then shifted his gaze to certain lists of items before he smiled and replied: 'There is nothing that can go wrong. A member of the Argentine Government is the sponsor. The Americans remain stupid and asleep and besides they dare not interfere in Argentina. And human greed remains what it has always been. Think what it means, Reinecke: millions of dollar-credits for the *Partei,'* and he rubbed his hands. Herr Reinecke licked his lips.

Mr Curtis Henry's brief connection with this story is that some three thousand miles away in his office at the Metropolitan Museum of Art he was taking the deposition and claim of a Dutch refugee, a chubby, shabby-looking little man, with the face of a care-worn child, by the name of Jan van Schouven.

He gave his address, one of the lower West Side, which confirmed the tale of penury and reduced circumstances hinted at by his clothes.

'And the art object to which you wish to lay claim——' said Curtis Henry, his pen posed over the blank he was filling in.

'Se *Old Woman uff Haarlem,* py Rembrandt van Rijn,' said van Schouven simply.

Henry put down his pen and whistled. 'Great heavens! You are *that* van Schouven?'

'I wass,' replied van Scholven with such simple dignity that all the questions Henry had been forming were stifled and he confined himself to the questions on the information blank.

'Family?'

'My wife iss with me. She iss ill . . .' Some memory of misery and hatred flared in the Dutchman's placid eyes for a moment, a sombre flash of indignities suffered. 'My son iss in the English flying. My daughter iss a nurse. Also in England.'

'Value of the picture?'

'It would bring between t'ree hundert and t'ree hundert fifty t'ousand dollars today.'

Henry had a sudden insight into what such a sum would mean to a once wealthy merchant who had obviously suffered complete ruin at the hands of the Germans. He read the next line: 'Proof of ownership . . .' and then checked himself, but van Schouven chose to reply.

'Se picture hass been in our family for generations. I belief your expert, Mr Chester Allen Buskirk, knows . . .'

Curtis Henry made a nose at the mention of one of America's foremost art critics and experts. 'Ah – Mr Buskirk is a little too internationally art-conscious for us. The world recognises the picture as your property.' He completed the form and then turned to the little refugee again.

'Ah – look here, Mr Van Schouven. I'm sorry, but you realise of course that at present we can do no more than list these properties and the whereabouts of their rightful claimants. There is very little chance of their being recovered for a considerable period. Even after the Germans have been defeated, we . . .'

Van Schouven rose and bowed. 'Sank you. I realise that. As a refugee honoured with a home in your great country, I only felt it my duty to assist you in your work. Some day se time will come . . .'

The thing was happening in his eyes again. Then it faded. He bowed again, put on his shabby hat, and went out.

It was on that same day at the end of the third leg of the triangle, five thousand three hundred airline miles from New York, that Mr Augustus Swinney was attending a cocktail party in Buenos Aires.

From the first, Mr Swinney had found himself fascinated by the intricacies of the diplomatic niceties, the frozen faces and the delicately balanced situations of a gathering under the sponsorship of a neutral nation.

Representatives of belligerent, semi-belligerent, and neutral countries were collected uncomfortably under the same roof, munched at the same buffet table, from carefully studied positions, in which well-tailored but chilly backs formed impregnable circles, or gathered in tight, unassailable little groups in various corners of the two brilliantly lighted and ornate salons given over to the guests, opening the ranks only to admit one whose nationality or politics fitted them into the particular group.

Thus the Germans remained a hard core, hard-headed, hard-shirted, dark-suited, immediately beneath the splendid crystal chandelier suspended over the centre of the inner room where the buffet table was located. Bright feminine bits of silk drifted towards the dark core, swirled, floated away. Small dark Argentinians, distinguished by their dark eyes and English clothes, revolved around the rim; the solid Prussian centre never changed or moved.

The British contingent, semi-official and obviously on hand to see what was in the wind, managed to achieve a bland unawareness of the enemy by rallying beneath an excellent Romney hanging in the outer room, a gloomy portrait of the Duchess of Colchester gazing down dispassionately at her countrymen forming their own tight little isle in the swirl of humanity brought out by the exhibition of a new art treasure acquired by Alfonso de Paraná, Argentine millionaire and collector, and sponsored officially by the grey, frosty, super-correct person of Dr José Calderriega, Sub-Minister of Culture of the Argentine Republic.

The British were bounded on the north by the Russians, who, looking as though they had slept in their clothes, held together a kind of lumpy and dishevelled front, and on the south by a small satellite island of correct and careful Swiss. A small group of Americans, thoroughly ill at ease, remained close to the door for immediate escape in the event of any total loss of social composure. Italians and French drifted disconsolate and homeless, unable to create any nucleus that satisfied them. In spite of strong rocks of nationalism, the party was kept fluid by the circulating movement of lovely women of indeterminate allegiance and the many glowing-eyed men whose allegiance was plainly and simply to the lovely women.

Mr Swinney, free American citizen, cosmopolite, due to his world wanderings as refrigeration engineer and expert for Swift & Co., the meat packers, unhindered by the social quavers that gripped other members of the American colony, drifted, moved,

searched, came and went as he pleased, shouldering his tall, lean
figure through the crush of uneasy celebrants.

He went everywhere, talking, chatting, listening with his skin
as well as with his ears, and avoiding only the existence and
perimeter of the dark, ugly core of Nazis, whose presence stank
in his nostrils.

That two and two added up to four he was still quite certain,
but of the real purpose behind this curious yet brilliant gathering
he was not at all sure, beyond that it was for the ostensible
occasion of viewing a painting, a canvas of sufficient importance
to cause the Argentine Sub-Minister of Culture to spread the
grey mantle of his sponsorship over the affair. It was only because
of this semi-official diplomatic mantle that such an extraordinary
mixed group was able to attend.

It was also, Mr Swinney knew quite well, because of the
quasi-Government sponsorship that social barriers were down,
to him as well as three-quarters of those in the rooms. Most of
those present would otherwise never have been permitted to set
foot in so much as the ante-room of the home of Señor Alfonso
de Paraná one of the wealthiest men in the Argentine, and a
social figure of importance in Buenos Aires and Paris.

The guest list apparently represented a cross-section of the
wealth, diplomacy, industry, and international society of Buenos
Aires. Mr Swinney was not unaware why *he* in particular had
been invited, since, holding the important position of chief
refrigeration engineer for Swift & Co., the meat packers, he did
belong to the upper stratum of industry.

He was also able to reason that since art is generally accepted
as an international commodity, this might well account for the
international nature of the gathering. But since Mr Swinney was
also well aware, as was everyone else present, that their host,
de Paraná, was an ardent Argentinian fascist, a supporter of
fascist Government policy and an enemy of the Allies, he was
alive with curiosity as to the real reasons underlying the gathering.

Where Allies and fascists met across the front lines, they shot
at one another. Here they mingled and circulated, sipping champagne and nibbling delicacies.

It was Mr Swinney's first experience of the grand diplomatic
and social lie that covered human behaviour under such circumstances, a lie that was acted out daily in Turkey before it swung
to the side of the Allies, in Portugal, in Switzerland, in Buenos
Aires. Mortal enemies met, rubbed shoulders, passed, pretended
they were not there.

As a cultured American businessman in his early forties, a man at home in five languages and most of the European capitals, this curiously childish kind of pretending amused rather than outraged Mr Swinney. It was the presence of a second lie that aroused his curiosity and vaguely disturbed him. He wondered whether the canvas hanging behind the closed doors of de Paraná's fabulous library, not yet thrown open to the guests, was actually, as rumoured, Rembrandt's famous *Old Woman of Haarlem*. He doubted it. And yet . . .

That was just it. No one had said that this was the picture they had been invited to see, and yet everyone seemed to know. No one said anything, and everyone knew everything – how the Germans were bringing goods into the Argentine, how quinine was being diverted from Bolivia and sent into Germany via Franco Spain, how secret information about a British meat convoy found its way into the hands of the commander of a Nazi submarine wolf pack, how even perhaps a Dutch art treasure might conceivably turn up in Buenos Aires, the Paris of South America.

Once one was careful to maintain the fiction of Argentine neutrality, one seemed to pick up information and knowledge by osmosis, through the pores of the skin. Someone might say casually: 'I understand that . . .' and the vague rumour understood would be closer to the truth than the news printed in the controlled press.

Mr Swinney's sane, precise mathematical mind explored and sifted rumour and personalities in an attempt to reduce them to simple denominators such as two and two, which could then be added up to four – the grey, icily proper Dr Calderriega conversing with the British commercial attaché, fat de Paraná, his small nostrils twitching, his dark eyes gleaming sensually above the grey pouches that underlined them, fingering a small, priceless Cellini group and discussing it with a famous French sculptor now resident in Buenos Aires, the tawny, monocled, correct Baron von Schleuder of the German Embassy staff holding a thin-stemmed, gold-speckled Venetian champagne glass between his stubby fingers and exchanging polite small talk with the wife of an Argentine cattle king . . .

Dammit, it was all so official and correct.

Mathematics and the consequences of the addition of simple sums were driven from the mind of Mr Swinney when he again caught sight of the magnificent woman with the upswept Titian-bronze hair and cat-eyes. She was standing in the inner salon not far from the buffet table conversing with the paunchy little fuss-

budget of a man with the rimless eye-glasses, the gay-nineties
stiff collar, and the obvious toupee.

'God, she's good-looking,' Mr Swinney said to himself. 'I
wonder who she is.' He had seen her twice before, once during
the noon *corso* on the Avenida Florida, and again in the American
bar of the Hotel Continental at cocktail time. Mr Swinney
was a bachelor by choice, but this did not prevent him from
becoming profoundly stirred by certain types of woman. Woman
with cat-eyes and the mysterious, introspective feline expression of countenance that went with them he found irresistible.

He edged through the throng and, entering the second salon,
moved closer. He busied himself at the buffet table and watched
her out of the corner of his eye. No doubt that her clothes had
originally come from Paris. Only the French knew how to reveal
a classic figure in daytime dress. The daring of the purple hat
perched atop the thick, bronze-coloured hair fascinated him. By
Jove, she had the skin to carry it. The set of her head on her neck
was a challenge to every man in the room. Mr Swinney noticed
other eyes upon her. He determined to meet the challenge in his
own way.

She and Fuss-budget appeared to know each other well. If
he could become acquainted with the fat little man with the
toupee . . .

De Paraná suddenly appeared and joined the two, claiming
the girl. Swinney hoped that he would name Fuss-budget, but he
didn't. He said: 'Forgive me for robbing you, my dear friend. It
is only for an instant. I swear I will return the Countess to you
in a few moments.'

Fuss-budget's head waggled archly at the top of his stiff collar
and he bowed and turned to the buffet table, loaded with the
delicacies of five continents. Mr Swinney contrived to be next to
him.

Mr Swinney was surprised to note that Fuss-budget did not
smell of mothballs as he had expected. For he was a small, self-
sufficient left-over from another era, the professional gentleman
of the old school, and obviously an epicure.

He tasted the grey Malossol caviar and nibbled at Hungarian
pâté, savouring texture and flavour. But the full expression of his
ecstasy he reserved for the paper-thin, near-transparent slices of
smoked, fuchsia-coloured ham. He tasted. He chewed. He
swallowed. He closed his eyes with reminiscent delight. When he
opened them it was to find a tall, spare gentleman with a craggy,
hawk-like face, long, strong nose, and dark hair, sprinkled with

H

grey at the side, eating of the same ham and smiling at him sympathetically.

'By Jove!' said Fuss-budget. 'Genuine Westphalian ham. Perfectly cured.'

'Delicious,' said Mr Swinney.

The little man polished his glasses with a scented silk handkerchief, replaced them, examined the old, dark-red ham from which the slices came, and helped himself to another portion. 'Haven't tasted a real one for years. Don't know why they can get it here and we can't up in New York.'

Mr Swinney could have told him. It was one of the things that one knew – by osmosis again – when one lived in Buenos Aires. It was small in bulk like so many other of the German products that one could always find in Buenos Aires stores – the Leica cameras, the fine lenses and optical goods, the rare drugs and medicines labelled 'I. G. Farben, Berlin.'

But he was not of the mind to alarm or astonish the little man, but rather to make friends with him.

'The secret lies in the process of smoking. But have you ever tried one of our old Argentine hams? We have our own process of ageing and curing. The hams are first soaked in wine for weeks.'

The little man's ears cocked like a terrier's and his nostrils flared.

'Really? You mean better than——?'

'Tenderer. The flavour is unique. They are never exported.'

Fuss-budget licked his lips, then glanced at Mr Swinney. 'But, ah – you are an American, are you not?'

'I am with Swift & Company. I should be delighted some time if you would care to sample——'

The man sighed regretfully. 'Unfortunately, I am flying back in the morning.' Then he added importantly: 'I flew down only yesterday at the invitation of Dr Calderriega. Hm – it would really be a new taste experience. Of course, there is no question as to the superiority of Argentine beef . . .'

Mr Swinney was thinking to himself: 'Now, who the devil could you be? Flew down from New York at the invitation of the Argentine Sub-Minister of Culture. I suppose I ought to know you, but I don't.'

De Paraná returned with the cat-eyed girl on his arm and returned her to Fuss-budget. 'Voilà, mon ami! As I promised.' The little man bowed in the manner of one careful not to disturb the set of a toupee. For an instant they made a little group of which Swinney was the outsider. Fuss-budget hastened to perform the politeness. He said to Mr Swinney: 'Ah, I did not catch your name, sir.'

'Swinney. Augustus Swinney.'

'Of course – Countess Amalie, may I present Mr Augustus Swinney? The Countess Amalie Czernok. You know de Paraná of course.'

The Countess Amalie gave Mr Swinney her wide cat-smile and accepted him with her eyes. He was startled to find them violet-coloured, the shade of her hat.

Later, when they were alone, he said: 'I schemed to meet you. Are you angry?'

She spoke with an accent that might have been French. 'Not at all. I saw you scheming. That is why I came back. It is always flattering to a woman when she sees an attractive man make up his mind to meet her . . .'

Mr Swinney made a mental note: 'Aha, then she was watching. I wonder whether she noticed me in the Continental.' He said: 'I intruded myself shamelessly upon the little man. By the way, who is he?'

'That is Mr Buskirk, the art critic. Surely you know Mr Chester Allen Buskirk. I met him many years ago in Paris. He is so sweet and old-fashioned.'

Buskirk . . . Buskirk, the art critic, greatest living expert on the old masters. Flown down from New York to Buenos Aires at the invitation of Dr José Calderriega. Now, what did that add up to if one was still convinced that in spite of the super-impeccability of congealed diplomatic face, two and two made four?

'You are French, Countess?'

'Part French, part Polish.'

'A combination that inevitably results in a beautiful woman.'

'You look like an American, but you do not talk like one. You have been to Paris too?'

Before he could reply, there was a sudden stir in the room, a kind of mass awareness of a change in the routine and the beginning of a movement through the second salon towards the massive carved-oak doors leading to the library.

The doors which previously had been shut were now swung back. The Countess Amalie drew in her breath and sighed: 'Ah, the picture. Now we are permitted to see the picture. Are you not excited?'

'You mean Rembrandt's *Old Woman of Haarlem*?'

'Then you heard too?'

'One hears a great many things. I don't believe it.'

'You do not believe it?' In the light from the crystal chandelier overhead, her eyes were wide and luminous. 'But why should it not be possible?'

'Because,' said Mr Swinney, flatly, 'they wouldn't dare.'

But he found out when he came into the library and saw what hung on the wall of Brazilian teakwood panelling that they did dare, after all, that two and two still added up, and four made a very ugly number.

In Munich, Kunstverwaltungsrat Bressar was burning the lights late in his office in the Pinakothek, poring over lists marked: 'Final shipment following liquidation Cracow Museum, Cracow, occupied Poland,' and occasionally earmarking items for the Argentine.

In New York, Jan van Schouven, the little Dutchman with the tired-child expression and the desperate eyes, stood in the dingy hall outside the dingy furnished room and listened to the doctor say: 'Madam van Schouven is a little better tonight. However, if it were at all possible I would say it was almost imperative that she be moved to a warmer climate, at least for a time. . . .'

And in a tiny cove just outside Avellaneda, some twenty-five miles south of Buenos Aires on the Río de la Plata, an impatient U-boat captain sat in the steel cell of his quarters reading over a three-weeks-old copy of the *Völkische Beobachter*, digesting for the tenth time the accounts of the Wehrmacht's glorious advances to the rear in Russia and wondering how long it would be before the orders came through from the Embassy in Buenos Aires to unload his cargo, pick up the return load of tungsten, molybdenum, platinum, and quinine, and put to sea. He was tired, anyway, of being a damned freighter. There was no Knight's Cross with oak leaves for that kind of work. . . .

Mr Augustus Swinney looked up at Rembrandt's magnificent and touching masterpiece, the *Old Woman of Haarlem*, beautifully hung on the panelled wall of de Paraná's library over the fifteenth-century Spanish fireplace, softly but glowingly lit to bring out all the deep warmth of the tones of gold and brown. He thought of the last time that he had gazed on its breathtaking perfection.

It had been in Amsterdam, he remembered, in 1938. He had dined at the home of a business acquaintance, Mynheer Jan van Schouven, a wealthy tobacco merchant with plantations in Sumatra. They had been discussing the possibility of the use of refrigeration for the preservation of tobacco in transit over long distances.

Van Schouven lived in a timber house in Amsterdam that was four hundred years old. After the evening repast Vrouw van Schouven and her young son and daughter excused themselves and retired. The tobacco-grower had led Mr Swinney into the library to drink Javanese coffee, smoke the strong black cigars of twisted Sumatran tobacco, and inhale the fragrance of a brandy that was laid down the year Wellington cornered Napoleon at Waterloo, not far to the south.

The ceiling timbers of the room were of blackened oak, the deep chairs of oak and leather. Candlelight shone on soft pewter and the glistening leather backs of old books. Many candles illuminated the glowing, lifelike portrait of a wrinkled old woman in a heavy carved gold frame that hung casually on the wall opposite the beamed fireplace where its surface would catch the reflection from the curling coloured tongues of driftwood flame.

Mr Swinney had not been able to take his eyes from it. Not only the portrait fascinated him, but the concept of its hanging. It was displayed not as an art treasure, but as a part of the warm, richly sombre decoration of the old room, as an object, Mr Swinney felt, that had occupied its place for a long, long time.

To van Schouven he said finally, indicating the portrait: 'How that lives, how warm and kindly it makes this room! . . .'

Van Schouven nodded, drawing on his black cigar until the end glowed. 'It iss called se *Old Woman of Haarlem*. My ancestor Piet van Schouven received it from Rembrandt in payment of a debt. Piet made for Rembrandt a pair of Leiden boots of Spanish leather. It iss so rechistered in his account book.' Van Schouven smiled his placid Dutch smile. 'Se story iss told that my ancestor considered himself ill used in se exchange. Se leather cost him eleven florins . . .'

That evening had always remained in Mr Swinney's memory as a kind of island of deep peace and the ancient culture of living, standing out brightly in the turbulent streams of his travels.

The Germans had brought fire and flame and their new order to Amsterdam. Now the *Old Woman of Haarlem* gazed down at him with her wise, aged eyes peering out from beneath the white wimple from the panelled wall of another library in Buenos Aires. The heavy, two-foot-square gold frame was a different one, but here was no mistaking the picture. To have seen it once was to know and recognise it for ever.

The spell of Swinney's memories was broken when the Countess Amalie spoke softly at his side. Curiously she used almost the same words that had come to Swinney at his first sight of the masterpiece: 'How it lives!' and then she added: 'What would one not give to possess such beauty!'

A kind of bitter wave shook Mr Swinney at the sound of the word 'possess' . . . 'possess.' To possess, the Germans had charred, blackened, and defiled the neighbour nations of Europe.

The guests had been filing into the massive library. They formed into their careful patterns, the Germans grouped in the far corner beneath the fifteenth-century Flemish tapestry whose warm reds and blues set off the pasty white of their faces, which were beginning to show signs of strain. The correct, tawny Baron von Schleuder was pale too. He kept licking his lips, affixing and removing his monocle, and staring at the picture.

The British shifted their island close to the massive carved Spanish table and whispered amongst themselves; the French and Italians gesticulated and made approving noises. The Argentines formed a group close to the picture itself, with the suave, grey, icily cold Dr Calderriega, de Paraná flushed and excited, and Chester Allen Buskirk polishing his glasses briskly as a nucleus.

Mr Swinney felt the tension that lay beneath the exclamations and the high-pitched conversations in the room and understood it. His own mathematics were complete. The sum of two and two still made four. The trial balloon was about to go up.

He said to himself: 'Clever Calderriega. He'll help them get rid of their loot, but he doesn't trust his dear Nazi friends any farther than he can see them.'

Mr Chester Allen Buskirk, having wiped the last speck off the windows of his lenses, adjusted his pince-nez, cleared his throat, and stepped towards the painting, which hung just above eye-level. An uneasy hush broken only by whisperings fell over the room.

Buskirk took full advantage of the centre of the stage. He cocked his head gingerly, he stepped away, he stepped closer to examine the texture of the paint, he stepped away again . . .

'God,' thought Swinney, 'you've got it in your hands, little man. Tell 'em it's a fake and you'll spike them. Surely *you* know who owns that picture. . . .'

Buskirk cleared his throat again, removed his pince-nez, and turned to de Paraná and Calderriega. 'Unquestionably authentic. Unquestionably Rembrandt's *Old Woman of Haarlem*!'

The German group stirred first, shifting and turning. Several of them used their handkerchiefs. Baron von Schleuder gazed sternly and fixedly at the picture and said: 'Colossal!' French and Italian shoulders were lifted higher, the Argentines broke into a torrent of excited Spanish, and the cynical whisperings of the British increased; the Russians glowered. There were no other Americans in the room besides Mr Swinney and Buskirk.

The fussy, self-important little art expert was perfectly conscious of the figure he was cutting. He drifted over towards Mr Swinney, attracted by the light from the tower of the Countess Amalie's bronze-coloured hair.

The Countess turned her wide-set huntress's eyes on the little man and said: 'What learning was embodied in that simple statement!'

Buskirk preened himself. 'Learning? No. It is an emotion. Learning may be prey to error; the emotions aroused by the perfect blending of intellect with light and colour, never.'

'Damn your emotion,' said Mr Augustus A. Swinney, sharply.

Buskirk started so that his pince-nez fell into his hand. 'I beg your pardon, sir!'

Mr Swinney's voice was cold and cutting. 'There is also such a thing as ethics.'

Buskirk was confused, but with the slyly feline eyes of the girl moving from him to Swinney and back again, he retreated behind an epigram:

'Art is not concerned with ethics, but with truth.'

'Bunk!' said Mr Swinney, his voice made harsh by his rising anger. 'You know to whom that picture belongs – and God knows where he is or what the Germans did to him. And yet, knowing it, you identified the picture for a pack of Nazi thieves in cutaway coats. . . .'

Buskirk became thoroughly flustered under the attack. Heat rising to his face fogged his glasses and he fell to polishing them furiously. 'I am acquainted with van Schouven. He is now in New York. He may have sold the picture. . . .'

'Did you inquire?'

Buskirk felt that he was being interrogated like a little boy and was being humiliated before the stunning and dramatic-looking Countess, who was now watching only Mr Swinney with a curious expression at the corners of her full mouth. He drew himself up and attempted extrication.

'That is none of my concern, sir. There is an American branch of the International Art Salvage Commission to which van Schouven can turn to press a claim. I do not deal with property rights, ha hum, but with the limitless horizons of eternal art. . . .'
He stole a quick look at the Countess Amalie and thought he detected a flicker of approval in her face and felt encouraged to continue.

'Truth in art is not a matter of a bill of sale, sir. The fruits . . .'

'Hush!' said Mr Swinney, curtly, the way one might have spoken to a child, but there was distaste on his lips. He looked down at Buskirk from his lean, clean height. 'You are a living, walking, talking anachronism. You are as bad as they. You condone. It is time the world learned a better truth than yours – that nothing matters but the difference between right and wrong.'

The Countess Amalie drew in a deep breath and veiled her eyes with her kohl-darkened lids.

Buskirk blustered: 'You are insulting, sir. I am here as the guest of a Government official.'

'That's just it,' said Mr Swinney, but he said it to the retreating, outraged back of the little art expert.

'You have hurt his feelings,' said the Countess Amalie.

'Damn and hell,' said Mr Swinney from the depths of his growing anger. 'It is sickening.'

He stopped speaking and the Countess turned her enveloping gaze on him interrogatively to see whether he would continue and tell what was sickening.

Mr Swinney did not do so. His thin lips closed and his indignant eyes roved over the room and the restless groups of people. But he knew – quite everything. The pattern was clear, unmistakable, and mathematically logical, but it was the perverted, graceless mathematics of the most evil men the world had ever known.

For three years the Germans had been looting captured Europe of its art treasures. Over and beyond what the Goerings and von Ribbentrops had pilfered for themselves and their estates, millions upon millions of dollars' worth of world-famous and historic paintings, sculptures, and antiquities had been pouring into Munich from gutted museums of Poland, Holland, France, Belgium, Italy, Czechoslovakia, Russia, and Norway, from galleries and private collections stripped bare, from ransacked homes.

Mr Swinney knew that in every occupied city Quislings had waited with lists prepared of every art object of value in the vicinity. Like locusts the Gestapo and party boys had descended upon the communities with vans and trucks and carted it away. Germany might be losing the war in the military sense, but her thieves had cornered the art market of the world. Now the discredited and bankrupt party heelers were preparing to fence the swag for the dollar credits needed to bolster their collapsing financial bastions.

The German mind was no mystery to Mr Swinney, who had travelled among them and done business with them. Crude and brash though their methods were, they knew they needed a sponsor for their transactions at least once removed from their persons, some group to act at once as window dressing, front, and buffer and raise some slight incense smoke screen of legitimacy to offset the stench of intrinsic German crookedness.

What was more logical than to turn to the strongest and wealthiest and most powerful South American nation, the only one whose Government was openly friendly and helpful to the Nazis and secretly hostile to the United States and the Allies?

Even Mr Swinney had to admit that the use of the name of Dr José Calderriega as sponsor of the exhibition had been brilliantly conceived. For if this show was not exactly a Government affair, yet Dr Calderriega was *of* the Government, as Sub-Minister of Culture. The Germans had calculated well that his name and position would stifle criticism and opposition from the outset.

The use of Alfonso de Paraná had been clever too. Known as one of the wealthiest men in the country, and connoisseur of art in his own right, with a notable private collection, the turning up of a famous picture in his possession was just the right touch.

But Mr Swinney had no illusions about de Paraná. He was an out-and-out fascist and Germanophile. Enough of the booty would stick to his fingers to make it worth his while, but his role was strictly that of middleman. Mr Swinney thought with disgust of the greed that would bring art dealers through these salons in the days to come, perhaps some of his own countrymen among them.

Nor did Mr Swinney need the rumours, or pickups, or snatches of conversation caught on the fly to tell him how the stuff was to get there. Light, small, compact, a rolled-up canvas by Raphael would fit into any cranny in an undersea boat; a twelfth-century triptych, a medallion by Benvenuto Cellini, a tapestry by Gobelin, ancient jewelled candlesticks from Polish churches, encrusted chalices of the early popes, would take up little more space. One U-boat could load enough boodle to pay for a day of war. Mr Swinney had no doubt that a Nazi submarine was lurking somewhere nearby, waiting to unload the rest of its cargo if it had not already done so.

Once they had got away with the transfer and sale of the Rembrandt as a trial, the Nazis would flood the market for all the traffic would bear. It all dovetailed, even to that pompous ass Buskirk.

Fascists or no fascists, Calderriega and de Paraná were no

fools. *They* knew their Germans and had cleverly protected themselves against having a fake put over on them. But in addition Buskirk's presence had served to set a further seal upon the affair.

A kind of silence fell over the room again, and Mr Swinney saw that the icily grey Dr Calderriega was about to say a few words. They came out in Spanish, as neat and clipped as his grey moustache, as tight and spare and reserved as his figure:

'Presence of this great painting . . . under the roof of Señor de Paraná . . . milestone in and monument to Latin-American culture . . . congratulations due this great art patron of Buenos Aires . . .'

The Germans nudged one another, smirked, raised their champagne glasses as in a military drill, and said: '*Hoch!*'

A few desultory 'Hear, hears' came from the British contingent; a Frenchman cried: '*Epatant!*' the Russians glowered silently and shifted their feet uncomfortably. People in the room milled about a little.

Mr Swinney's gorge rose. 'Fire and damnation,' he thought to himself. 'Not only I know; *they all know!* Every one of them! Everyone here knows, and the Germans and that grey Argentine and the fat one with the pouches know they know, and are ramming it down their throats.'

This, then, was the second lie that was being circulated there that afternoon, as lightly as the canapés and the Venetian cocktail glasses, as hushed and hidden as that other diplomatic fiction of the non-presence of diplomats of countries engaged in war.

The British knew— it was in their tight lips and frigid bearing. The Russians knew, and showed it in their scowls and uneasily moving feet. The Swiss, the Slavs, the French, the Italians knew it. The Spaniards were laughing up their sleeves. The fashionably gowned women knew it, and showed it in the sly casting of their eyes and the heads bent forward to whisper. The men from the embassies had known it for weeks and merely moved a little more stiffly from the hips.

Everyone was privy to the same logic, the same reasoning, the same rumours, the same information as Mr Augustus A. Swinney, simple loyal American citizen, refrigeration engineer and fascist-hater.

But no one said anything.

Over them all, like an unseen, viscous garment, constricting and attenuating thought and movement and behaviour, lay the cloak of diplomatic conduct. The soft net of protocol was tougher than steel. They might know what they knew, or whisper behind their hands what they pleased, but until something was said or

utter impossibility of a man, the employee of a large American firm, leaving Buenos Aires accompanied by one of the most valuable pictures in the world. But in meantime I strongly suggest that you hold the further development of this transaction in abeyance. I will be in touch with you and with Señor de Paraná later in the evening.

In New York City, where it was an hour earlier, Curtis Henry said to his wife over cocktails: 'I can't get that little Dutchman, van Schouven, out of my mind. He's got such dignity. There's a fellow who once had the best of everything, probably living on nothing now . . . I doubt whether even his own countrymen here know how hard up he must be. I wonder what one could do for a chap like that. Probably nothing.'

In the damp, bare dingy room that looked out over the dirty, noisy, winter-bound slum street, Jan van Schouven pondered over what the doctor had told him of the dire necessity of moving the woman with whom he had lived for all his life in faith and harmony to a warmer climate and wondered what he should do, for there was nothing more left to sell. And because he did not know, he did something he and many of his people had learned to do since the coming of the war. He turned to prayer and asked for help.

In South America, too, darkness had fallen over the little cove outside of Avellaneda where the captain of the U-boat was playing *skat* with the first officer. He said: 'What the devil is the matter with that fellow von Schleuder that we did not hear from him? Why can't we get that damned bric-à-brac ashore and get out of here?'

The first officer took a trick. 'We will probably hear from him tomorrow.'

The captain spat. 'Tomorrow – tomorrow. Always tomorrow. Some day tomorrow will be too late for Germany . . .'

It was shortly after seven o'clock when Mr Swinney emerged from the warehouse on the Calle Garibaldi, still tenderly lugging a square wrapped bundle under his arm. The edges of the heavy carved and gilded frame peered out from heavy swathings of burlap that Mr Swinney had wrapped around it to keep it from harm or damage.

He had to walk a block or two before he found a taxicab. He gave the driver the address of his apartment, No. 17 Avenida Manuel Quintana, and was more than a little impatient of the heavy traffic in the central part of the town because he was expecting visitors. He was rather anxious to arrive before his callers.

At that, he just did. Gabino, his houseman, let him in.

'Anyone call, Gabino?'

'No, señor.'

'Very well. I am expecting some visitors. I will answer the door myself. If I should need anything I will call you.'

Mr Swinney lived in a modern three-room apartment on the sixth floor. The large multipaned windows of the living-room looked out on the quiet, tree-lined avenue. A small vestibule led from the outer door to this room. Beyond was a small dining-room and a bedroom.

Mr Swinney placed his package on the chrome mantel over the modern decorative but non-functional fireplace facing the entrance hallway, but he did not remove the protective burlap wrapping. Where the bright gilt of the frame protruded, it showed up like pirate gold against the severe stainless steel of the mantel panelling.

Thereafter he had only time to light a cigarette and go to his bookshelf and briefly examine a small volume before the door buzzer sounded. Mr Swinney replaced the book and opened the door. It was, as he had expected, Dr José Calderriega, Sub-Minister of Culture of the Argentine.

Dr Calderriega came through the vestibule and into the living-room with a quick, nervous step, but he paused on the threshold for an instant as his gaze fell upon the mantel. He said: 'Ah.'

'Yes,' said Mr Swinney. 'Won't you sit down, sir?'

Dr Calderriega sat on the edge of a chrome fauteuil, a perfection of a man in every small, icy detail, from his polished shoes to his faultless head. Age had not altered his appearance or the smoothness of his skin; it had merely frosted him. There was also frost in his voice as he inquired:

'You are Mr Augustus Swinney?'

'I am.'

'May I inquire before going any further, Mr Swinney, whether this was a practical joke?'

'No,' said Mr Swinney softly, but definitely. 'It was not a practical joke.'

Dr Calderriega's lips relaxed and he nodded slightly. Mr Swinney thought: 'Now that he has ascertained that I am neither drunk nor a maniac, he has had to back off and begin all over again. I must be careful to keep this conversation on a high diplomatic plane or he will be shocked and disappointed. Well, we shall see.'

'Mr Swinney, we will overlook your indefensible behaviour if you will permit me to leave with the picture and restore it to Señor de Paraná.'

'That is generous, Dr Calderriega. I regret, I cannot permit it.'

'I see. And what do you intend to do with it?'

'Secure it until I am able to restore it to its owner.'

'The owner is Señor Alfonso de Paraná.'

Mr Swinney rose with a small sigh. 'Under those circumstances I can no longer discuss the matter with you, Dr Calderriega. Stealing is a matter for the police. I suggest that you call them. I will notify the American Embassy that I am ready to submit to arrest.'

Dr Calderriega sighed also, but like a dried leaf blown on ice. 'Sit down, Mr Swinney. There is – ah – no question of the police – at the moment. What is it you want?'

'To return the picture to its actual owner, Mynheer van Schouven.'

Dr Calderriega coughed. 'You are certain of your ground? Supposing no proof of previous ownership exists?'

Mr Swinney nodded. 'I understand the Germans have shown their usual thoroughness in destroying all records, indices, and proofs of ownership in connection with their national thieving expeditions. However——' He paused, but he was not looking at the Sub-Minister. His eyes had wandered to his bookshelves across the room. He then tried very hard to suppress a grin, but was unable to and let it happen. He went over to the shelf and plucked out a small red volume, the one he had examined previously.

'The Germans, Dr Calderriega, should have liquidated one of their most prolific cataloguers before they undertook their tour of looting. The evidence of their own uncle Karl Baedeker will yet brand them as the most shameless nation of burglars the world has ever known.'

He thumbed through the little book. 'Do you remember these little guide-books clutched to the breasts of Americans rushing about Europe? Baedeker's *Belgium and Holland*, 1930, page 257, Amsterdam – the Rijks Museum. I quote: "First floor . . . third room . . . on the right is hung Rembrandt's masterpiece *Old Woman of Haarlem*, parenthesis, on loan for five years by its owner, J. van Schouven, close parenthesis. This magnificent head, in the warmest tones of the master, depicts . . .' Well, the canvas is quite well described. Any court of law would recognise this as evidence.'

Dr Calderriega exhaled slowly and correctly. A single glistening bead of water no bigger than a seed pearl appeared beside the close-clipped grey moustache. Finally he said softly: 'Do you really believe, Mr Swinney, that you will be able to remove this picture from Buenos Aires?'

Mr Swinney considered the question for a moment before he replied: 'Yes, I believe I will.'

'Permit me to say that you are playing a dangerous game, sir.'

'Permit me to say that you are too, doctor. Your name appears upon the invitation as sponsor to the exhibition of Señor de Paraná.'

A second bead, in perfect balance, appeared on the other side of the Sub-Minister's lip. Mr Swinney wondered whether they were both congealed there.

For the first time Dr Calderriega's voice took on an edge, like a figure skater grating a blade on a turn: 'You understand, sir, that the Government is not officially involved.'

'Naturally,' said Mr Swinney with a slight bow. 'It is obviously beneath the dignity of the government of Argentina to assist in – ah – the disposal of purloined articles. Still, publicity would be regrettable. The Argentinian people might not understand. . . .'

The shudder that Dr Calderriega gave at the word 'publicity' was almost human.

'However,' continued Mr Swinney, 'it seems to me that no publicity is necessary, if—'

Dr Calderriega leaned forward slightly. 'If——?'

'If the art market in Buenos Aires were closed to – foreign export, the subject would never come up, I feel certain . . .'

'Ah. It is perhaps fortunate that the Ministry of Culture has the final say in – such matters.'

'As you say, it is most fortunate.'

Dr Calderriega rose and gazed for a moment at the object on the mantel. Something approaching a groan burst from him. 'It is impossible! Impossible! Do you realise that there will be other – forces interested in the repossession of that picture, forces that will stop at nothing – absolutely nothing?'

'That,' said Mr Swinney succinctly, 'is your worry as much as mine, Dr Calderriega. I wish you luck. Good evening.'

Shortly after the Sub-Minister had left, Mr Swinney went to the window and looked down into the street. He saw two policemen in their dark-blue uniforms with black leather puttees, Sam Browne belts, and peaked caps with red bands. They strolled fifty yards up the street, then stopped and strolled back again.

Mr Swinney smiled. He thought: 'I'd give a lot to know whether they're there to keep me in or to keep others out . . .'

He did not trust Dr Calderriega. When a man walks the thin crust of such scandal, disgrace, and disaster as the Sub-Minister trod, he might also be tempted to join those forces that would stop at nothing.

He wondered when those would begin to arrive.

It was nearly nine o'clock before Baron von Schleuder let himself out of the self-operating lift at the sixth floor of Number 17 Avenida Manuel Quintana and pressed the button outside Mr Swinney's door.

Upon being admitted, the Baron entered briskly and with an air of busy determination. He was a large man with one of those large-featured faces which look as though they had been fashioned roughly in putty. His tawny, leonine hair was slicked back from his forehead and he wore his monocle. He, too, paused at the living-room threshold, stared stonily at the exhibit on the mantel, and said: 'So.'

Mr Swinney made no comment, nor did he invite the Baron to sit down. Instead he remained silent, waiting for the conversation to open. The Baron permitted his monocle to drop into his left hand and said: 'Mr Svinney?'

'Yes?'

'Von Schleuder! Cherman Embassy!' His sentences came out curt and harsh, like military commands. 'We will speak about this picture.'

Mr Swinney replied: 'Very well. Who are you representing? Señor de Paraná?'

'Certainly not!'

'I see. The German Government, then?'

Baron von Schleuder opened his large lips to reply and then closed them firmly and glared at Mr Swinney.

'It is not a question of who I represent. The picture must be returned immediately.'

'I don't recognise your authority.'

'By what right do you presume to keep this picture?'

'Well,' said Mr Swinney reflectively, glancing at the gilt-edged bundle on the mantel, 'let us say the right of immediate possession. You had it. De Paraná had it. Now I have it. I might add that I got it the same way your Government did. I took it.'

Von Schleuder's thoughts playing over his heavy face were as transparent as a newly washed window.

Mr Swinney said quietly: 'Are you thinking of trying to take it from me physically? It would raise the most awful row. People would come . . .'

'Ach!' said the Baron, 'don't be ridikelous. That kind of extravagances is for romances.' He suddenly made an elephantine gesture that was supposed to indicate change of attitude, good-fellowship, and a newfound understanding. 'Let us play all the cards on the table, Mr Svinney. We wish the picture returned of your own will. What is your price?'

Mr Swinney looked as innocent as a newborn child. 'I would have to get in touch with the owner, Mynheer van Schouven from whom the picture was originally stolen by the Germans. I doubt whether he would wish to sell it to you.'

The Baron was not amused. He abandoned his jovial air as quickly as he assumed it. 'Ah so! Well, you have ask for trouble. You will have only yourself to blame.'

'That's better,' said Mr Swinney. 'That's how we love you.'

The Baron gave Mr Swinney a measuring and even slightly quizzical look in which he raised his brows a full inch, like a tenor on a high note.

'Well,' he said at last in the conversational tone of one who is about to take his departure, having concluded his business, 'at least we understand one another. I hope you do not get hurt, Mr Svinney. If you attempt to remove this picture from this room, much less from Buenos Aires, you will do so at your own risk, is that not so?'

'Thanks,' said Mr Swinney. 'I'll let you know when it gets to New York. Then you and Calderriega both will be able to relax. And, ah – I usually shoot at burglars.'

The Baron smiled a quiet, lemony smile, replaced his monocle, glanced once more at the object on the mantel, and departed. Mr Swinney went to the window and saw the Baron emerge into the street. Three men climbed out of a car parked at the kerb. The Baron spoke to them briefly, entered the car, and drove away. The three remained standing in the shadows. Mr Swinney was under no illusions as to what *their* presence meant.

Mr Swinney was also under no illusions as to his position. He was in a fix and he knew it. If because of circumstances Calderriega and von Schleuder were unable for the moment to avail themselves of normal procedures to recover the painting, neither was Mr Swinney in any position to ask for protection. Once he succeeded in getting the picture out of the country, the game would be won. But Mr Swinney gave a kind of rueful snort. He would have given much at the moment for an idea as to how that was to be accomplished.

Augustus Swinney was a businessman with a strong sense of justice, and not an adventurer, even though his quixotic impulses and deep-seated hatred of his country's enemies sometimes landed him in strange situations. Nevertheless he took natural precautions.

From a drawer he secured a small .32 automatic, tested its action, saw that it was loaded and a shell in the chamber, and slipped it into his pocket. He then wrote out a list of groceries and canned goods on a slip of paper and summoned Gabino.

'*Vaya al bodega.* The one on the corner of Vincente Lopez is open until ten. When you return, knock and call out. It will be locked.'

From the window he watched the houseman emerge from the service entrance down the street. The three Nazis in the shadows did not budge, but one of the two uniformed policemen detached himself from his post on the other side of the street and strolled after him.

'Damn!' said Mr Swinney.

When an hour passed and the houseman had not returned, he knew. He reflected they would not hurt him. The servant had probably been arrested on some trumped-up pretext, thoroughly searched, and held.

Then it was to be a siege. Mr Swinney locked and bolted the rear service door, fastened the short chain to the front door leading to the lift and stairway, and inspected his larder. With careful rationing there was enough food – cereals and a few items of tinned goods – to last him for quite a while. He was glad to note a plentiful supply of coffee. He would need that to keep awake. He set about brewing himself a potful at once.

In the living-room Mr Swinney sipped the thick, strong drink, considered his situation and his chances, and tried to figure from whence the attack would come. The procession of polite diplomatic visitors he knew was over. The next parties to ring his doorbell would mean business. And if they came in force – well, even a dead American refrigeration engineer in a burgled apartment could be hushed up in a dictatorship.

Shortly before midnight Mr Swinney heard the humming of the automatic lift and the click and thump as it stopped at his floor. After a moment's pause the buzzer sounded.

'Polite of them!' he said to himself. 'Well, it's about time. As the Baron put it, I asked for it.'

He slipped the safety catch of the gun in his pocket and went to the door. 'Who is it?'

No reply. Mr Swinney wondered whether he was being a fool and whether the next move would not be a fusillade through the door. Nevertheless, leaving the short chain on, he opened the door to the width it permitted.

He smelled, not gunpowder, but the sweet, exciting fragrance of perfume, caught a glimpse of white skin and bronze hair and a drape of fur.

'Amalie!' said Mr Swinney, and took the chain off the door.

The Countess Amalie was framed magnificently by the doorway. She wore an evening sheath of black satin without a single ornament to distract from the immediate form beneath it. The fur drape of chinchilla made a background for the wide cat-eyes slanting into the high cheekbones.

She said: 'Am I terrible? If you misunderstand, I shall hate you to the day I die.'

'My dear Countess,' said Mr Swinney, 'won't you come in?' He understood very well, and her presence thrilled him to the core. He had met many women of the genre of the Countess Amalie in Europe and had invariably found the experience stimulating and enchanting. They made practically no demands . . .

He had recognised the type immediately the first time he had seen her. The meeting in the salon of Señor de Paraná had confirmed it to him. He had read the answer in the first glance they had exchanged. In a masculine and quite unrefined manner, Mr Swinney had entertained great hopes for the development of a beautiful friendship with the Countess Amalie Czernok. Mr Swinney had not travelled extensively for nothing. Then the somewhat florid events he had precipitated had quite driven thoughts of her out of his head.

Misunderstand indeed! That was how the game began.

She crossed the threshold and faced the steel and chrome mantel and the gilt-edged, burlap-wrapped object that reposed thereon. Her gaze never left it as Mr Swinney removed the downy, feather-light, exquisite fur from her shoulders.

'That is why I had to come,' she said – 'to tell you what I felt. For no other reason . . .' The sensual mysteries of centuries lay behind her cat-smile.

'I have thought of nothing else since it happened – your courage to do this thing for our people. I thought that I had seen and known brave men. I am European. I have seen what our people have suffered and I have met courage, but until today I have never known the meaning of pure . . .'

Mr Swinney's nerves were badly jangled by what he had been through. He felt suddenly like a soldier who knows that on the morrow he returns to the firing line and, because time as well as desire is of the essence, is impatient of delay.

He faced her, put his hands to her shoulders, and said: 'Amalie – for God's sake – stop talking.'

'Oh God,' said the Countess. 'I can't help myself . . . What is it you have done to me?'

Mr Swinney held her in his arms and sought for the key to the barrier that was between them, the resolution of the mood that made her suddenly shake with sobs.

She said: 'I do not know what has happened to me. I cannot help myself. And now I am afraid.'

'Afraid?'

'For you, my dear – what will they do . . . A moment ago what you had done seemed the bravest, noblest deed in the world. And now –'

She escaped him and he let her go. She went to the mantel and with her fingers touched the gilt frame, the burlap wrapping, then turned to him. 'Oh, I hate it – I hate it,' she burst out. 'It will come between us . . . Can I help being a woman? There are too many of them – they are too strong. What can one man do against them alone? Don't you understand? If they . . .'

Mr Swinney went to her, but not precipitately, because he did not wish to frighten her further. Not until she was in his arms again did he say: 'My dear, what can we do – now?'

'Give it up. We can't fight them alone. I could not bear to lose you – now.'

Mr Swinney heaved a deep sigh. 'Maybe I'm a fool, Amalie. It was different until you came here. Perhaps you are right.'

'My dear – my dear . . .'

There were no more barriers – so much so that at first Mr Swinney had some little difficulty in extricating himself. Rage and cold distaste aided him. The Countess was facing him, her cat-eyes as wide open and mouse-wary as they would go. He took the feather-light chinchilla and dropped it around her shoulders.

'All right,' said Mr Swinney. 'Get out.' He said: 'Go back to the company you came from, the spying sluts of Stieber and Bismarck and all the rest of the master race, whose dirty work you do.'

He said further: 'Go back to the Middle Ages, where you belong. You are old-fashioned, outmoded. We are tired of you and we are tired of your Germans. The whole world is tired to death of you all. You smell of blood and money and the dead. When we finish with this job, there will be no room left for you or any other of their filthy works . . .'

The Countess Amalie, who could recognise a closed book when she saw one, went quietly, without a word, and with only a hint of genuine regret in her wide, violet eyes.

Mr Swinney locked and chained the door and went out into the kitchen and heated himself some coffee. It was while he was drinking it that he remembered the look in her eyes. He said to himself: 'Swinney, you're an idiot. Couldn't you have been so damned noble a little later?'

Then he set himself to the task of remaining awake. But there were no further incidents of any kind that night.

In the morning, while he was shaving, Mr Swinney reviewed the debit and credit sides of his performance, and for the first time since he had insulted him he thought of Chester Allen Buskirk, the stuffy little Old World gentleman and art critic, and his conscience hurt him a little.

The man was a product of a dead and bygone era. He had meant no harm; he had even been honest, according to his own lights. Mr Swinney wished there were some way in which he might convey to him that he regretted his behaviour towards him.

The idea of how this might be done came to him with such suddenness that he cut himself shaving, which was hardly worth the salvaging of social amenities with a man he would never see again. But Mr Swinney staunched the blood without regrets or rancour and went out to see that the time was after nine o'clock, which meant that his office would be available.

He picked up the telephone and dialled his office number. There was a clicking on the line, which told him no more than he expected. The phone was tapped. He didn't care; he got his secretary on the line and said: 'I may not be in for a while – might be a week. If anything turns up, you can reach me at home.'

Then he gave some business directions and concluded with 'Is Miguel there? Put him on.'

Miguel was the refrigerator foreman. When he came on the line, Swinney said: Hello, Miguel. Swinney speaking. Have we any of those special hams left? You know, the old ones?'

'I am not sure, señor. Shall I look?'

'I'll wait. Take a look. Try locker nine. There were some there last month.'

After a five-minute wait the foreman came back on the line. 'Sí, señor. I have found one.'

'Good. Do it up. Attach one of my cards. Miss Diega will give you one. Have her write on it: 'My compliments and apologies.' Right? Jump into your car and take it out to the airport and de- liver it to Mr Chester Allen Buskirk. He is leaving on the eleven- o'clock plane. Let me know if he received it. That's all.'

Mr Swinney looked out of the window to see whether the new shift had come on yet. It had. Both the local police and the Nazi honour guard had been changed.

He thought what he would do if he were in the enemy's place, and the logic of what must be their reasoning struck him as simple as the adding of two and two. They were prepared to wait him out. Mr Swinney's problem was equally simple. It was to stay awake. He wondered just how long a man could go without sleep and still function.

At one o'clock Miguel telephoned. 'The señor received the ham, sir. He say thank you.'

'Now, that was nice of him,' Mr Swinney thought to himself.

The second night without sleep was bad, but the third was plain hell, and Mr Swinney did not know how he could go on.

He had thought to devise a way to steal cat-naps by setting his alarm clock to ring after a half-hour of sleep. But the second time he tried it, he woke up at the last faint tinkle of the bell to find the mechanism quite run down. Another moment and he would have slept on through.

Twice there had been action on both nights, once at the front door and once at the back. He had gone there and called through the door: 'Skip it, boys . . .' He heard them departing, and the last time he heard them laughing.

Also, the second day his telephone was cut off. Mail and papers were no longer delivered. He lost track of time and dates, even though he marked the calendar, but his exhausted brain was playing him tricks. He learned all there was to know about the deadly and exquisite torture of sleeplessness, and several times he was on the verge of giving up.

Then he would down more coffee, prod himself, force himself to pace the apartment, show himself at the window. He would become confused and look at the calendar to see the time instead of his watch.

He had marked off the days – Tuesday, January 11 – Wednesday, January 12. Thursday, January 13, took on the terrible aspects of a mountain peak he might never achieve. They, on the other hand, were fresh and strong. If he fell asleep . . . they would force the door . . . He fought on desperately . . .

On Thursday, January 13, Mr Augustus Swinney, having somehow survived the night, took an icy shower, shaved, put on clean linen and a fresh white suit, plucked a geranium from his window box and stuck it in his buttonhole, put on his Panama hat, and went out.

As he closed the front door of his apartment he did not so much as throw a glance at the thing still resting on the chrome mantel, where it had been ever since he had put it there so long, long ago. . . .

        ✧   ✧   ✧

The Baron von Schleuder answered his telephone. 'He has gone out? Kurt is following him? He is breakfasting at the Continental? Yes! At once. No – wait! I will come immediately . . .'

Dr José Calderriega also answered an insistent ringing of his private line.

'What? Left? At the Continental? An officer is still there? No one else has come or gone? No, no! Do not enter until I arrive.

They made quite a party in the foyer of No. 17 Avenida Manuel Quintana, too many of them to crowd into the automatic elevator all at once, so Dr José Calderriega and Baron von Schleuder, eyeing each other warily, went up ahead, leaving the others to follow and taking only the police department expert with the skeleton keys.

The keys, however, proved to be quite unnecessary, because, upon trying the handle of the outer apartment door, it proved to be unlocked.

Outside of hundreds of cigarette stubs and some empty coffee cups the apartment was unchanged as the two men remembered it. There was even the burlap-wrapped affair on the mantel. Dr Calderriega, in spite of his age, was the first to reach it, but the Baron helped him unwrap the protective sacking and reveal the empty frame and the note in the middle of it, which was brief and to the point.

Dear Dr Calderriega – or von Schleuder:
Will you oblige me by returning this frame to Señor de Paraná or whoever owns it, as it does not belong either to me or to Mynheer van Schouven.
The 'Old Woman of Haarlem' is now in New York City.
I beg that you will believe me and refrain from ransacking my apartment. I shall be forced to present a bill for whatever damage is done to my premises.

Very truly yours,
AUGUSTUS A. SWINNEY

They did not believe him and tore the apartment to shreds, and later on Dr Calderriega paid a large bill without a murmur. But they did not find the *Old Woman of Haarlem*, for a very simple reason. Mr Swinney had told the truth.

In New York City, Mr Curtis Henry pounded on the door of the third-floor room of Jan van Schouven, shouting:

'Van Schouven! Van Schouven! Open at once! I must see you.'

The little Dutchman emerged looking pale and worn and more child-like than ever.

Curtis Henry said: 'Van Schouven! You must come at once.

I – I am so excited I can hardly speak. I have not yet got it straight. It is about the *Old Woman of Haarlem*. The ass Buskirk telephoned me. He was in a state himself. Something about a ham from South America and the Rembrandt painting. He has just returned from Buenos Aires and discovered the canvas wrapped around a ham that was given him. He is frightened to death of scandal, realises the picture was stolen from you, and insists you come at once. If it is true——'

'If it is true,' said van Schouven, 'God is merciful in answering the prayers of those who love Him. . . .'

Off Avellaneda, a score or so of miles south of Buenos Aires on the Río de la Plata, the muddy brown waters of the river gurgled and stirred some two days later and finally healed the breach that had been made in its viscous surface by the disappearance of a steel conning tower.

The U-boat commander was in a wretched temper for reasons beyond the discomfort of already cramped quarters, further narrowed by carefully wrapped and buttressed packages, packages that if divested of their straw and canvas coverings might reveal a carved Gothic eleventh-century saint, a Botticelli Madonna, or a Florentine chalice. . . .

The second-in-command looked in. 'At least we are going home, no? Cleared at 13.05.'

The U-boat commander regarded his junior with distaste and delivered himself quietly of the German equivalent of 'That's a hell of a way to run a war.'

In Munich, Professor Kunstverwaltungsrat Bressar entered his littered office in the Pinakothek at nine o'clock in the morning in an irritable mood, which was not improved by the spectacle of his assistant, Herr Reinecke, standing at his desk pale and greasy and licking his lips.

'Good morning, Reinecke.'

'G-good morning, Herr Kunstverwaltungsrat.'

'Na! What are you standing there like that for? What is the matter with you?'

'Herr Professor – a – a cable has come. It is not good. Buenos Aires has refused to permit the – shipment to land. It is being returned . . .'

And in Buenos Aires, at the far other end of the hypotenuse of the triangle with Munich and New York, Mr Augustus A. Swinney was having a cocktail.

But this time he was having it all by himself in the fashionable Boston Bar in the Calle Florida.

He was feeling considerably refreshed after sixteen hours of solid sleep. He was also further refreshed by a brief item in *La Prensa*. He had the paper folded to it and could not refrain from reading it over and over again.

It was a New York Associated Press dateline, headed: 'Negotiations for Old Master,' and read: 'Negotiations were completed today for the acquisition by the Metropolitan Museum of Art of Rembrandt's famous canvas, *Old Woman of Haarlem*, from its owner, Jan van Schouven, Dutch refugee and former wealthy tobacco merchant, for a price reputed to be between $350,000 and $400,000.'

Mr Swinney would have given much to see Buskirk's expression when he cut away the outer wrapping of his special ham and found himself looking into the wonderful, warm old face of the *Old Woman of Haarlem*.

Mr Swinney knew it had been sheer panic that had caused him to cut the portrait from the frame that evening when he had fled with the picture to his office, and wrap it around an old smoked ham to hide it. The idea had come to him when he had noticed how much the back of the canvas resembled the age and smoke-stained wrappings of these delicacies. Cellophane inside to protect the surface of the canvas, and a few 'Swift & Co., Buenos Aires, S.A.' packer's rubber stamps had completed the job.

But Mr Swinney would have been quite as willing to admit that the idea of palming it off on Chester Allen Buskirk and letting him take it to New York was nothing less than sheer inspiration.

Mr Swinney was conscious of a troublesome, stimulating perfume and the feeling that someone was looking over his shoulder. He turned and looked up into the cat-face of the Countess Amalie Czernok, who had just finished reading the A.P. item.

She tapped him gently on the shoulder and said: 'You are a devil!'

Mr Swinney rose to his feet. He said: 'Amalie! You ought to be pretty angry with me.'

'I – I am not sure that I am not.'

Mr Swinney had had much time to rest and think. He said: 'As to a woman, I want to apologise to you for the things I said to you . . .'

The Countess reflected for a moment and her tongue showed for an instant, red like a kitten's at the gates of her teeth. She replied: 'As a woman, there is no need to apologise. At no time did you say – that I was unattractive . . .'

She smiled her slow cat-smile and went on, but her look re-

mained with Mr Swinney for quite some time and kept his
thoughts from dwelling too much and exclusively on the *Old
Woman of Haarlem*. After all, *she* had been dead more than
four hundred years, while Amalie was very much alive. He
reflected that only a fool bore a grudge against a beautiful
woman. . . .

The Dowry

••

From my war diary, written in Rennes, France, August 18, 1944, after a day spent in Brittany with the Maquis, the men of the French Resistance:

'. . . *Every Maquis encampment was betrayed at some time or other by one of three things – loose talk, gipsies, or a woman. The Nazis paid from 5,000 to 20,000 francs for the betrayal of a patriot and found plenty of takers with dirty souls who would sell out a member of the F.F.I. for money. The Maquis knew well enough who was betraying them, but as long as the Gestapo was in the saddle, there was little they could do about it. But now it is different, and all over Brittany sit the miserable, frightened, filthy women with the stain of greed and treachery on their souls awaiting their trial, and the certain poniarding that will follow. As one of the Maquis had inscribed on his Sten gun, 'Victoire et Revanche!'*

'*There is a horrid story of a woman who married a villager, and gave a wedding breakfast. This wedding breakfast is a big event in Brittany. She invited a patriot member of the underground to attend and then betrayed him to the Gestapo, who surrounded the house during the wedding feast, took him away, tortured and killed him. That is how the woman got her marriage portion. Note: A good short story here. Think about it!*'

I thought about it a great deal, because I couldn't forget it, or any part of that day of August 18 when Sonia Tomara of the 'Herald Tribune,' Rozelle Hargrove of N.E.A., herself a born Breton, and private Johnny Anderson of Milwaukee, our jeep-driver, and myself drove from Rennes to Saint-Brieuc, Pontrieux, and Paimpol in northern Brittany, part of which was still in the hands of the Germans, to find the leader of the Maquis and visit the secret camp of these courageous guerrilla bush fighters. The story was written upon my return to the United States and published in Cosmo under the title, THE DOWRY.

We four were the first Americans to enter the little Breton seaside village of Paimpol, a few hours after the patriots had captured the town and taken the German garrison prisoner. Later that day we were taken to the secret camp of the Maquis, and there it was that we heard the story of Yolande from the lips of a young captain of the underground who had known her and who but a short time before had had a bitter share in her final destiny.

The tragedy was still fresh in the minds of all, for they had known her since she was a little girl in and around Paimpol. We saw the house in which she had lived and where she sold out the patriot for thirty pieces of silver, and on the execution ground, a small field next to the camp, we stood on the new-packed earth beneath which she slept. The men of the F.F.I. had not waited long to exact justice. The watchword of the Bretons, always a tough and primitive people, was 'Pas de pitié!'

I remember the first time I heard the phrase, on the way to Paimpol, when we stopped by the bank of a canal and watched them fish the dead body of a German sergeant out of the water. He had been executed for shocking and nameless brutalities the night before. As the battered corpse was laid on the stone landing at the edge of the canal, children were shouting and laughing and the villagers looked down upon the remains with great interest and enthusiasm.

Evidently someone in the crowd must have said something that contained a modicum of sympathy, a passing word for something that had once been a human being, even though he had not lived like one. There was an old peasant on our side of the water in cap and jacket, with snow-white hair, whose ears it reached. He removed his long pipe from his mouth and shouted across the canal: 'Pas de pitié!' His old voice rang over the water like the bells of doom. It was the voice of all tortured France speaking. This was the hour of revenge.

Yet there had been some pity for Yolande, and that was why I knew I wanted to write her story, because through it I might be able to project something of the France that I saw at the moment of her liberation.

While the essentials of the story, the events and the background, are true, the details of the story, the relationships of the characters and their intimacies, are fiction. I haven't the faintest idea what the readers of 'Cosmopolitan' thought of THE DOWRY *because not one of them wrote to tell me.*

It was in the Summer of 1944 that my long-standing ambition to become a war correspondent was fulfilled when 'Cosmopolitan' sent me across as correspondent and European editor on the finest assignment for which any writing man could ask, and for this I will owe a lifelong debt to Miss Frances Whiting, then editor-in-chief, who made it possible.

For it was more than an assignment. There was a bit of soul-saving involved. Miss Whiting was both editor and friend. And as an editor she knew that I was going to pieces as a writer because, owing to circumstances, I had been unable to get to the war. As a friend she saw that this was profoundly affecting me and might have permanent consequences. I was brooding over missing out on the greatest story of all, and my state of mind was reflected in my work.

As it had twice before, Cosmo underwrote my trip overseas. My only instructions were: 'Go over and look at the war. When you come back, write about it if and when you feel like it. We won't press you.' I went to England and France, into Paris with Dick Tregaskis in a jeep among Leclerc's tanks the day of liberation, smelled powder, got scared, got shot at, and came home with my gloom and megrims dispelled and a sackful of material, which before the war ended yielded three articles, three short stories, and a three-part serial. Two of these short stories, THE DOWRY and VERNA have been included in this book.

With them go my gratitude and affection for Miss Whiting, who helped me around many a rough corner in my career in the past and who by this final assignment did more for me than any other person or persons in the entire editorial and publishing field. And I do not know which is more grateful, the writer or the man. Both of us salute her.

THE DOWRY

Inland from the savage granite coast of northern Brittany the country softens to peaceful rolling farmlands, roads winding through brier rose and hawthorn hedges behind which lie, half concealed, the stone cottages and stout barns of the thrifty Breton peasants, sweet lands bathed in sunshine or veiled by the grey curtains of mizzling rain that drift in from the sea, a country whose outward appearance belies the fierce, primitive, untamed nature of its inhabitants.

It is a land of giant spreading oaks, of orchards of apple, pear, and plum, coloured with the red and purple fuchsia and flaming laurel, scented with the blossoms of mimosa, eucalyptus, and camellia. It is also a land of high romance and dark superstition, of sorceries, banshees and torrigans, and memories of ancient pagan religions whose monoliths, the druid menhirs rise like solitary giants from meadows of purple heather, and the dolmens, and mystic circles of moss-greened, granite cromlech stones stand half-hidden in fields of gleaming gorse and tangled brier.

Some twelve miles in from the sea sleeps the old market town of Tregoulac in the Department of Côtes-du-Nord, a village of tall, archaic timbered houses that lean forward until they appear almost to meet across the narrow cobbled streets, houses topped with crazily peaked towers, gables, dormers, and chimney-pots, tossing to the sky like sails and pennons flying from ships of stone.

Tregoulac is thirteen centuries old, but ancient though it be, it is yet young compared to the antiquity of the bloodstreams that course through the veins of the Bretons of the district, descendants of Celt and Briton and Saxon conqueror, Roman and Gaul.

Modern times and improvements have dimmed the old customs. Life centres in the market square and the church and cemetery of St Guldas at one end, the starched white coifs and full-blown black skirts and coloured kirtles are seen only on the figures of the very old women who still bring their curved earthen pitchers to the fountain of the Virgin set in the mossy churchyard wall, and pause there to kneel and pray for a moment for the living and the dead.

The Christian religion, overlaid upon the deep-rooted and still untamed paganism inherited from their ancestors, plays a tremendous part in the daily life of the people. The Bretons live in close association with death, their friend, the '*Ankou*,' whose ghostly horse and cart are heard by the peasants, padding and creaking down the hedged lanes in the dark of night on his tireless rounds. They have a Christian version of an old saying of the druids : 'The dead are so many, the living so few,' and they have no fear of death. For the Breton to die is simply to emigrate.

The war in the spring of 1943 had neither changed nor much disturbed the town or the inhabitants of Tregoulac and the surrounding farms. The Germans had occupied but by no means conquered the country and its people.

The Nazi garrison in field-grey occasionally tramped the narrow, cobbled streets and sometimes tan and green military cars roared into the market square to discharge groups of grim S.S. men in their black and silver uniforms with the death's-head at their peaked caps. The townsfolk simply ignored them.

I

Perhaps, with their departure, a citizen of Tregoulac would be missing thereafter from his usual haunts, never to return. And nothing would ever be said, or even whispered.

Or a glaring black and white poster printed in French and Breton, would appear on the dark wall of the churchyard or the smooth sides of the Hôtel de Ville, the town hall on the market square:

REWARD! 20,000 FRANCS WILL BE PAID FOR INFORMATION LEADING TO THE ARREST OF THE TRAITOR AND ENEMY OF THE PEOPLE KNOWN AS 'PANTHÈRE,' SUSPECTED LEADER OF THE UNDERGROUND.

[SIGNED] COL. HEINZ VON BRAUNHELM,
DEUTSCHE KOMMANDATUR.

Then the townspeople would pause in little knots before the proclamation to read, silent and tight-lipped, even their dark eyes veiled and quickly downcast as they walked away. If they were those who knew something of the whereabouts or identity of the mysterious Panthère, the information remained locked in the iron cavity of their hearts. For the Breton is above all fiercely loyal and an implacable enemy.

It was as though the Germans felt and feared the deep, mysterious nature of the people and their unchallengeable connection with the dark and stormy past of this haunted corner of France, for they left them strictly alone except for the occasional desperate man-hunts aimed at controlling and destroying the slowly growing underground and resistance movement.

Thus life and business went on as usual in Tregoulac under the German occupation. That spring the town was far more concerned with the progress, or rather lack of progress, of the match between Yolande Plouhet, daughter of Jean and Marie Plouhet, proprietors of the little butter-and-egg shop behind the church on the rue Saint-Eloi, and Louis Guizenec, who owned a small but prosperous farm and apple orchard a kilometre or so from the village.

All Tregoulac knew that dark-eyed Yolande Plouhet was madly in love with Louis Guizenec, had been for more than a year; that he favoured her, but that the matter of the dowry stood between him and the consummation of her heart's desire. For the parents of Yolande were far from wealthy, and the handsome, blue-eyed, fair-haired farmer was known to be exceedingly thrifty and beset with ambition. He had his eye on the plot of fertile land adjoining his farm.

It had grown to be a kind of standing jest in and around Tregoulac, and natives who left the vicinity on business trips or to visit relatives would inquire upon their return: 'Well, has Farmer Louis given way yet on the matter of the dowry and married Yolande Plouhet?' Or: 'What is the news? Has Yolande Plouhet managed to raise the cash yet to wed Louis Guizenec?'

But it was no joke to Yolande, who was dying of love for Louis. She was torn between her ardent desire for him and submission to the custom of the country, which acquiesces in the right of a prospective groom to demand that his bride bring him a sufficient dowry to help him rise in the world and thus secure the happiness of the forthcoming marriage.

Yolande, to all appearances, was a modern girl living in a modern age. Like the other youth of Tregoulac, she had abandoned the starched coif of the district, the colourful peasant garb, and wooden sabots. She wore skirt and blouse imported from Rennes, a city she had visited several times as a child in the company of her godfather, a well-to-do tanner of Tregoulac.

She clacked over the cobblestones in high heels, and was no stranger to the ministrations of the hairdressing parlour and beauty shop at the corner of the market square. She was handsome, with dark, brooding eyes and full Oriental mouth, the lower lip protruding slightly. On Sundays she never failed to attend Mass at the Church of St Guldas, with her parents, a small, brown figure sitting with head bent in piety, hands folded, eyes lowered, except when guardedly and with infinite caution they strayed to the side to catch a glimpse of the sturdy figure and sand-blond head of Farmer Louis.

But beneath her simple, unobtrusive exterior Yolande was a Breton of the Bretons, a smouldering mixture of passion, desire, mystery, and superstition. She was as primitive as her ancient ancestors, the Celts, the squat, dark Oriental race that had come flooding westward through the Carpathian passes in the age of the birth of Europe.

She lived in a world peopled by creatures of old legends, ghosts and sorcerers and pagan gods. She prayed dutifully to all the accredited saints in the calendar, but stepped softly in the presence of the great druid oak at the cross-roads outside Tregoulac, and old memories in her venerated the menhir stone on the northern edge of the town, now topped by the Christian cross, its smooth surface carved in modern times with the symbols of Christ.

When first her dark eyes, shining from their square-cut lids, had rested upon the figure of Farmer Louis, one market day, she knew that she loved him; she had gone to the church and lit a candle to St Anne and prayed that Louis would be made to look upon her with favour. But that night, too, she had stolen out into the fields in the moonlight, lacing sprigs of mystic vervain into her hair. She had repaired to the dolmen of *Ma Douez* and had performed those ancient rites which were requisite.

And, indeed, the gods, both new and old, had rewarded her prayers, for Louis returned her affection, if not her love, though not to the degree of becoming either dizzy or careless in the matter of the dowry.

Louis Guizenec was a sturdy peasant, close-mouthed and uncommunicative, a little slow-witted, but a man who knew his worth. He was a Saxon strain, which accounted for his fair hair, blue eyes, and tall frame. He lived for his farm and his acres, and was not averse to a marriage that would increase the number of the latter and the prosperity of the former. On the other hand, he was not the kind of man to throw himself away for a pretty face or a neat ankle. A dowry of twenty thousand francs would enable him to purchase the desirable property adjoining his. If the girl who provided it were comely, so much the better, but if not he was no man to complain either. The important thing was to get ahead in the world.

Like so many of the inhabitants of the district, he had traffic neither with the Germans nor with the resistance movement. He was a man who minded his work and his own business, brought his produce to market and sold it for the best price it would bring. All he asked was to be let alone to till his acres and nurse his orchard, and this the Germans were constrained to do. Life under the occupation had not altered for him except for the understanding he had reached with Yolande.

And as for that, he was a patient man and could afford to wait. For the dowry he demanded was far beyond the means of either Yolande or her parents. But it flattered his vanity that the girl was so much in love with him, and when in a night of courting in the churchyard cemetery of St Guldas, where the couples of Tregoulac came to plight their troth as their elders had done before them, she had promised him with tears in her eyes – nay, sworn by the sacred bones of her grandfather – that she would secure the sum if he would but give her time, he had agreed. After all, he was no worse off than he had been before, and certainly the dark-eyed girl attracted him strongly.

And so, beneath the calm demure demeanour exhibited as she waited behind the counter of the butter-and-egg shop, Yolande burned with desire for Louis as her husband and suffered and planned how she might come by the money and tortured herself with her love.

She was swept between admiration for Louis's thrift and his keen business sense in holding out for the sum he demanded, and poignant, wishful dreams of a Louis who would take her in his arms and whisper that for love of her he would waive the dowry. Then these sweet fantasies would be replaced by fear and anguish and gave rise in her head to ever wilder schemes to secure the sum.

Ah, the war, the times, and the occupation. Before, a girl might journey to Paris and take employment. There were many ways of making money in Paris. Now she could not even journey to Rennes.

Yolande had paid a painful visit to her godfather, Yves Gourin, the wealthy tanner, on one of his infrequent appearances in Tregoulac, for since the occupation his business had appeared to flourish and he was absent on long trips more and more. At least, Yolande had always considered Yves wealthy, but when she told her story and, trembling, made her plea to the old man for the money, he had shaken his silvery head sadly.

'It is not possible, my daughter. It is a large sum that Louis places upon his – ah – desirability. A more modest man might make a better husband. Such a sum, if it were available, might be better spent in these times.'

Yolande was to remember this remark later. But now she was only stricken with a sense of hopelessness and despair. She burst into tears.

'But, Godfather, I love him. What shall I do?'

Her question was a memory of her childhood and better days. When as a little girl she had come to her godfather with some childish trouble, she had been wont to turn up her little round face to him and with quivering lips ask: 'But, Godfather, what shall I do?'

Invariably the answer had been a gentle smile and the words : 'Pray, my daughter, have faith in God and pray!'

And it was thus he answered her now: 'Pray, my daughter, and perhaps a way will be found. Do not let your desires blind your faith in the good God . . .'

Not her tears, but anger now blinded Yolande.

Pray . . . pray . . . always pray. Had she not exhausted the pantheon of deities, pagan as well as Christian, with her nightly supplications? And the aching pain of love for Louis that was ever present in her heart was suddenly replaced by hatred for the gentle old man with the sharp, keen face and white hair down to the shoulders of his embroidered jacket. He had the money. She knew it. He could give it to her if he wanted. It was easier to say 'Pray' than to part with the sum that would have bought her eternal happiness.

But no sign of her emotions appeared upon her face beyond the tears that still welled from her eyes, tears of desperation and helpless fury, and even these she dried now and took her leave.

She walked through the narrow winding street from the home of her godfather and passed through the market place on her way back to her father's shop. She paused before the poster affixed to the front of the leaning façade of the Hôtel de Ville and read it again:

REWARD! 20,000 FRANCS WILL BE PAID FOR INFORMATION LEADING TO THE ARREST OF THE TRAITOR AND ENEMY OF THE PEOPLE KNOWN AS 'PANTHÈRE,' SUSPECTED LEADER OF THE UNDERGROUND.

COL. HEINZ VON BRAUNHELM,
DEUTSCHE KOMMANDATUR.

The sun was warm and the air soft, but she seemed to grow cold as though the winter mists had begun to blow in from the sea. Twenty thousand francs! The four eyes of the zeros seemed to stare stonily into her heart and she stared back like one possessed. Twenty thousand francs! The sum of the dowry, if one but knew who and where this Panthère might be. Traitor and enemy of the people, the poster said. If one could but be so fortunate as to have such information within one's grasp! Her mind leaped straight to a vision – her wedding party and Louis at her side – Louis for ever at her side. The vision dizzied her and she swayed with its delight. It was still with her, wreathing the corners of her mouth in a smile, as she entered the shop.

It was not until late that night alone in her bed above the little garden that opened out behind their house that the thought came to her that whoever this mysterious Panthère might be who was so badly wanted by the Germans, he was a Breton, and a Frenchman, and to betray him would be the blackest crime of which the human soul was capable.

And then she was ashamed and frightened, and cowered in her bed and wondered whether God, *le bon Dieu* who dwelt high in the spire of the Church of St Guldas on the market place, had been watching and had looked into her heart as she had stood before the poster in the square.

Time passed. The poster remained on the walls unheeded. Yolande busied herself with concocting one frantic scheme after another for raising the twenty thousand francs. Then one day, by a sheer accident of fate, she came into possession of a terrible piece of information. Panthère, the mysterious and unknown leader of the resistance movement in the Tregoulac district, was none other than Yves Gourin, her godfather. There could be no doubt of it, nor of the redoubled efforts the Germans were making to break his identity and find him. A munitions convoy on the coast road had been ambushed and blown up. Tregoulac itself was again filled with S.S. men, and Gestapo agents were everywhere, spying and interrogating. The inhabitants remained tight-lipped, wary-eyed, and unmoved. The flurry would pass. It always had.

And Yolande, grown quieter, paler, more lovesick than ever, carried the dreadful secret locked away in her breast, whence it rose to torture her night and day.

If only she had not stumbled upon it. Sometimes she tried to convince herself that it was not true, that it was only a bit of local gossip. But then there was corroborating evidence – Yves's unusually long and repeated absences from Tregoulac, ostensibly on business. And then she remembered the remark he had made to her about the money: 'Such a sum, if it were available, might be better spent in these times.'

She knew now what he was doing with his money. And an echo of the anger that had flamed in her heart the day he had denied her flickered up. Resistance movement indeed! One was no worse off under the Germans than one had been before, and besides it was obvious that they had come to stay. Twenty thousand francs for a lost and futile cause. Twenty thousand francs for her happiness. And what if Yves Gourin were to die? He was an old man. . . .

Yolande struggled like a linnet trapped in lime against the evil and treacherous thoughts that crept into her head. Time and again she barred and doubled-bolted the doors to her mind, sealed them with fervent prayers to the saints to protect her, and still they gained entrance. If only Panthère had been someone unknown to her. If only she had never found out. She evoked memories out of her childhood relationship with Yves, his kindnesses and many little beneficences to her, the presents he had bought for her on the great fête days of the *Pardon*, the dress for her first Communion, and the wonderful trips to Rennes.

She went to church more often to ask to be cleansed of all thoughts of evil. But she did not make confession. And she avoided the mystic pagan monuments in the neighbourhood. True, they were only old and innocent stones and monoliths of granite, some of them with cup marks, hollows to be anointed with honey, wax, or oil, but the Church had interdicted such sacrifice and the stones themselves, had banished them into pagan darkness, and in that darkness dwelt memories of cults and practices, love of the body of man that transcended all else, love of love.

And yet, for all the torture through which she was going, Yolande knew that never, never would she eternally damn her soul with such a foul betrayal of one who was not only a patriot and a brave man, but a second father to her.

But that was before the talk began to go around Tregoulac about Louis and Henriette Jerzual, the dumpy, snub-nosed daughter of Hervé Jerzual, the prosperous owner of the principal hotel on the market square.

It was the kind of talk that suddenly springs up in a village here and there, casual gossip. It was that Henriette had been making eyes at Louis in the tavern room of the hotel, and her father possessed and was willing to pay the sum of twenty thousand francs' dowry in order to secure his not too attractive daughter a good marriage. And the farmer who owned the plot of ground adjoining Louis's farm was anxious to sell and had put a price on it, take it or leave it.

The talk stabbed to the heart of Yolande like a poniard.

It was just gossip. Even Louis denied it fervently to Yolande when she taxed him with it, and swore it was not so. And she would be reassured for the moment, but any instant her reassurance would be demolished like a house of cards by a word or a glance or even something imagined. But one kept on hearing things – Louis and Farmer Bodeur, who owned the plot of ground, were seen in long discussion. Louis was spending more time than necessary in the taproom of the hotel, where Henriette served the tall pitchers of cider and rich slices of local salmon. . . . Who could blame Louis? After all, a man had to think of his future and could not wait for ever. And besides, though she was far from a beauty, Henriette was a hard, willing worker and would make Louis a good wife. Too bad about the little Plouhet. . . .

Yolande, filled with the demons of jealousy and fear, went through agonies that were well-nigh unbearable. Where there was smoke, there must be fire, and the thought of losing Louis to another suffocated her until she thought she would die.

She could not sleep at night and would lie in her bed thinking of Louis, the look of him and the smell of him, the feel of him, the way his blue eyes shone from his brown face, the hard roundness of his thighs, tight in his work breeches, the strong jut of his jaws clutched around a pipe-stem, and the odour of fields and leather harness, of horses and of man that enveloped her when he held her in his arms.

And from out the dark pits of hell the demons of jealousy brought forth a picture of Louis and ugly Henriette together in their marriage bed and held it before Yolande until she writhed and screamed in the darkness and shut her eyes and hid, sobbing and crying, under the covers, calling his name and the name of the saints, and names of druid gods and sorcerers, too, long forbidden, but never forgotten.

Now she could no longer banish the dreadful temptation to sacrifice Yves. He was so old. What was death but a translation, an emigration to paradise? What was the passage of one who had lived out his time to the necessity of assuaging the fires that were consuming her? An old man would vanish from the scene as so many had before him, and a young, strong-beloved body would be delivered to her arms, hers for eternity.

And who would ever need to know, or suspect, if one were clever – if one told Louis one thing and her parents another, if one laid one's plans so carefully that there could be no slip, if one made certain the bird would not be flown when the trap was sprung? . . .

The marriage of Yolande Plouhet and Louis Guizenec took place in the early summer of 1943, and the guests assembled in the gay little garden behind the cottage of Jean and Marie Plouhet, after the ceremony at St Guldas, for the traditional Breton wedding breakfast.

In her little room, overlooking the garden, where she was changing her clothes after the church ceremony and donning the traditional Breton costume of wide flowing black skirt heavily banded with velvet and embroidery, with beautifully worked over-apron of coloured satin, Yolande was swept alternately between delirious joy and waves of fear.

Louis was hers, but yet she skated on the brink of disaster. The twenty thousand francs in crisp pink and green banknotes reposed in her wedding chest atop the heaps of snowy linens and clothes that would supply her new household. Louis had seen it there and accepted her promise that he would receive it after the wedding. Her parents she had told that Louis had finally agreed to waive the large sum he had previously demanded and accept the more modest dowry that she herself had amassed.

She dressed herself mechanically, hardly knowing what she did, except that consciously she slowed the process, lingering over each movement, and always her eyes would come to rest upon the heavily carved lid of the oaken chest beneath which the money burned. It was not yet hers to bestow. If she failed, she would have to return it. And sometimes when she paused stock-still and found herself staring at the chest, she was seeing the square harsh face of a man bearing a white sword-scar and surmounted by a black military cap to which was affixed a death's-head in silver. She would remember what she had said and what she had promised. Then waves of sickening apprehension would flow over her until her legs trembled so she felt she would sink to the floor.

There came a knock at the door. Yolande's hands flew to her breast to stifle the wild beating of her heart. It was Annique, her best friend and bridesmaid, who said: 'Yolande, are you coming? Everyone is waiting. Your godfather, Yves Gourin, has just arrived, and . . .'

Yolande said slowly: 'Yves has come?'

'Oh yes, and *Monsieur le Maire* and all the guests are assembled. . . .'

Yolande took her friend by the shoulders, and turned her around, pushing her towards the door. 'Go. I am almost ready. I will be down in a moment.'

When she was alone, she staggered, her knees collapsing under her, and fell across the carved chest, weeping tears of relief. She had received a message from him promising to return to Tregoulac in time for her wedding. When she had noted his absence at the ceremony in the chapel at St Guldas, she had had such a seizure of fear and terror that she had hardly been able to give voice to the responses that joined her through all eternity to Louis Guizenec. But now Yves was really there.

She pulled herself together and swiftly repaired the ravages made by the tears. She fastened the fine coil of lace and linen that had been her mother's and her grandmother's before her, and through it she twined a sprig of orange blossom. When she was quite ready, she went to the window looking out upon the rue Saint-Eloi and stood there for a moment, passing her handkerchief once across her brow as though she were faint. Then she turned and proceeded slowly down the stairs and stood framed in the doorway that opened on the scene of gaiety and festivity in the little garden.

There was much to meet her eyes, the long trencher tables laden with the wedding breakfast, round, dark loaves of bread and pitchers of wine and cider, plates of meat and vegetables, the huge *pot-au-feu*, gleaming pink and silver salmon, dishes of sweets and cakes, the two blind *biniou*-players seated with their ancient bagpipes on a raised platform, the ribbons and wreaths and decorations, the milling guests, the imposing figure of the Mayor in his frock coat of office. She saw none of these.

Her gaze rested only on the person of Yves Gourin, whose tall figure and shining white hair falling to his shoulders caught the eye. He was pulling at a long pipe, smiling, his fine face gleaming with pride.

And then thereafter Yolande's eyes sought out and found and remained upon the figure of her husband, who stood at the far end of the garden surrounded by cronies, a cider cup in his hand. She dwelt upon every feature, the aquiline bridge of his nose, the fair hair at his neck, the slope of his shoulders, the firm pillars of his legs, doting upon them, devouring them with love and swelling passion.

There was first a shout as the guests greeted the bride, and then an old, old woman of the village, Mère Locmariac, came forward and, kneeling at the feet of the lovely bride, in the old tradition, offered up a prayer for the dead, the dead of the families and all of those assembled there, whose presence and blessing she invoked.

And Yolande Guizenec listened to the invocation of the dead and feasted her eyes upon her husband.

Mère Locmariac finished her prayer. She rose and kissed the bride on both her smooth cheeks and the first shrill wailing of the *binious* arose from the platform of the blind pipers, in a haunting melody that filled the garden, drowning out the rustle and murmur of the guests at the beauty and the paleness of the bride, and drowning other sounds too, the roar of cars in the street without, and the tramping of heavy-shod feet on the cobblestones.

Now that the ceremony to the dead was over, the tune of the pipes shifted to a gay and lilting dance, the traditional *jabadao*, and the guests rustled and shifted and murmured, looking to see who should be the first to have the honour of dancing with the bride.

Yolande Guizenec went straight to her godfather, Yves Gourin, laid aside her bridal bouquet, and made him a curtsy. Then, to the applause of the assembled guests, the old man laid down his pipe, bowed, took his godchild by the hand, and together they began the ancient and stately round of the *jabadao*.

And this was the way the black-uniformed German *Schutz-Staffel* troops surrounding the house found them when they came streaming in through the door, flooding over the stone garden wall, filling and blocking every exit.

In the first shock, no one moved except the soldiers of death taking up their positions commanding the garden, and in a moment they, too, froze into immovable figures of silent menace. The wedding guests stood like statues, some of them with cups half raised to their lips, or their hands at the plates of refreshments on the tables. None looked at his neighbour. The blind *biniou*-players, sensing the catastrophe through their skins, left off playing, and the last wind from the collapsed bags of their pipes came as a kind of low, dying moan. In the centre of the garden stood Yolande and Yves Gourin, petrified, she with an arm about his waist. There came the smart tramp of heavy boots in the corridor of the cottage and the metallic snick and click of the cocking of weapons. A German strode into the garden, an officer with a harsh face crossed by a long, white scar. At the peak of his black cap was a silver death's-head. He paused for an instant to survey the scene from the threshold. Then he marched straight to the old man with the long white hair standing next the bride and spoke sharply:

'Yves Gourin, you are under arrest!'

The awful moment was broken by the cry of Yolande, who reached up and threw her arms about her godfather's neck. 'Oh no, no!'

Still no one moved. No one even dared to look. Only Yolande saw the expression on the face of her godfather, the queer glitter that came into his eyes, which turned into a look of unutterable loathing and contempt. Then, slowly, he reached up and unfastened her arms from about his neck with a kind of shudder as though he were touching something reptilian and put them away from him. Without a word, he turned and followed the officer from the garden. A few moments later the gay, festive little enclosure was as empty of soldiers as it had been before. Outside one heard motors starting up with loud explosions and finally fading away in the distance.

Then only did the people in the garden return to life, stirring, speaking softly, shifting, forming into little knots, while Yolande ran to Louis and threw herself sobbing on his breast. The drone of the *binious* resumed again, but it was a Breton lament rather than a dance tune. Afterwards they played merrily again, though not for long, for the spirit was out of the celebration and none was in a mood for dancing. When the food and drink had been consumed, the wedding guests went home.

Later in the day a cart drew up in front of the little shop in the rue Saint-Eloi, and Yolande and her earthly possessions, her pots and pans, her bedding and clothes and linens in the carved

wedding chest, and her twenty thousand francs, were transported
to the home of her husband.

Yves Gourin was never seen alive again, and the Germans saw
to it that the town heard about what had been done to him before
he died. But the town also knew and whispered about the fact
that he had passed with his lips sealed and that the Germans had
been unable to wring from him the names of his accomplices in
the underground.

And there were other things that began to be whispered and
gossiped and traded in and about Tregoulac, things spoken
softly across the wooden tables at the tavern, after cautious looks
about, brief sentences exchanged on corners beneath the leaning,
pot-bellied houses, dreadful things spoken across the stone and
blackberry brier fences of the quiet farmlands.

Who was it had betrayed Yves Gourin to the Germans? Ah
well, never repeat it, but one hears . . . The price that farmer
Guizenec paid for his new plot of land was exactly twenty thousand francs, was it not? Remember the amount of the reward
on the poster, which has now been removed? Whence had one in
such modest circumstances as Yolande Plouhet procured such a
sum for her dowry? Why did she appear in her wedding dress at
the second-storey window fronting on the rue Saint-Eloi before
joining the guests in the garden? Jean Pelicot, the postman, swears
he saw her signal with her handkerchief, and a few moments
later the street was full of Germans. Ah, and most damning, did
she not single out Yves to be the first to dance with her at the
wedding? And was she not hanging on his arm when the Germans surrounded the house and burst in upon them? Such a
black deed could hardly be possible. And yet, when one puts
two and two together . . .

Time went on and the talk and the whispers grew, though they
did not reach the ears of Louis Guizenec, who was concerned
only with the expansion of his farm; but Yolande heard them,
or rather felt them. At first she was afraid, but later she rallied.
What if they suspected? There was no proof. No one, nothing
could disturb her happiness with Louis.

But things were happening beneath the surface of the little
town, mysterious boilings and seethings. More and more of the
young men of Tregoulac and the district were vanishing into the
bush. One heard of the growing strength of the F.F.I., the French
Forces of the Interior, the Maquisards and their secret camps, an
underground army growing day by day, mysterious parachutings
from aeroplanes that flew over in the night, growing caches of weapons and ammunition, growing boldness on the part of the men

of the Maquis. The Gestapo officer of the district himself was said to have been ambushed and captured by the F.F.I., and the Nazi garrison in Tregoulac was doubled.

And now when Yolande came to town alone, there were those who would not speak to her any longer, but stared at her stonily, or turned and walked away when she approached, and into their looks she read an implacable hatred.

Her mood changed to one of defiance. Very well, then, they knew. And what if they did? They dared not do anything to her. The Germans were there to protect her. They would always protect her.

And then in the late winter there was talk in Tregoulac of a coming Allied invasion of France.

To Yolande it was just talk. And if it happened, she had no doubt that it would be defeated. The Germans were so strong. There were so many of them. The coast defences were impregnable. The Allies would be swept back into the sea, the Maquisards captured and crushed. And in the meantime, the moment of now, through the very ticking of the clock, she had her Louis.

But in the early springtime, when May brought the rose-pink pear and the snowy apple blossoms to bloom, she felt a vague uneasiness, a tightening of the nerves, the kind of heaviness one feels on a stifling summer's day when all nature stills, the storm clouds gather on the horizon, and one leans one's ear to catch the first faint, distant rumbling . . .

Not even when the armies of liberation landed in Normandy, though, did she give way to fear. She took courage from the long lines of German tanks and cannon and lorries laden with stout troops in field-grey that rumbled through the town. None could defeat this dreadful might. It was impossible that the swelling combers of war could break over this Army and threaten the happiness of her possession of Louis.

June turned to July. One heard more and more disquieting things – break-through at Saint-Lô, a German army fleeing, another cut off. And then all of one night Yolande lay awake and shivering beside the warm, sleeping body of her husband and listened to the distant thudding of the cannon at Saint-Malo carried to her through the quiet of the starry summer night.

She tried to comfort herself that it was a far-off thunderstorm, but she knew that it was not, for it never ceased, or changed, and every so often she heard a dish rattle or stir in her china cupboard, and sometimes there would be a heavy thump of air upon a window casement as from a distant explosion. And she lay there all through the night cold as ice and not daring to creep to the warmth of Louis.

It was a few days later that Yolande brought the week's yield of butter, milk, and eggs to market in Tregoulac to find the town alive and boiling with military traffic, staff cars, weapon-carriers, road buses, lorries. The Germans were loading them with every evidence of haste, carrying boxes and crates and caissons of munitions out of houses and headquarters. It was then that Yolande noticed for the first time that all of the vehicles were pointed, not west, towards the front, but eastwards, the line of retreat. Already the first of the trucks and carriers were beginning to roar and rumble out of town.

An icy chill seized her heart as she watched. And now as she reached the market square with her horse and cart, a rattle of small-arms fire broke out from the north-west part of the town, backed by the rhythmic 'cha-cha-cha-cha-cha' of machine-gun fire. She heard a German soldier say the word: 'Maquis!' and then the speed of activity in the square redoubled. Trucks started away with only half a load.

Yolande screamed once, loud and long, but no one paid any attention to her. A Reichswehr soldier carried a duffel bag out of a house and dumped it into a small open military car. Yolande ran to him and shouted: 'What is happening? Where are you going?' She tugged at his arm, her hair flying, her face all white and twisted.

The soldier looked at her in surprise, shook her loose, and climbed into the car. He said: 'Back to Germany – I hope – before your damned Maquis catch us. . . .'

Yolande clutched blindly at the side of the car as though by holding it she could halt the entire exodus. 'But you can't! You can't leave me! You can't go!'

The soldier sniggered and said: 'Too bad we discovered each other so late, Fräulein! Well, *au revoir*!' and he clashed the steel car into gear and jerked it away from Yolande and off through the market square, leaving her sprawling on her hands and knees on the cobblestones. Somebody near by laughed loudly. And from the upper window of a house across the square, the tricolour of France suddenly cascaded in folds of red, white, and blue and hung there mockingly in the brilliant sunshine. . . .

It was two days later, looking out on the farm from the window of her kitchen, that Yolande saw them coming carefully in single file across the fields, towards the house.

There were six of them, men and boys, ragged and whiskered like pirates from their long stay in the bush, clattering with weapons and grenades that hung from their belts, their work clothes nondescript and dusty. But each wore a red, white, and blue arm-band around his left sleeve.

The leader, a tall, bearded boy, was clad in the khaki battle-dress dropped him by the British. The cross of Lorraine was fastened to his beret, and there were three blue stripes sewn to his left shoulder. Over his back was slung a Sten gun, and he carried an automatic pistol.

They moved slowly with a kind of leaden purpose, and Yolande stood motionless at the window, watching them. She did not cry out, or scream, or try to run. She knew that Louis was ploughing in the new field beyond the woods, a quarter of a mile away.

The men stopped, deployed before the house, and looked warily for a moment. Then the leader saw Yolande through the kitchen window. He said something to his squad and they relaxed their weapons. They came into the kitchen and stood there looking at her.

There was a curious moment of embarrassment during which some of them shifted their feet and looked away.

The leader cleared his throat. He said: 'Yolande Guizenec, we have come for you.' That and no more.

She made no reply, beyond a kind of long, tired sigh, a mere exhalation of breath that never seemed to end. Then with fingers that fumbled a little she undid her apron and hung it carefully over the back of the chair. She reached up behind her as though to give her brown hair a sort of pat into arrangement, but paused in mid-air and let her arms fall to her side.

When the leader went to the door, she fell in behind him without a word, the other five following. She did not give so much as a backward glance. And so in single file the seven moved away from the farmhouse and across the green and yellow fields. . . .

I saw the grave of Yolande Guizenec when I visited the secret camp of the Maquis in the Tregoulac district in Brittany last summer shortly after the men of the resistance movement had swept the Boches from their land, and heard her story.

It was not really a grave, but just a bare patch of trampled earth in a grassy field along with eight others, next to the grove that concealed the tents and headquarters of the Maquis camp. But it was set a little aside from the others, this bare patch, so that she slept alone. A cleft stick had been thrust into the ground in the centre of the brown earth, and in the cleft there drooped the wilted, browning bud of a wild rose.

The story was told me by the young, bearded captain of the
F.F.I., standing there in his khaki battledress, the double-barred
cross of Lorraine pinned to his beret, black Sten gun slung across
his shoulder, two German potato-masher grenades hung at his
belt. His *nom de guerre,* the only name by which he was identified was Captain Nemo.

And, we stood in the little field with patches of newly turned
brown earth over the remains of those who had died a traitor's
death.

Captain Nemo said: 'We did not mete out to her the death
we reserved for the other traitors, the poniard stab in the breast.
It was permitted to her to be shot. . . .'

I asked: 'Why? Surely it was a dreadful crime she committed,
more wicked than most.'

The captain nodded. He looked down and with his toe stirred
the edge of the brown earth where it met fresh green grass. Then
he replied: 'Yes. She was a traitress. She betrayed her country
and her dearest friend. But we had known her all our lives. Many
of us had played with her in Tregoulac when we were children
together. And then besides—'

He paused, and I said: 'Yes?'

Captain Nemo looked at me, and his dark eyes were no longer
the eyes of a boy. He said: 'It is hard to punish, to mete out justice, and yet it must be done. You see, she did – what she did –
because she was in love. And so it was permitted, even though
bullets are scarce, that she be shot through the heart. She fell
there, against that young oak tree. . . .'

Verna

One of the biggest surprises I had in France, the war summer of 1944, was the number of personable young females on hand attending the war. Most of them were technically behind the lines, though I saw nearly as many up front in various capacities. What with long-range shelling, day and night bombing, buzz bombs, and the ubiquitous land mines, the phrase 'behind the lines' was a mere technicality.

There were lady war correspondents, nurses, Red Cross workers, U.S.O. camp-show cuties, French and Belgian girls in uniform, acting as liaison with the underground armies, and all of them were good-looking. Somehow the poor numbers just didn't get to go to the war. No one has yet written the story of these modern camp-followers in the greatest of all wars, and the trouble with it is that it does sound like the cheapest kind of fiction, in which the beautiful girl is always turning up at the author's convenience some place where the reader damn well knows there wouldn't be any such thing. But the fact is they were there. I don't know how it was in Italy or the Pacific, but France was ankle-deep in handsome adventurous creatures. When finally after certain difficulties I was able to make the Hotel Scribe in Paris the day the city was liberated I found at least three girl war correspondents who had arrived there ahead of me, and one of them, Miss Lee Carson of International News Services, would have given La Bacall a run for it on the score of sultry good looks. The day before, two English girl correspondents, one a stunning iceberg blonde and the other a handsome redhead, nearly got themselves killed by an 88, trying to get into Paris via Versailles, where there was fighting.

Most touching of all I found the U.S.O. girls, silly-looking yellow-haired, red-mouthed kids in Camp Shows uniforms, singers and dancers and show girls, batting around France, living under dangerous and difficult conditions, and doing at all times the best they knew how.

When I landed in France by air from London, arriving at a Comm Z. base near Valognes, and went to field mess under a tent, there, parked at a table, was a little unidentified mouse with dyed yellow hair, the stocking-liner from her tin hat perched on her impudent head. She was dressed in a too big o.d. uniform

274

and had large, solemn, wide-awake brown eyes that seemed to take in everything. New to the ways of this war, I was simply flabbergasted by her presence. She was minding her own business and quite nonchalantly living the life of the soldier under arms in the field. She might have stepped right out of a Broadway chorus line, and probably did. She was a Camp Shows girl, a little dancer whose business it was to entertain war-weary troops.

I never forgot her. I can close my eyes today and still see that sweet, incongruous little figure. I never even spoke to her, or inquired who she was, but she moved into a niche in my heart, or perhaps my imagination, and became Verna, a symbol for a new and inconspicuous but nevertheless touching kind of gallantry. Thereafter I saw several Camp Show units in action, and when I returned from abroad on the 'Queen Mary,' Fred Astaire and Bing Crosby were fellow passengers with the units they had taken around the ETO, and always, backing up the stars, there were these same daffy kids with two eyes, two ears, and a nose and mouth, and the dyed yellow hair, who gave out with the smiles and the sex appeal and the shapes, bad singers and worse dancers, but wonderfully brave girls, it seemed to me.

I knew I wanted to write a story about them, or one of them, and the first vague idea for the piece probably had taken shape within my mind from the first moment I saw the little chorine in the mess tent at Valognes. Upon my return I worked it out and hit upon the ending, which of course is pure fantasy, but which, I assure you, very well could have happened in the Paris of the late summer and winter of 1944. For the character of Colonel Speed McIvor I borrowed the personality, zip, and speech of Colonel Jock Lawrence, an old friend, and Public Relations Officer for the European Theatre. He didn't mind.

I'd like you to meet my girl, Verna.

VERNA

Soldiers abroad during the war appreciated the great stars of stage and screen who gallantly sacrificed time, comfort, and safety to cross dangerous waters and play for them in their camps and areas within sound of the big guns and the crump of falling bombs. But the show people they really loved and took to their hearts were the small, unheralded, unsung, hard-working wandering groups like Camp Shows Unit No. X117.

Unit No. X117 boasted no important stars, or anyone who had even been heard of outside of cheap cabarets. It was headed by a fat comedian named Eddie Stinson, recruited from the second-rate night-club circuit. Eddie had a round face and flabby jowls, and when he came out wearing a too small derby on the top of his head, you knew he was going to be funny.

The rest of the troupe consisted of Sammy Sisk, who played the banjo and acted as master of ceremonies; a magician billed as The Great Zerbo; an accordionist, Pete Russo, who furnished the music; Connie Clay, a singer, who in private life was Mrs Eddie Stinson; Maureen Pearl, an acrobatic dancer; and Verna Vane. Verna was Eddie's stooge.

This unit travelled the battle-torn lands of Europe, from Rouen to Reims to Strasbourg, from Strasbourg up to s'Hertogenbosch and Nijmegen and down again through Liège and into shell-shattered Aachen, playing their little vaudeville show in heat and cold, in dust and downpour, wherever there was a soldier audience that needed them, no matter how small.

Sometimes they performed in halls, but usually it was on a platform set up in some open field against a background of wrecked farm buildings, or black smoke mounting from the horizon, or a burned-out Tiger tank cocking the long barrel of its 88 to the sky like an admonishing finger. They were always within sound of the muttering guns. Sometimes the whine of an enemy shell would make discord to Pete Russo's music, or the distant querulous chaffering of automatic small arms would drown out Eddie's gags.

There were no prima donnas in the little troupe. None of them were any better than they should have been as performers, but they made up in zeal and sincerity what they lacked in polish. Their frequent proximity to the fighting lines, the occasional bombings or sporadic shells, excited more than frightened them. They rather gloried in their toughness and ability to take it when the going got rough, and they soon got used to the noise and the danger. The one exception was Verna. The war terrified her to her very marrow.

She did her best to conceal the palpitating fear that was always with her, and you might not have guessed how afraid she was unless you looked into her dark eyes and saw how haunted they were.

Her uniform of khaki slacks, heavy boots, and oversize field-jacket with the winged insignia of the Camp Shows on the left

shoulder made her look smaller than she was. From beneath her
steel helmet, balanced precariously on her small head, her hair,
dyed to a light straw colour fell to her shoulders. The long black
lashes that curled up from her blued eyelids were real, but the
colour in her cheeks came from her make-up box and was spread
thickly to hide her perpetual pallor.

Everything terrified her – the sudden coughing of a truck
motor, the sight of tanks or guns, the proximity of side arms.
When a C-47 transport plane flew overhead, she seemed to shrink
together inside the bulky field-jacket. She would start at any
loud noise, and the sound of some machine gunner in a neighbouring field clearing the barrels of his weapon preparatory to
moving up brought on a violent trembling. She could not help
herself. She was afraid of being hurt or of being killed. Her
nerves were unable to gear themselves to war.

Verna's real name was Marie Wojcik, and she was a waif who
came from somewhere around Chicago and the chorus line of
cheap burlesque houses and third-rate floor shows. She had
drifted east through Detroit and Pittsburgh, working and struggling for the break she was convinced would come some day.
Verna was inseparably wedded to show business and what she
referred to as her career. Her unquenchable ambition was stardom, and she was convinced that nothing could keep her from
achieving it. She was absolutely unaware of her complete lack
of talent for the stage.

It was while she was starving in New York that Verna joined
Unit X117 to go overseas. It was steady work; she would eat;
and above all, it was experience. And in the reaction of the first
soldier audiences before whom she performed in the comparative
quiet of England, she thought she saw a kind of forecast of the
triumphs her career would some day bring her. In their whoops
and whistles and cheers and laughter she had a glimpse of the
ovation that would take place on that night of nights when as the
singing and dancing star of a musical-comedy hit she would shine
before the smartest, most sophisticated, and wealthiest audience
in the world. In her dream, rich men and poor would be at her
feet, and the newspaper columns would be filled with her praises.
She would wear diamonds and rubies.

For it was only the glittering superficialities of fame that
attracted her and fired her ambition. She did not know there was
something else, something deeper. And probably the reason she
could not know was that there was nothing in her to give, beyond
a quick generosity to others who like herself were lonely and on
their own in a vast and overwhelming world.

Verna could neither sing, nor dance, nor walk, nor create illusion, but she was pretty and could bare her thin, childlike body to be looked at and part her small pink mouth in a bright, fixed smile.

She had mastered the mechanics of a few steps and had acquired one tap routine which she would perform stiffly and without rhythm to the music of *Little White Lies*. Verna also had one song – if there was a microphone, for otherwise she could hardly be heard. With her eyes large and round with effort, she would purse her lips close to the mike and quaver something that went: 'My yarms are so wempty, since you wenna way.'

Those were Verna's two specialties, but more often than not she didn't even get through them because Eddie Stinson, the fat comedian, used to break her up. That's the way the act was organised. It all depended on how Eddie was feeling and the way his gags were going over.

Verna was the first of the girls to appear during the performance. Sammy Sisk would step to the microphone and say: 'And now we present that popular little singer of songs straight from the Stawk Club in Noo Yawk,' a colossal lie which nobody ever questioned. 'Come on up here, Verna.' And Verna would come on, wearing nothing but a pair of silk tights with a small silver fringe around the hips and a spangled bra into which she usually put some padding because her little breasts did not quite fill it out. Her legs were too thin, but shapely.

Eddie Stinson would be on-stage too, smoking a big black cigar and wearing his too small derby hat, a ludicrous contrast to his khaki uniform. As soon as he caught sight of Verna he would pull violently on the cigar and emit clouds of smoke, and the G.I.s would holler and whistle and give the wolf call.

Then while Verna stood there making with the smile, Eddie would remove his cigar and ask the audience: 'Are you guys thinking the same thing I am?' which brought forth yells and guffaws, and when those died away he fed them the topper: 'I was wondering if it was gonna rain tomorrow?' which was good for another laugh.

And so it went, with Eddie Stinson mugging and making cracks, or getting behind Verna and clowning while she sang, and sometimes you might hear a line or two of her song or a couple of taps, but more often you would not because of the laughter. At the end, however, when Verna retired she would always get a terrific hand. Sometimes they would keep right on applauding and she would have to take a bow.

It was curious the way the soldiers liked her. Verna thought

it was her performance. She did not know that she was so
amateurish that she did not project at all as an entertainer, but
the soldiers just enjoyed looking at her because she was so skinny
and kind of earnest, wistful, and helpless and reminded them of
kids they all knew back home . . .

The troupe crossed over into France, and Verna came up
against something she could not handle. Outside of Vervins, the
first time the Luftwaffe night bombers came over and tried to
plaster a troop concentration a half-mile away, she cowered in a
corner of the cellar and hid her face and howled. Thereafter
even at the distant sound of aeroplane motors she would begin
to whimper, disturbing the rest of Maureen Pearl, the dancer
with whom she shared quarters.

Rides in jeeps and trucks over the roads of France with their
ever present warning signs: 'Mines Cleared to Ditches,' were an
agony of apprehension to her. As they moved up closer to the
lines, the ceaseless thudding and rumbling of artillery, coupled
with the occasional whine of a shell exploding a mile or so away,
added to her terrors, and the distant sound of small-arms fire
brought on fits of uncontrollable trembling.

Only during the brief minutes when she was on-stage did
Verna appear to regain control of herself. Whenever and wherever
they played, she would appear in her little pants and bra, to give
out with the smile, mutter her song, and do her dance while
Eddie Stinson clowned.

She grew thinner and hollow-cheeked under the strain, and
Eddie Stinson, who was a kindly person, discussed sending her
home. When it was put up to Verna, she flatly refused to go.
She cried and begged and promised not to disturb anyone any
more. She admitted she could not help being frightened, but
swore that nobody would ever know about it again.

The members of the unit wondered why Verna wanted to stay
when she was so unfit for it, and Zerbo the magician came closest
to the answer when he said: 'The kid thinks she's a trouper.
Maybe she's got more guts than all of us.'

Verna did think she was a trouper. It did not fit into the
pattern of her career as a future musical-comedy star to quit
when the going got rough. She lived by slogans and catch
phrases. 'The show must go on,' was one of them. Too, something
in her heart had been touched by the drawn, dog-tired faces of
the fighting men. Their weary attitudes and harried eyes, their
terrible loneliness, awakened echoes of her own loneliness and
struggles. She was happiest when she was bringing them cheer
and forgetfulness with her art. If she went away, she felt some-

thing would be taken away from them and they would be disappointed.

For she was convinced that she gave delight with her performance and did not recognise that what little art was connected with it belonged to Eddie Stinson. Of the memory of her that remained indelibly in the minds of the soldiers who saw the little show – a sweet, awkward kid from back home – a memory that remained long after Eddie Stinson's jokes had been forgotten, and the men lay in their foxholes or moved forward under fire, she had no conception.

But she kept tighter rein upon herself and through the dreadful rumbling nights stifled her sobs in the khaki field blankets so as not to wake Maureen, and the members of the troupe respected her effort and refrained from kidding her, and even stopped making cracks about her 'career,' which, if anything, was more of a trial to them than her nervous reaction to the dangers of war.

During periods in quiet sectors, when the threat of imminent dissolution seemed removed and the strain was off her, Verna chattered ceaselessly about her career. Everything was made to have a bearing on this career, which was to culminate when she got her break in a Broadway show. She knew the names of all the critics and big shots who would be there; she envisioned where she would live, and the parties that would be given, and the clothes and furs she would have, and the stories in the newspapers. She wouldn't drink whisky because it might hurt her voice, and refrained from smoking for the same reason; she practised her time steps ceaselessly and all in all went maddeningly on the nerves of the other members of the troupe.

While they were no stars themselves, they were professionals and competent in their lines and it was more than obvious to them not only that Verna would never make the grade, but that she could not even get and hold a job in the chorus line of a modern Broadway show. They knew their own limitations, and it irritated them that one so wholly lacking in talent and ability should ceaselessly din her aspirations in their ears. They were too harassed to realise that there is a certain divinity in such blindness and yearning as Verna displayed.

The Germans retreated across France and Belgium, the Americans and British and Canadians pursued them, and Unit X117 trouped close behind the advancing armies. In Liège, where the show spent a week, Verna met a young captain of engineers by the name of Walter Hruban who fell in love with her, and she, as much as she was able, with him.

Captain Hruban was a stocky blond boy from Calumet,

Michigan, with innocent blue eyes and muscular body. He was engaged in the construction of a supply depot in the vicinity of Liège. He saw Verna at a Saturday-night show and she went straight to his heart. He contrived to meet her, and his shy adoration of her was as apparent to the other members of the troupe as it was to Verna.

Verna liked him first then loved him. He was not like the other officers or enlisted men who hung around her, eyeing her hungrily or merely using her presence to ease the loneliness or homesickness that was in them. From the very first, Walter Hruban made her feel that she was the sun that rose and set upon his happiness, the moon and the stars and the universe to him. It was a new sensation to her to be so genuinely loved, and it warmed a response in her. She became giddy, lovesick, and wholly human for the four days of their courtship, during which they were inseparable.

The members of the troupe watched with eyes that were fond rather than cynical, for it seemed a just and sweet solution to the problems of Verna. Maureen Pearl was even a little jealous, for Hruban had exuberant masculinity.

On the fifth day Captain Hruban asked Verna to marry him. They could be married right there – he would get permission from his superior officers. Then Verna could go back to the States and stay with his family until the war was over, when he would return and join her.

Verna disengaged herself from his arms and said: 'Gee, Walter, you're sweet. I wish I could.'

He took her hands and held them to give force to his persuasion. 'But why can't you, honey? You know I'm crazy about you. I'll do anything to make you happy. You love me, don't you, honey?'

When she looked at Walter, his tanned face with the yearning blue eyes shining out of it, it made her feel all choked up. She said earnestly: 'Gee, Walter, I love you so much it makes me wanna bust.'

'Then why can't we get married, honey? Look, I could fix it so——'

Verna pulled her hands out of his. 'Honest, I can't, on accounta my career.'

The boy looked startled as he contemplated this unexpected obstacle and then came immediately to the solution. 'Aw, why, gee, honey. You could go on with the stage after we were married. I wouldn't stand in your way. If you wanted to do that until I got back, why——'

Verna refused to look at him. 'It ain't that, Walter, but when you have a career, you hadn't ought to marry.'

'Gosh! I don't see why not. Plenty of actresses marry.'

'Yeah, but it don't last. They always get a divorce. You're too sweet, Walter. I wouldn't want you should get mixed up in all that kind of thing.'

'Why, but, Honey! I wouldn't want to divorce you – ever. Why should we if we care for each other?'

Verna conjured up the familiar pictures of the future she had so long made for herself, pictures that were more real than life itself: Verna in furs and wraps, with her limousine and chauffeurs and her name in lights. And she even thought she could read lines from some future gossip column: 'Verna Vane, the musical comet-y star will have it Reno-vated. She and her groom have occupied separate establishments for a year.' The thought gave her a little thrill. To Hruban she said: 'You don' unnerstand, Walter. It's different in the theatre. Some day I'm gonna be a big star.' And she went on to tell about the great future that awaited her, and the sacrifices that had to be made to realise it. Because she believed in it, she made Walter believe it too, and, heartsick, he felt her slipping from him. He had nothing to offer her but himself, love and marriage, and with a sigh he realised that he had aspired too high. The glory and the brilliance that would some day be Verna's were not for such as he, and a new kind of awe came into his attitude towards her.

That night, after the show, they were together in his quarters when the flying bombs came over, their motors throbbing and popping and stamping in the night sky, and Verna began to tremble and shake as they listened for the cut-out, and Walter took her in his arms and said: 'Gee, Honey, don't be afraid. They never come down around here.'

But one did, a few hundred yards away, and the pregnant silence that followed the shocking discontinuance of its obscene passage was annihilated by a shattering explosion that rocked the building, and the night was filled with cries and the tinkling of broken glass.

Verna clung to Hruban, crying hysterically: 'Oh, God, I'm so scared! Oh, hold me tight. Don't let me hear any more; don't let me see anything. I'm so terrible scared, I jus' can't stan' any more.'

Hruban held her tightly and let her hide her face. He kissed her and tried to stop her trembling, and when she answered his kiss he said: 'Why, you're nothing but a poor frightened kid. I'm gonna look after you. You're mine.'

She stayed all night with him, gratitude mingling with passion, love with the need to find escape from fear and loneliness. Walter mistook the warmth and generosity that was a side of her nature and in the morning talked again of their marriage.

But the dreadful night had yielded to a cheerful sun, lighting a bright blue day, and as the memories of darkness receded, Verna produced her career again. He was sweet, she loved him awfully, but she had to think about her future.

She left him miserable and baffled. He could not understand or reconcile the two Vernas, one the actress, the great star she had convinced him she would be, and the other the trembling, shaken child who had crawled to him for comfort.

Two days later the unit with Verna moved into captured Aachen.

It was while they were there that Maureen Pearl asked Verna: 'What about that nice kid back in Liège? He wanted to marry you, didn't he?'

Verna, who was mending her tights, looked up. 'Oh, sure.'

Maureen was a big dark girl with a wide mouth and an acid disposition. Verna's complacency infuriated her. Didn't the little fool know the real thing when she saw it? she asked: 'Well?'

'Oh, I couldn't marry him,' Verna said, 'on accounta my career.

'Oh, for God's sake, your career!'

Verna shook her head. 'I don't think it's right for people in our profession to get married – I mean, if you're gonna be a big star. I went for him in a big way, only it would have interfered with——'

Maureen interrupted bitterly: 'You little sap! Letting a chance go by to grab a sweet kid who was nuts about you. You ought to have your ears slapped. Your career! It's time somebody told you the facts of life, baby. You're having your career right now. That's all there is, sister. You can't sing, you can't dance, you can't act, you can't even walk. You haven't got the talent of a trained flea. You'll never do any better in show business than you're doing right this minute. Why don't you get wise to yourself?'

Verna looked up from the silver-fringed tights on her lap and with no ire whatsoever said: 'Oh, you're just jealous, Maureen,' and went back to her sewing, wrapped in the unassailable cloak of her conviction, leaving Maureen in a kind of helpless anger that assuaged itself in spiteful thoughts of the bitter lot that would be Verna's in the future. She would face failure after failure until the flash beauty of her youth faded and all hope vanished for ever.

Unit X117 found itself in Bastogne when the von Rundstedt offensive exploded upon the surprised American forces. The little troupe, shepherded by a Lieutenant Jed Smith, a Special Services officer assigned to guide them, tried to escape from the town and drove smack into positions held by German Royal Tiger tanks. They got their jeeps turned around and fled back into town, pursued by machine-gun fire, with Verna screaming hysterically all the way.

With the town surrounded, the lieutenant found them a deep cellar beneath a shell-battered schoolhouse, and there they cowered for five days listening to the shocking din of the battle overhead, with Verna hiding under a blanket, more dead than alive from pure terror.

The other members of the troupe were badly frightened too, for while the lieutenant tried to minimise the danger, it was one thing to be behind the lines of battle within range of an occasional shell, and quite another to be in the centre of a vicious German drive and completely surrounded. To the terrors of bombardment and the ceaseless 'Cha-cha-cha-cha-cha-cha' of automatic weapons fire, the sharp 'Brrrrrrp!' of the German machine pistols in the woods on the edge of town was added the fear of capture and consignment to a German concentration camp until the war's end.

The cellar was filled with the stink of burned cordite and smoke from near-by burning buildings. Later another odour was added, as wounded men were brought there. There were no nurses, and not enough medical corps men were available. Maureen Pearl, Connie Clay, and the men of the unit did what they could for the casualties. Verna was utterly useless. She lay on some straw covered by a blanket, her shoulders shaking and her teeth chattering ceaselessly.

Christmas morning Lieutenant Smith came down into the cellar and addressed the unit. He said: 'Look, things aren't so bad any more. We've pushed 'em back beyond the edge of town. There's supposed to be a column of our tanks about five miles away. Anyway, the Krauts haven't got us yet. How about putting on a show for the guys who can get to it, this afternoon? They'd sure appreciate it. We could fix up a place in the schoolhouse upstairs, with a stove, maybe.'

Nobody said anything at first. Eddie Stinson looked down and swallowed. Zerbo muttered: 'You can have that, brother.' Sammy Sisk tried a gag: 'How would I look without a head?' but nobody laughed. The fat comedian finally said: 'Well, I dunno.'

The lieutenant gazed from one to the other and said: 'I

wouldn't want you to do anything you didn't feel like doing. It's up to you. We got a lotta walking wounded that would get a hell of a kick out of a show. Why don't you put it to a vote? Whatever you say goes.'

Eddie said: 'O.K. We'll take a vote and stick by it. I vote yes. If the lieutenant says it's safe, I guess it's all right.'

Connie Clay and Sammy Sisk agreed with him. Pete Russo, Zerbo, and Maureen Pearl voted no. Eddie Stinson said: 'That's three and three.' They all looked at Verna shaking in her corner and knew there'd be no show, but Eddie went through the motions, anyway.

He called over: 'Verna! The lieutenant wants us to give a show this afternoon. We're taking a vote. What about you, kid? How about giving 'em a little of the old song and danceroo?'

The quiet that followed his question was broken only by the moaning of a boy with a shell fragment through his hip. Then Verna sat bolt upright staring at them out of her fear-haunted eyes. She was trying to say something, but the chattering of her teeth would not let her, so instead she nodded her head. And the nod was yes.

Pete Russo said: 'Well, for cryin' out loud! I thought you'd be the last one to be that dumb.'

Maureen said bitterly: 'Our little heroine! The show's gotta go on! She cannot disappoint her audience. Nuts!'

Verna just nodded again. Eddie said: 'O.K., lieutenant. Four to three. I guess we'll put on some kind of show.'

It was bitter cold in the schoolroom on Christmas afternoon. There was one small oil stove up on the platform, but the wind and snow that swirled in through the shattered windows nullified its heat.

The enclosure was packed to the doors with soldiers, the walking wounded in their blood-soaked bandages; men relieved from the lines, steel-helmeted, their carbines or tommy guns cradled in their arms; jeep-drivers, supply men, paratroopers, cooks, Signal Corps boys, engineers, crews out of disabled tanks.

Outside, but more distantly, the sounds of the battle still raged, the rattling clank of tanks and half-tracks mingling with the short bursts of automatic-rifle fire, the irritable whine of shells, and the '*poom-poom-poom*' of the quarrelling tanks; aircraft snarled overhead.

And there on Christmas Day Unit X117 gave its show, bundled to the ears against the cold, with the notable exception of Verna. When Sammy Sisk said: 'And now, fellers, I take pleasure in presenting that popular little singer of songs straight from the Stawk Club in New Yawk, Miss Verna Vane,' Verna came on in her little silk panties with the silver fringe and the padded spangled brassière holding up her too small breasts. Only at the insistence of the lieutenant was she wearing her steel helmet athwart her yellow hair.

When she came out, Eddie Stinson blew clouds of cigar smoke, and the men yelled and cheered. He said: 'Well, look what Sanny Claus brought!' and they whooped. He said: 'Howdja like to find that in your stocking?' and they howled.

Somehow Verna had managed to stop the chattering of her teeth, and she was giving with the smile. She had applied body make-up, but underneath she was blue with cold. There was no microphone, and when she opened her mouth to sing, only a croak came out; it was drowned by a burst of fifty-millimetre firing from the edge of town, and Eddie hollered: 'Quiet!' and got another laugh.

Pete Russo switched into *Little White Lies*, and Verna struck her taps against the floor while Eddie Stinson said in a loud aside: 'She just does that to keep warm!' and clowned through the number with her, and when it was over, the sound of the cheers and the applause drowned out the ugly symphony of war, and Verna just stood there, smiling and looking like that shy, good-natured kid from back home while the soldiers stamped and whistled and wolf-called and not one of them so much as guessed that for her this had been a kind of Gethsemane.

When Bastogne was relieved and the road south-west was again clear, Camp Shows Unit No. X117 was the first to drive out to safety after the wounded, and within a few hours was away from the sound of the hammering guns. Afterwards there was even a little publicity in the papers about the unit that was trapped in Bastogne and that gave a show on Christmas Day, though of course there was no mention of Verna.

It was several weeks later that the unit was headed west towards Mons to play in a hospital there, rolling over paved roads in a safe and quiet area in a four-jeep caravan. Verna was riding in the last jeep with a corporal who was telling her that she was a pretty cute trick.

It was a winter day of grey clouds with a threat of more weather and the roads were deep in snow and ice, so they drove carefully. There was not even aircraft overhead to disturb the quiet beauty of the winter landscape.

Then from ahead there came a deep rumbling with overtones

of noisy clanking. Verna's hands flew to her breast, and she said :
'Oh, God!'

The corporal smiled and said: 'Take it easy, kid; that's just a
column of Shermans moving up. But we'd better get the hell off
the road until they get by. Those damn things are liable to skid
all over on this ice.'

The three lead jeeps had already pulled off the road and into a
field through an opening in a fence. The corporal put the jeep
into its heavy traction gear and swung through the gate and wide
of the other two cars. There was a kind of click and a whirring
as a dark object leaped up out of the snow to the right of the
jeep and the next instant exploded with a jarring roar and a dirty
mushroom of black smoke.

The corporal was wounded in the hand and the thigh by bits
of shrapnel, but Verna never knew what hit her. She slumped
quietly out of the side of the jeep and lay there in the snow,
head down, a little, quiet, tattered khaki bundle that would never
move again.

The others had piled out of the lead jeeps and came running
over as the corporal yelled: 'God, a German *Sprengmine!* We
musta dragged the wire under the snow. Somebody look after the
kid. I'm hit.'

But they saw at once that there was no longer any need to do
so. Connie and Maureen knelt sobbing in the snow by her side
while the men stood looking down helplessly at the hole torn
through her steel helmet, and the grey tanks with their admonishing guns pointed straight forward rumbled past the little tragedy
in the field, without pausing. Eddie Stinson, his fat jowls shaking,
repeated over and over again: 'Oh, the poor kid. The poor
damn little kid.'

The mortal remains of Verna Vane of necessity gathered
accompanying papers, a dossier that included the manner of the
end that had come to her. As a matter of routine the report
crossed the desk of a Colonel Speed McIvor, once a publicity
director for Magna Pictures in Hollywood, but now Public Relations Officer for SHAEF, stationed in Paris.

He glanced at it idly, then picked it up and read it through,
his fingers reaching for the row of buzzers on his desk. He pushed
them all. A major, two captains, a lieutenant and a WAC sergeant
materialised.

'Hey,' the colonel said, 'what about this Verna Vane who was
killed by a mine near Mons? Who is she?'

The major began to explain, but the colonel, who had a hair-trigger mind, was 'way ahead of him. He interrupted, talking in short, rapid sentences:

'Jees, it's a story, isn't it? What are we sitting around for? First girl from a camp show killed in combat. Well, it was a mine, wasn't it? It says there's no next of kin. Poor kid must be an orphan. Ought to have a bang-up military funeral. Gave her life for her country, didn't she? Guys firing a volley over her grave. Hell, we can do better than that in this town. Do it in a big church. Who's the guy in charge of Notre-Dame Cathedral? Get him on the phone. The kid was in that show that was trapped in Bastogne. That's a great yarn, isn't it? Make every paper in the States. The general might even come. Get me his adjutant on the phone. See that a piece gets into *Stars and Stripes*. Put in a call for the ranking chaplain. Find out about getting a guard of honour. Boom! We're in business. Beat it, everybody!'

The rest of that day, by methods known only to a live wire from Hollywood, considerable red tape was snipped, and a piece appeared in *Stars and Stripes* the next morning to the effect that the general would attend funeral services in Notre-Dame on Sunday for Verna Vane, American girl killed in action.

The colonel moved fast, but thereafter events over which he had no control began to move even faster. With the publication of the item in the soldiers' newspaper, word was permitted to sift through that a certain highly placed French Personage was miffed that he had not been asked to attend a ceremony important enough to call out the presence of the American general.

The colonel burned up three telephone wires, and the Personage was invited and accepted. McIvor thereupon made his first acquaintance with something known as protocol, and his telephones were very busy. Also the colonel began to sweat. He had only been trying to organise a good story for back home. Now it was too late to back out.

It seemed there was a Russian general heading a military mission in Paris. There were also Dutch, Belgians, and Poles, Norwegians, Yugoslavs, and Brazilians, not to mention dignitaries from Canada, New Zealand, and Australia, and a marshal from Great Britain. The presence of the American general along with the French Personage at the ceremony made it imperative they be invited, if Allied solidarity was to be preserved. The colonel did a rush job on invitations.

The cathedral choir offered its services, and the F.F.I. sent a delegation and a wreath. The Air Forces said they'd better be in on the show if the colonel wanted any more transportation, and a colonel of Artillery sent a sharp note demanding to know whether they were the forgotten branch. There was some bitterness as to which of the two senior chaplains should read the service.

But, at that, things worked out better than might have been expected, and on a cold but sunny January afternoon in Paris, passing through an aisle of massed tanks and half-tracks, the remains of Verna Vane arrived on a gun caisson for her first and last world première.

She had really achieved everything her poor little heart had ever desired. Her wrap, the stars and stripes that draped her coffin, was of silk, and upon it she wore the jewels she had craved so much. For while her own country had deposited only the modest Purple Heart upon her casket, the more expansive and slightly bewildered Russians had taken no chances and sent the Order of Suvorov in gold and enamel and diamonds. The Belgians awarded the Order of Leopold, and the Dutch the Order of William, a white cross surmounted by a jewelled crown.

Ten thousand candles flickered down the great nave of Notre-Dame, and the winking reflection of their myriad lights glittered from the bemedalled breasts of the great gathering of notables from every Allied land. The American general was flanked by the French Personage on one side and the gleaming Russian general on the other, and then, rank on rank, sat the dashing, colourful military and the more sombre diplomats.

And the ten thousand candles shone upon young grave faces and row upon row of khaki uniforms, for the G.I.s on leave in Paris had come to be Verna's audience.

None of the glittering foreign dignitaries had the slightest idea who Verna Vane was, or cared, but the doughboys knew. They had seen her at Rennes and Le Mans and Nancy, outside of Metz and north of Luxembourg, in Brussels and Liège and Maastricht, in shattered Aachen and besieged Bastogne, and they remembered the thin girl in the little pants and the thingamajig across her chest who couldn't sing or dance a hell of a lot, but who had stood there smiling wistfully at them while she took an awful lot of kidding from that fat guy. They remembered how she had reminded them of all those sweet kids back home . . .

There was music too for this big show, the booming of the great organ and the swelling of the choir intoning the majestic Mass, and while the glorious chant rose to the vaulted roof, an Air Forces Piper Cub flew overhead and dropped a wreath on the square outside the church and the artillery pieces lined along the Seine thudded the last salute.

K

The members of Camp Shows Unit No. X117 were there, at the side of the cathedral behind the dignitaries.

The Great Zerbo said: 'It's funny, isn't it, about her and her career? She got it, anyway.'

Sammy Sisk said: 'Gee, this is better than Madison Square Garden.'

Eddie Stinson's fat jowls shook, and he kept repeating: 'The poor damn kid.'

Maureen Pearl said to Connie: 'If the poor thing had used the brains she was born with and married that guy who was so crazy about her, this never would have happened,' but Connie only wept and said: 'Oh, I think it's so beautiful.'

Sitting jammed between khaki-clad figures, far back, so that the distant shining casket was but one tiny brighter drop in the great pool of light in the centre of the cathedral, was a captain of engineers who too was remembering Verna. He was recalling that once this being, this glamorous star, now so far, very far removed from him, had lain sobbing in his arms, crying: 'Oh, God, I'm so scared! Oh, hold me tight!'

He had held her tightly to his heart, and for that enchanted moment she had been his. And he said a small prayer and was profoundly grateful for the wonder and the beauty of the thing that had happened to him, Walter Hruban, just one guy in a hell of a big army.

As must end all shows, so this one too came to a close with the last rolling chords of the organ, and when the audience had filed out of the cathedral they placed the casket upon the caisson once more, the guard of honour lined up behind, and they took Verna to the American cemetery, fired the farewell volley, and there buried her with her shattered steel helmet hung over the small, plain white cross that marked the haven of her final exit.

The Enchanted Doll

A number of my short stories as well as novelettes and novels have been made into moving pictures, some of which vanished without trace; others managed to make an incredible amount of money for their producers. None of them with but one single exception, ever gave me genuine satisfaction or pleased me wholly. Either my story had been tampered with or my characters miscast, or sometimes even the whole point of the story garbled or lost.

The fact that a number of these were resounding commercial successes, as I have indicated, and made millions for the producing company, is quite beside the point. I originated them and when I saw them on the screen I was disappointed and frustrated.

The one exception to this dismal catalogue was a half-hour television short, a two-reeler made by Mr Douglas Fairbanks Jnr., as a part of a television series he was making, based on this little short story I wrote some years ago.

I remember when the film had been finished sitting with Mr Fairbanks in his projection room in his studio outside London and for the first time ever watching the total translation to the screen of not only all of my characters but the spirit of my story and its emotional content as well. Miss Geraldine McEwan, the actress he employed for the part of the unhappy heroine, was tender, wistful and endearing and brought the girl I had imagined most exquisitely to life. The role of the young doctor was excellently portrayed by Mr Douglas Fairbanks Jnr. himself. The story never set any rivers on fire, nor did the film I imagine shatter any television screens, but at least for once sitting in a darkened projection room and watching actors and actresses portray characters

291

I had invented and speaking lines I had written, I was made happy.

Somewhere, some time – I cannot remember the place or the period – I passed a shop, saw therein a painted doll and fell in love with her. It might have been in some small retailer's in a side street, or in the toy department of a great store like Harrods or Selfridges. This little effigy had been created by some specialist, an artist who hand-painted the face, and the expression thereon was extraordinarily sweet and life-like and the little figure touched my heart. I wish now I had bought it, I was ashamed to do so and unable quickly enough to think up some legitimate excuse.

And probably the reason I didn't buy it was because this doll touched something even deeper than that seat of emotions we call the heart, and I didn't wish to face up to it or acknowledge it by anything so dynamic or matter-of-fact as a purchase. And anyway had I bought her what would I have done with her?

For the more deep-seated emotional centre that had been touched, I knew later as I sat writing this story, was my never satisfied longing for a daughter. Sons I had had (to whom this book is dedicated) but as long as I can remember I have entertained a yearning for a girl child. This longing was never fulfilled.

Don't be alarmed; THE ENCHANTED DOLL *is not that kind of story, in fact it is quite different, although it does make a bow to the interest in psychology and psychiatry which was in great vogue at the time that I wrote it. But then that is what the subconscious versus writing is like. Those things which we dredge up from the dark corners in the attics of our brains are never used directly but emerge transformed or as parallels or substitutes. Only the trained psychiatrist or the original human involved would recognise the impetus. Some day, some psychiatrist with a literary flair will write a fascinating book. He will take half a dozen of the world's best short stories and analyse them against the lives of their writers.*

This story was first published in Great Britain and marks the beginning of my divorce from the American short story market, for no American magazine would print it, nor could I ever find out why. The editors of the four important and high-paying American magazines decided that their readers would not like it. The editor of a British woman's magazine, with enormous circulation, decided that their readers would like it.

Does this mean that the British audience is more adult than the American? Or that we, the British reader and I, understand one another better? I like to think so.

THE ENCHANTED DOLL

It was three years ago today that I first saw the strange and alluring doll in the window of Jim Carter's stationery and toy shop near Abbey Lane, just round the corner from my consulting room where the brass plate with the black lettering on my door reads – STEPHEN AMONY, M.D.

And I feel impelled to try to set down on paper some record of the things which resulted from that meeting, though I am afraid it will be a crudely told story, for I am not a writer, but a doctor.

I remember just how it was that day, the autumn sun shining across the Thames, mingling with the soft coal smoke from the ships on the river and the street smells of the poor neighbourhood. The flowerseller's stall at the corner was gay with dahlias, asters and chrysanthemums and a near-by barrel organ was playing *Some Enchanted Evening*.

As I turned the corner and came to the toy shop, I was made once more aware of the poor collection of toys in the dusty window and I remembered the approaching birthday of my niece. So I stopped and examined the window to see if there might be anything appropriate, and browsed through the bewildering array of unappealing objects – a toy red fire engine, crudely made lead soldiers, cheap cricket balls, pads and bats, all a-jumble with boxes of garishly coloured boiled sweets, bottles of ink, pens, pencils, gritty stationery, paper-backed novels and comics.

My eyes eventually came to rest on the doll tucked away in one corner. She was overshadowed by the surrounding articles and barely visible through the grime of decades collected on Jim's window, but I could see that she was made all of rag, with a painted face, representing a little girl with the strangest, tenderest, most alluring and winsome expression on her countenance.

I could not wholly make her out, due to the shadows and the film through which I was looking, but I was aware that a tremendous impression had been made upon me, that somehow a contact had been established between her and myself, almost as though she had called to me. It was exactly as though I had encountered a person, as one does sometimes a lovely girl, or a stranger in a crowded room, with whose individuality one is indelibly impressed and which lingers on.

I went inside and replied to Jim's greeting of: ''Morning, Doc, what can I do for you? You out of tobacco again?' with – 'Let me see that rag doll, the one in the corner by the roller skates. I want to send something to a little niece of mine . . .'

Jim's eyebrows went up into his bald head and he came round
the counter, the edges of his shabby jacket flapping. 'That doll?'
he said. 'That doll now could cost quite a bit of money, probably
more than you would want to pay. She's special made.'

Nevertheless he took her from the window and placed her in
my hands, and here it was that I received my second shock, for
she had the most amazing and wonderful quality. No more than
a foot long, she was as supple and alive to the touch as though
there were flesh and bones beneath the clothes instead of rag
stuffing.

It was, indeed, as Jim had said, hand-made, and its creator had
endowed it with incredibly life-like features and lively grace,
that it gave one the curious feeling of a living presence. Yet there
was even more than that to her. Could a doll be said to have sex
appeal in the length and proportions of her legs, the shape of
her head, the swirl of her skirts over her hips? Was it possible for
an emotion to have been sewn into the seams marking the con-
tours of the tiny figure? To hold it was to feel a contact with
something warm, mysterious, feminine and wonderful. I felt that
if I did not put her down I should become moved by her in some
unbearable fashion.

I laid her on the counter. 'What is the price, Jim?'

'Four quid.'

It was my turn to look astonished. Jim said, 'I told you, didn't
I? I only make a couple of bob on it. I don't need to make no
profit on you, Doc. You can 'ave it for three pounds fifteen. Over
in the West End in some of them big shops she gets as much as
six and seven quid for 'em.'

'Who is "she"?'

'The woman from Hardlea Street who makes 'em. She's been
there about a couple of years now. She trades 'ere. That's 'ow I
come to get one once in a while.'

'What is she like? What is her name?'

Jim replied: 'Can't say exactly – something like "Calamity."
She's a big, flashy, red-haired woman. 'Ard! Wears a lot of furs.
Not your type, Doc.'

I couldn't understand it, or make the connection between the
woman that Jim described and the exquisite little creature that
lay on the counter.

'I'll take her,' I said. It was more than I could afford, for my
practice is amongst the poor where one goes really to learn medicine. Yet I could not leave her lying there on the counter amidst
packets of matches, dusty boxes and papers, for she was a creation that gave me the feeling that some part of a human soul had

gone into the making of her. I counted out three pounds and fifteen shillings and felt like a fool.

I felt even more of a fool when I had got her home and was repacking her to send to Birmingham. Again I experienced the impact of the tiny figure and realised that I had the greatest reluctance to part with her. She filled the small bedroom I have behind my surgery with her presence and brought an indescribable longing to my throat.

When I returned from posting the parcel to my niece, I thought that would be the end of it. But it wasn't – I couldn't get it out of my head. I thought about it often and tried to reconcile the emotion it had aroused in me with what Jim had told me of the flashy, red-haired woman who had created the object, but I could not. Once I was even tempted to pursue the matter, find out who she was and perhaps see her. But just at that time chicken-pox landed in our neighbourhood and drove everything else out of my head.

It was a few weeks later that my telephone rang and a woman's voice said: 'Doctor Amony?'

'Yes.'

'I passed by your place once and saw your notice. Are you expensive to call privately? Do you cost a lot for a visit?'

I was repelled by the quality of the voice and the calculation in it. Nevertheless I replied: 'I charge five shillings. If you are insured or really cannot afford to pay, I charge nothing.'

'Fair enough. I could pay five bob. But no more. You can come over? Callamit is the name. Rose Callamit. It's the house on Hardlea Street, next to the greengrocer's. Just walk in – it's on the second floor.'

I arrived at the house and mounted two narrow, musty flights of stairs, dimly lighted and creaking. A door was opened an inch or so and I felt I was being subjected to scrutiny. Then the unpleasant voice said: 'Dr Amony? You can come in. I'm Rose Callamit.'

I was startled by her. She was very tall with brick, henna-dyed hair and an over-powering smell of cheap perfume. She had dark eyes, almond shaped and slanted slightly in an oriental fashion and her mouth was full, thick-lipped and heavily made up. There was a horrible vitality and flashy beauty about her. I placed her age at somewhere between forty-five and fifty.

The deepest shock, however, I sustained when I entered the room which was one of those front parlour-bedrooms of old-fashioned London houses, furnished femininely, but with utter vulgarity, with bad prints, loud satin cushions and cheap glass scent bottles. But hanging from the wall, lying about on the bed, or tossed carelessly on the top of an old trunk were a dozen or so rag dolls, all of them different, yet, even at first glance, filled with the same indescribable appeal and charm as that of the similar little creature that had made such a profound impression upon me. I realised that I was in the presence of the creator of these astonishing puppets.

Rose Callamit said: 'Tall, dark and handsome, eh? Ain't you kind of young to be doctoring people?'

I answered her sharply, for I was angry, uncomfortable and irritated. The rediscovery of these beautiful and touching creatures in this cheap, disgusting atmosphere and in connection with this horrible woman had upset me. 'I'm older than you think, and my looks are none of your business. If you don't want me to treat you, I'll go.'

'Now, now, doctor. Can't you take a compliment?'

'I'm not interested in compliments. Are you the patient?'

'No. It's my cousin. She's ill in the back room. I'll take you to her.'

Before we went in, I had to know. I asked: 'Do you make these dolls?'

'Yes. Why?'

I was filled with a sense of desolation. I mumbled, 'I bought one once for a niece . . .'

She laughed. 'Bet you paid plenty for it. They're the rage. Come on then.'

She led me through a hall into the smaller room at the back and opened the door partly, shouting: 'Mary, it's the doctor.' Then before she pushed it wide to admit me, she cried to me loudly and brutally: 'Don't be surprised, Doctor, she's a cripple!'

The pale girl, clad in a dressing-gown, in a chair over by the window was caught with a look of utter despair on her countenance. I was disgusted and angry again. The way the woman had said it was itself crippling. She was not only telling me that Mary was a cripple, she was reminding Mary.

She could not have been more than twenty-four or twenty-five. She seemed to be nothing but a pair of huge and misery-stricken eyes, and what was shocking was how low the lamp of life appeared to be burning in them. She was very ill.

From that first visit I remembered the underlying sweetness of her presence, the lovely brow and shapely head, now too big for her wasted frame, the translucent, blue-veined hands, hair now limp and lustreless. She had a mouth shaped to incredible pathos, soft, pale coral and ready to tremble. But I saw something else that astonished me and gave my heart a great lift. She was surrounded by small tables. On one of them were paints and brushes, on others, rag material, linen, stuffing, thread and needles, the paraphernalia needed for making dolls.

Her present illness and her deformity were two separate things; yet it was the latter that caught my attention even from the door, something about the way she sat, and made me wonder. The technical name for her condition would be unintelligible to you, but if it was what it looked to me at first glance, it was curable.

I asked: 'Can you walk, Mary?' She nodded listlessly.

'Please walk to me.'

'Oh, don't,' she said. 'Don't make me.'

The pleading in her voice touched me, but I had to be sure. I said: 'I'm sorry, Mary. Please do as I ask.'

She rose unsteadily from her chair and limped towards me, dragging her left leg. I was certain I was right. 'That's good,' I said, smiled encouragingly and held out my hands to her. Something strange happened. For a moment we seemed to be caught up in each other's eyes. I felt she was being swept away and drowning in the dark pool of her misery and despair, while the air all about me seemed to be quivering with the force of her silent cry to me for help. Her hands lifted towards mine for an instant in imitation of my gesture, then fell back to her side. The spell was broken.

I asked: "How long have you been like this, Mary?'

Rose Callamit said: 'Oh, Mary's been a cripple for almost ten years now. I didn't call you for that. She's ill. I want to know what's the matter with her.'

Oh yes, she was ill. Sick unto death perhaps. I had felt that as soon as I came into the room. With my glance I invited the big, vulgar woman to leave the room, but she only laughed. 'Come off it, Doctor Amony. I'm staying right here. You find out what's the matter with Mary and then you can tell me.'

When I had finished my examination I accompanied Rose into the front room. 'Well?' she said.

I asked: 'Did you know that her deformity could be cured? That with the proper treatment she could be walking normally in . . .'

'Shut up, you!' Her cry of rage struck like a blow against my ears. 'Don't you ever dare mention that to her. I've had her looked at by people who know. I won't have any young idiot raising false hopes. If you ever do, you're finished here. I want to know what's wrong with her. She won't eat or sleep or work good any more. What did you find out?'

I replied: 'I don't know yet. I found nothing suspicious organically. But there is something terribly wrong somewhere. I want to see her again. In the meantime I'm prescribing a tonic and a stimulant. I'd like to look in again after a few days.'

'You'll keep your big mouth shut about curing her leg, you understand? Otherwise I'll get another doctor.'

'All right,' I said. I had to be able to return to visit Mary again. Later we would see. . . .

When I picked up my hat and bag to leave, I said: 'I thought you told me it was you who made these dolls.'

She looked startled for a moment as though she had never expected the subject to come up again. 'I do,' she snapped. ' I design 'em. I let Mary work at 'em sometimes to help take her mind off she's a cripple and will never get a man.'

But when I walked out again into the bright autumn day with the children playing on the pavement, or throwing a ball up against the old Brewery wall and the traffic grinding by, my heart told me that Rose Callamit had lied and that I had found the sweet spirit behind the enchanted doll. But the cold clammy messenger of a doctor's instinct warned me also that unless I could determine the cause of her decline, that spirit would not be long for this earth.

Her name, I found out later, was Nolan, Mary Nolan, and she was slowly dying from no determinable cause. I was sure that her cousin had something to do with it. Not that Rose was killing her consciously. The red-haired woman actually was frightened. She wanted Mary alive, not dead, for Mary was her source of revenue.

After I had made a number of visits, Rose did not even bother to keep up the pretence that it was she herself who made the dolls, and I was able to piece together more of the picture.

When Mary was fifteen, her parents were killed in an accident which also resulted in her injury. A court had awarded her in guardianship to her only relative, the cousin Rose Callamit. When Mary's inheritance proved meagre, Rose vented her spite on her by harping on her deformity. Through the years of their association, the older woman had made her deeply sensitive to and ashamed of her lameness. Her theme was always: 'You are a hopeless cripple. No man will ever look at you. You will never be married or have children.'

When Mary came of age, her spirit apparently was broken and she was completely subjugated to the will of her cousin, for she continued to remain with her, under her sway, living a lonely

and hopeless existence. It was about this time that Mary first began to make the rag dolls, and Rose, for all her vulgarity, greed
and indolence, had the shrewdness to recognise their unique
quality and irresistible appeal. After she had sold the first ones
she kept Mary at it from morning until night.

Mary was afraid of her cousin, but it was not that which
was killing her. It was something else, and I could not find
out what. Nor was I ever allowed to see her alone. Rose was
always present. Never had I been more conscious of the manifestation of good against evil than in that room with the girl, whose
poor, suppressed nature fluttered so feebly in her wasted body,
and the gross woman with greedy eyes and patchouli smell who
exhaled the odour of wickedness.

I did not mention my belief in the possibility of cure for Mary's
lameness. It was more important to discover what it was that was
destroying her. Rose would not let her be moved to a hospital.

For ten days, I thought I had arrested the process that was killing Mary before my eyes. I stopped her work on the dolls. I
brought her some books to read, some sweets and a bottle of
sherry. When I returned for my next visit, she smiled at me for
the first time, and the tremulousness, the longing, the hunger, the
womanliness and the despair of the smile could have broken a
heart of stone.

'That's better,' I said. Another ten days of no dolls. Rest, sleep,
read. Then we'll see.'

But her cousin glowered and there was an unpleasant expression about her mouth.

When next I came to visit Mary, Rose was waiting for me in
her own room. She said: 'You needn't come any more, Doctor
Amony. We don't need you now.'

'But Mary . . .'

'She's fit as a fiddle. Good-bye, Doctor. . . .'

My eyes wandered to the old trunk in the corner. There were
three new dolls lying on top of it. Was it only my imagination, or
was there a new quality to these mute, bewitched figurines? Was
each in its way a birth and a death in one, a greeting to the
beauties, desires and pleasures of life and, at the same time, a
farewell?

I had the most powerful impulse to push the monstrous woman
aside and crash through the doors to see my patient. But the
habits of medical ethics are too hard to break. When a physician
is dismissed, it is his duty to go unless he has reason to suspect
that his patient is meeting with foul play. I had no such reason.

I had failed to determine the cause of Mary's illness; Rose was undoubtedly calling another doctor, for she needed Mary's work for an easy living, and would unquestionably try to protect her own interests.

Thus, with great heaviness of heart, I departed. But I thought about Mary night and day.

It was shortly after this that I became ill myself. Imperceptibly at first, then finally noticeably; loss of appetite, loss of weight, lethargy, irritability, at nightfall half a degree to a degree of temperature, and moments of weakness when I felt as though somehow I could not go on with my work. I asked a doctor friend to examine me. He thumped and pounded and listened, and eventually reported: 'There's nothing wrong with you, Stephen. Take things a little easier. You've probably been overworking. Nature's protest.'

But I knew it wasn't that.

I began to look shocking; my skin was losing its tone, my cheekbones showed and I was hollow-eyed from loss of sleep. I did not like the look in my eyes, or the expression about my mouth. Sometimes my nights and my dreams were filled with fever and in them I saw Mary struggling to reach me while Rose Callamit held her imprisoned in her ugly arms. I had never been free from worry over failure to diagnose Mary's case.

My whole faith in myself as a doctor was badly shaken. A desperately stricken human being had called upon me for help and I had failed. I could not even help myself. What right had I to call myself a doctor? All through one awful night of remorse and reproach the phrase burned through my brain as though written in fire—

Physician, heal thyself.

Yes, heal myself before I was fit to heal others. But heal myself from what? If anything, my symptoms resembled those of Mary Nolan. Mary! Mary! Mary! Always Mary!

Was she my sickness? Had she always been from the first moment that I had encountered that extension of her enchanted spirit embodied in the rag doll in the toy shop?

And as morning greyed my bedroom window and the traffic clattered by, I knew my disease. I was in love with Mary Nolan. When I could couple the words – 'love' and 'Mary,' when I could look up and cry – 'I love her! I want her! I need her person and her soul at my side!' it was as though I could feel the fire of healing medicine glowing through my veins.

It had always been Mary – the warmth and yearning, need and tenderness that she expressed with her presence, and the odd, off-beat beauty of her, too, a beauty that would only reach its full flower when I had cured and restored her in every way.

For now, as the scales fell from my eyes, and my powers were released again through the acknowledging of the hunger, love and compassion I had for her, I knew Mary's sickness in full, to its last pitiful detail, and what I must do and why I must see her alone if only for a few minutes if she were not to be lost to me and the world for ever.

That morning I telephoned Jim Carter and said: 'This is Doctor Amony, Jim. Will you do something for me?'

'Anything, Doctor. After what you done for my kid, you name anything.'

'Do you remember Mrs. Rose Callamit? The doll woman? Well, the next time she comes into the shop, find some means of telephoning me. Then keep her there in some way. Talk, or do something, anything to make her stay. I need twenty minutes. Right? Got it? I'll bless you for the rest of my days.'

I was terrified that it would happen while I was on an outside call and each time I returned to the surgery I looked in at the shop, but Jim would merely shake his head. Then one day at five o'clock in the afternoon the phone rang. It was Jim. He said merely: 'It could be now,' and rang off.

It took me no more than a minute or two to run the few hundred yards to the house where Mary lived. I ran upstairs two steps at a time. If the door was locked I would have to get the landlady. But I was lucky. Rose had expected to be gone only a few moments apparently and the door was open. I hurried into the back room, and found Mary.

There was so little of her left.

She was sitting up in bed, but now the absolute pallor had been replaced by two red fever spots that burned in the middle of her cheeks, a danger sign more deadly than the wastage of her hands and body. She was still surrounded by the paints and bits of coloured cloth and threads, as though she did not wish to die before she had put together one more image, one more dream.

She looked up when I came in, startled out of her lethargy. She had expected it to be Rose. Her hand went to her breast and she said my name. Not 'Doctor Amony,' but 'Stephen!'

I cried: 'Mary! Thank God I'm in time. I came to help you. I know what it is that has been making – making you ill——'

She was in that state where nothing escaped her. She felt my hesitation and knew I had avoided saying, '. . . that is killing you,' for she whispered: 'Does it matter now?'

I said: 'There is still time, Mary. I know your secret. I know how to make you well. But you must listen to me while I tell you . . . your life depends on it.'

A change came over her. She closed her eyes for an instant and murmured: 'No. Don't – please. Let me go. I don't want to know. It will be over soon.'

I had not thought that she might be unwilling or unable to face it. And yet I had to go on now. I sat down and took her hand. 'Mary. Please listen. When a body is undernourished we give it food; when it is anæmic we supply blood, when it lacks iron or hormones we give it tonic. But you have been drained dry of something else without which the soul and body cannot be held together.'

Her eyes opened and I saw that they were filled with horror and a glazing fear. She seemed about to lose consciousness as she begged: 'No! Don't say it . . . !'

I thought perhaps she might die then. But the only hope for her, for us both, was to go on.

'Mary! My brave, dear girl. It is nothing so terrible. You need not be afraid. It is because you have been drained of love. Look at me, Mary!'

My eyes caught and held hers. I willed her to remain alive, to stay with me, to hear me out. 'See, Mary, a person has just so great a reservoir of love to expend. It is drawn upon through life and must ever be replenished with tenderness, affection, warmth and hope. Thus the supply is always renewed. But yours has been emptied until there is nothing left.'

I could not be sure that she still heard me. 'It was Rose Callamit,' I continued. 'She took away your every hope of life, love and fulfilment. But what she did later to you was a much blacker crime. For she took away *your children*!'

There, it was out! Had I killed her? Had it been I, who loved her beyond words, who had administered the death blow? And yet I thought I saw a flicker of life in those poor, stricken eyes, and even perhaps the faintest reflection of relief.

'Oh, yes, they were your children, Mary, those enchanted creatures you created. When you were convinced that you had lost your chance to be a woman, you compensated for it by embodying your hopes, your dreams, and like every creator, whether mother or artist, a piece of your heart went into each of the dolls you made. You created them with love; you loved them as you would have loved your own children and then each one was taken from you and nothing was given to you to replace them. And so you continued to draw them from your heart until your life was being drained away from you. People can die from lack of love.'

Mary stirred. The glaze passed from her eyes. I thought I felt the response of faint pressure from the cold hand in mine.

I cried: 'But you won't, Mary, because I am here to tell you that I love you, to refill you to overflowing with all that has been taken from you. Do you hear me, Mary? I am not your doctor. I am a man telling you that I love you and cannot live without you.'

I caught her incredulous whisper. 'Love me? But I am a cripple!'

'If you were a thousand times a cripple, I would still love you. But it isn't true. Rose Callamit lied to you. You can be cured. In a year I will have you walking like any other girl.'

For the first time since I had known her I saw tears in her eyes and a tinge of colour to her cheeks. Then she lifted her arms to me with an utter and loving simplicity.

I picked her up out of the bed, with the blanket wrapped around her. She had no weight at all; she was like a bird. And she clung to me with a kind of sweet desperation so that I wondered where the strength in her arms came from and the glow of her cheek against mine; she who but a moment ago had seemed so close to death.

A door slammed. Another crashed open. Rose Callamit stormed into the room. I felt Mary shudder with the old fear and bury her face in my shoulder.

But Rose was too late. It was all over. There was nothing she could do any more, and she knew it. There was not even a word spoken as I walked past her, holding my burden closely to me, and went out of the door and down into the street.

Outside, the sun shone on the dusty pavement; no wind blew; children were playing noisily in the street, as I carried Mary home.

That was three years ago and I am writing this on an anniversary. Mary is busy with our son, and is preparing to receive our second born. She does not make dolls now. There is no need.

We still have many kinds of anniversaries, but this is the one I celebrate privately and give humble thanks for – the day when I first saw and fell in love with the message from Mary's soul, imprisoned in the enchanted doll that cried out to me from the grimy window of Jim Carter's toy shop near Abbey Lane.

The Glass Door

‡‡

THE GLASS DOOR *is the result of a one-minute falling in love I experienced with a girl on Madison Avenue one morning.*

I was walking down the Avenue on some errand or other and passed a new hotel they had just finished there. Through the glass door of the not-yet opened building I saw the girl in the bride's costume on the staircase being photographed.

She was a beautiful creature but over and above there was something extraordinarily appealing in the expression of her face. For the instant that I stood there on the pavement (I was not the only passer-by stopped by her beauty either) she satisfied all of the secret yearnings a man carries about with him, and I was in love with her.

I remained thus for sixty seconds watching her and enjoying that romantic fulfilment never attained in reality. She was, of course, a model being photographed for an agency and her face and figure would later be used to emphasise the necessity for life insurance, or silverware, face cream or under-arm security.

My down-town errand drew me onwards, I walked off, the spell was broken. The love affair was over. But out of the sixty seconds' longing for a girl I would never see again, grew the story of THE GLASS DOOR.

I can recall several more such instances or one might even call them instantaneouses. There was a bare-back rider in Ringling Brothers Circus in New York who eventually turned up in one of my Hiram Holliday stories, and another, a red-haired girl with a basket on her arm rounding the corner of a street in Amsterdam and of whom I only had a glimpse from my car as I turned off in the other direction, and she evolved into the subject of a fantasy romance published in 'Esquire' magazine.

THE GLASS DOOR *became and remains one of my favourite short stories for several reasons, and perhaps one of the chief ones is the economy one is able to practise as a writer in achieving the culmination of a desired romance.*

I think one of the hardest lessons ultimately learned by the incurable romantic is not to pursue too closely the object of his desires. I remember falling in love in Dallas once for forty-five seconds with a dress model for a famous department store. She was quite unlike the ordinary mannequin in that while her face was young and lovely, she had grey hair and was a grandmother. This romance differed in that I was offered the opportunity of meeting her, but by that time I was old enough to have learned the lessons I just spoke of. I declined the meeting and retained her thus in my memory, fresh and unspoiled.

All this leads to further development of the premise that there is more to writing than fame and fortune. At the expense of a little paper and ink one can become Don Juan, Casanova, Lothario and all the rest of those virile frauds rolled into one. No love is unattainable, and having been attained no woman is disillusioning or ever falls short of the dream. For, once she has supplied the initial impetus and stimulus and with her face and figure or no more than the tilt of her head, the softness of her eyes or the pure line of brow or jaw, in the imagination we are able to fashion her as we would have her, and certainly not as she ever is.

If such behaviour is 'escapism' and in itself childish and fatuous, what is one then to say of the original and initiating romantic impulse which is experienced by all and sends every man chasing skirts. He knows that when he catches what he is after it won't be what he thought it was. Nevertheless this has never discouraged pursuit. Another way – the writer's way, is to win all along the line. Boy gets girl! Boy gets dream too. Fiction, ancient, classical and modern is filled with woman characters who have been enjoyed by their creators.

The writing of THE GLASS DOOR *was pure gratification and the reading of it now, many years later, brings back pleasurably that sixty-seconds of romantic fulfilment when I stood outside on the Madison Avenue pave and gazed with worshipful longing at the incarnation of a long cherished dream.*

Wendy Carrel has not aged, though I have; she is still as she was, young, lovely, bitter, disillusioned and cynical and withal retaining her innocence and purity of heart as she too cherishes the fragile seedling of romance against the cold, hard winds of reality. She cried out for the one man who would fulfil her and I still respond to that cry.

I am not so sure about those modern writers of realism who so skilfully portray the less savoury human characters and apparently relieve their tensions thereby, and who they think they are in their stories, what vicarious experience they enjoy, but the writer of romance or the romantic writer, whichever way you will, not only enjoys his unobtainable goddesses but can even enjoy himself as well after he has completed his matamorphosis. He is a chameleon who undergoes changes to confrom with each story he is to tell and each hero in whose guise he appears.

Thus in THE GLASS DOOR *I who am I, and quite unlike Edward Anstey, become a curious combination of brilliant scientist and poet. That I am neither of these makes no matter. During the telling of this tale I am and likewise it makes my twist at the finish slightly more modest and becoming.*

Step with me then if you will through that Glass Door that fiction-wise is open to all of us.

THE GLASS DOOR

She was the most beautiful girl I had ever seen. I had never encountered such a tender and exquisite expression on the face of any human being as I saw on the countenance of the bride standing on the staircase.

I know there are more lyrical ways of saying this, particularly for a professional poet, which I happen to be. But in trying to tell a story in narrative prose, a medium unfamiliar to me, I have realised that the simpler the statement, the more easily is it understood, the more force and conviction it appears to carry, which is not the case with poetry. After I had seen her, I knew I would never forget her.

Even as I stood there on Madison Avenue, my face close to the glass of the door, with a half-dozen other passers-by in the street, gazing at this lovely apparition within, I knew that I was deeply moved by her beauty, but even more by the emotion, the mystery and the promise of the look that came into her face and filled her eyes to brimming as she posed at the turn of the stairs, holding her bridal bouquet.

I wondered what could be the thoughts passing through her head to make her look so glowingly beautiful, so warmly human and yet withal so spiritually divine, and I felt an overwhelming longing to be near her.

Never anywhere on earth, I was certain, would I find anything more beautiful than those hidden thoughts that were illuminating

her face, that were turning the corners of her lips and bringing
to her eyes that shining tenderness, that feeling of being filled
almost to overflowing with the substance of the soul.

Of course, I said to myself, *she is a bride. She is in love.* And
yet this left me unsatisfied, for the object of her affections
appeared to be nowhere about. There was a photographer on
the ground level, viewing her from beneath his black cloth, while
an assistant set and grouped floodlights at his direction. A woman
arranged the folds of the bridal gown that fell in a cascade of
white satin and cream lace to form a shimmering pool a few
steps beneath her feet.

I thought to myself, *Either she has just been married or is
going to be married. In any case, there can be no hope for me,
and what am I to do, now that I have seen her and can never
again put her out of mind?*

And only a moment before, I had been walking down Madison
Avenue in the Sixties, returning from lunch to my office in the
Ajax Building, owned by the Ajax Chemical Laboratories, for I
am in the way of being an amateur chemist; that is to say, I earn
my living with it on the side, my real profession being the writing
of poetry, at which I have had considerable success. Only last
week I sold a poem to a magazine for twelve dollars, and the
month before I received cheques for seven-fifty and five dollars
for verse. Now everything was changed.

The place where I had paused to look was the new Tarleton
Hotel, which had opened only a few days ago, and some of the
entrances were still locked and not yet in use. It was at one of
these where I was standing with the crowd, looking inside. Had
it not been locked I should have pushed inside and asked her
of what she was thinking there on the staircase that made her
look so beautiful.

Inside the hotel there was a kind of broad foyer with a grand
and glittering staircase with double wings curving left and right
upward from the landing some dozen steps. It was on this landing
the bride stood, one hand resting on the golden rail, the other
holding her streamered bridal bouquet.

She was as tall and slender as a calla lily. Her gown and veil
and train were all in white and cream. Her arms were sleeved,
her hair capped with an orange-blossom wreath; she was sheathed
in lace and satin – all but her face, white and pink with youth
and radiance and perfection.

So must Helen have looked, for this girl, too, was without flaw.
It is difficult for me, a poet, to set her attractions down un-
metered, for she had those qualities and perfections that are the

aim and end of every poet's search – the long dark lashes curled over deep-indigo, ocean-blue eyes, the lyric curve of her chin, the sweet artistry of her mouth. She looked as though Phidias had made her of painted marble and then breathed life into her.

Stragglers departed, and thus it was that I found myself pressed close to the long door when the change came over her that turned her from a statue to a woman, from a waxen figure of perfection to a human being with all the hopes, yearnings and sorrows, the hints of hidden joys and secret laughter, the tragedy of one who, with every capacity for love and living, is yet unfulfilled.

Who was she? What was she? Whose was she? What thing had she discovered to light this inner fire that so transformed her? To the threshold of what paradise had her mind led her? How could I touch or share this discovery that, if but for a moment, might bring man closer to the divinity for which he searched so tirelessly?

There it was. The entire scene – the foyer, the steps, the silken hangings trembled with it. The people within, too, seemed stricken and immobilised through it, as though time had stood still for them, and for that instant the photographer, his light man and his female assistant stood fixed under a spell. There came a moment when her beauty seemed too much to bear, when it seemed that one might be blinded in punishment for having looked upon it, and I turned my head away.

When I looked back, the expression was gone. It was over. The light man moved one of his standards closer. The angle of the bouquet of white roses and lilies of the valley was changed. It was two o'clock of a May day on Madison Avenue in New York. I moved away from the door and walked downtown towards my office. But nothing, not the green buses or the yellow cabs, the shining shop windows or the people on the street, looked the same to me or ever would again.

I tried to put her out of my mind. I could cloud her face and form, but I could not shut out the music that she had loosed in my universe. It was then that I first knew what a bad poet I must be, for I could not distil a single line of the songs, the hungers, the yearnings, the discords, the joys and the tears that I felt so keenly from the moment I had seen her. I sat at the deal table of my third-floor cold-water, walk-up flat and listened to the crash of the Third Avenue Elevated thundering by, and each passage meant that another five or ten minutes had sped and I could not write a word or commit a thought to paper. If this was what it meant to be in love, if this was what it was to be a poet, and a poet in love, both were hell.

A week later I saw her again, on 57th Street west of Fifth Avenue. She had hailed a taxi and was just about to get into it. Even though she was clad in a suit and blouse, and wore a piece of crimson veiling in her hair, I recognised her at once.

And yet I had time to notice that in many ways she was changed. The perfection of her features was unaltered, but she looked tired and dispirited. There was no hint of the mystery or the miracle I had seen through the glass door of the Tarleton Hotel. She was as beautiful, from the crown of her lustrous hair to her tiny patent-leather feet, as any man or poet could ever desire for his own, but the soul that had animated her when she posed as a bride on the staircase was missing.

Another moment and she would have been gone. Could I expect the laws of chance that had crossed our paths twice in this teeming city of eight million to repeat again? Now more than ever, it seemed that I had to know.

I ran up to her and said, 'Excuse me! Wait, please! Forgive me, but I must speak to you.' I was badly flustered and must have looked very foolish, for I am not prepossessing or ordinarily attractive to women. When I was a child I was considered plain. I was so excited and disturbed now that I forgot even to remove my hat. My face felt red and I was perspiring.

She paused, her gloved hand on the door handle of the cab, and looked at me as though to see whether it was someone she knew. I felt chilled at the strange kind of hardness I saw in her eyes now, and the bitterness that appeared to gather at the corners of her mouth. Made up as carefully as an actress, neat, dainty, efficient and cold, carrying a small bandbox; the thought struck me that she looked like Miss New York, the Fifth Avenue Girl. And my heart was crying out within me, *Where are you? What has become of you? Where did you go?*

For a moment, a faintly puzzled expression crossed her face. Then she continued to turn the handle of the cab door.

I cried out, 'Wait, I beg of you! One moment! I know you! You were the bride on the staircase. Never has any woman looked more beautiful. Could you wait just an instant? I - I want to get you an ice-cream soda and ask you something.'

I was so badly upset and not at all the person I had imagined myself to be, cool, collected and in command of the situation. We happened to be standing just outside of Hicks' soda fountain. I could have killed myself for being such a fool. A man of the world would have offered her a drink.

She turned and looked me over slowly and with a strange kind of calculation, from head to foot, and then said, with even a hint of amusement in her voice, 'Well, at least that's a new approach!'

I felt myself even more ridiculous, towering over her, since I am so tall that I am inclined to stoop. She was mistaking my desperate attempt to speak with her as an ordinary kind of pick-up. I said, 'Look here, I don't mean it as an approach, but it is terribly important that I talk to you for just a few minutes.'

She looked up again at me, still with the puzzled air. 'You did invite me for a soda, didn't you?'

At this moment the cab driver intervened. He said, 'Lady, would it be too much to inquire whether you want this cab or don't want this cab? Either way is O.K. with me, but if you would make up your mind, we might be able to restore the normal flow of traffic on Fifty-seventh Street and earn the undying gratitude of the Police Department.'

I saw her chin come up and some colour mount into her face. She said, 'I don't want your cab, and I don't like sarcasm. Goodbye.' To me, she said, 'No one has offered to buy me a soda for longer that I can remember. You did say you knew me, didn't you? I want a chocolate, all black with a double scoop of ice-cream.'

The first thing I noticed as we sat up at the soda fountain and she took off her gloves to eat her soda was that there were no rings of any kind on her fingers. I could have shouted.

I introduced myself to her. I said, 'My name is Edward Anstey. When I said I knew you, I meant I felt I knew you. I saw you that day when you – you were posing on the staircase of the Tarleton Hotel.'

She reflected for a moment, and then remarked, 'Oh, The Universal Insurance Account. The slogan underneath it will read, "How are You Going to Protect HER?"' Then she asked, 'Why does your name ring a kind of bell? Where do I know it from? Or do I?'

I replied, 'Perhaps you saw the April issue of the American Review. I had a poem in it called "The Sky Dwellers."'

She looked at me sideways as she sucked at her straw. 'You write poetry?'

I could understand her disbelief, for no one ever looked less like a poet than I. I have those Midwestern, washed-out eyes and a too long face.

I replied, 'I am a poet by profession. I sell my poems. I sold one to *Advance Age* last week.'

She gave a short laugh, and, oddly, not a very nice one. 'This *is* different,' she remarked.

Her name was Wendy Carrel, and she was a model. I didn't ask her, but I gathered she was the most beautiful, famous and successful model in New York.

I felt suddenly embarrassed that I had intruded upon the time of such a person. I said, 'I am sorry. I have kept you from an appointment. I didn't realise.'

She said, 'Never mind. I was only going home to soak my feet and read a book.'

I looked at her in amazement. 'Home? I would have thought a girl like you would never be home. I mean that men would be after you all the time for dates.'

Wendy Carrel's soda made a little bottom-of-the-glass gurgle. She looked up at me with an entirely different expression on her face, and said coolly and succinctly, 'Men? I am sick to death of men. I am sick of their dates and their suggestions and their passes. and their clumsy tries, their innuendo and double talk, and their stupidity and greed, and what I am expected to do in return for a dinner or a show. I spend most of my evenings home alone. And that is where I am going now. Thank you very much for the soda.'

I said, 'But I haven't asked you the question yet. That day on the staircase when you were posing as a bride. There was a moment – something happened to you – to your face. You were beautiful before that, so beautiful that it took my breath away. But for that instant you were divine. What were you thinking of? What changed you? Can you remember?'

From the look on her face as she studied me for a moment before she replied, I could not tell whether she had forgotten or, remembering, was not going to tell me. For one brief instant the shadows seemed about to lift from her. Then she looked me straight in the eye and said in a matter-of-fact tone, 'I haven't the slightest idea. I never think of anything when I am posing. The ideal of feminine beauty in this city appears to be a perfectly blank expression. I try to achieve it.'

This, then, was to be the end of the quest. What I had seen could have been an accident, a reflection of the glass door, a trick of lighting. I said, 'I am sorry. Thank you very much for being so kind.'

But it was not quite over. She said, 'Don't look so disappointed, as though I had robbed you of something. It was you who came after me, like all men come after me.' But then she added, as though something were still puzzling her, 'Is it really true that you are a poet?'

I said, 'Yes. I even live in an attic. That is, on the top floor of a walk-up.'

'And I suppose you would like me to come up so that you can read poetry to me?' She was bitter again.

'I wouldn't read poetry to you.'

'At any rate, you are frank.'

'I didn't mean that. I would try to use every moment to find what I saw that day, to learn whether it was there.'

'No, thank you. No sale.'

My heart felt like lead. The quest was finished. The adventure pursued might have been pleasurable, but I didn't want it with her, beautiful as she was, because of what I thought I had seen.

She rose, took her little model's bandbox and purse, and said with a kind of hard camaraderie, 'It was a good try, Anstey. Sometimes it works and sometimes it doesn't. Write this one off.'

I went out with her to get her a cab. It was the rush hour and we stood on the kerb together, searching, looking right and left for an empty. She was my responsibility, but now I wanted to be rid of her. When you are going to grieve for something lost you want to be alone.

I turned to look towards Fifth Avenue, and thus surprised the bleakness and misery on her face. Much of the hardness and cynicism had gone out of her, leaving the pain and innocence of a forlorn child. She had become a desperate human being with problems that were too much for her. Suddenly what I thought, or felt, or thought I wanted, all the poet's dreams and beautiful illusions, didn't seem to matter any more. But she did. Her need for help was immediate.

I said, 'Wendy! You're miserable, lonely and unhappy. Come home with me.'

She turned to me. Her features were dark, her mouth twisted in an ugly manner, and the bitter note was in her voice.

'Oh, all right. What's the difference?'

I had a double gas burner in an alcove, and I made scrambled eggs with calf's brains and stewed tomatoes, and we had bread, cheese and coffee, and a bottle of Richbourg that I had bought with my last cheque from the *Advance Age* for my poem called 'The Catbird.'

At first, Wendy was as nervous as a witch and as restless as a cat in a new home. While I cooked, she sat on the edge of chairs, chain-smoked or got up and wandered around the room and studied things, my books and pictures and possessions. She relaxed more during dinner, but afterwards she suddenly said to me accusingly. 'Where did you pick up the nickname "Clip"?'

'When I used to play end at Wisconsin, I guess. One of the kids in my outfit overseas remembered it. It's one of those things that stick.'

'Then you are the Anstey written up in *Passage* last week under Science. "Dr Edward I. (Clip) Anstey, brilliant chemist who won the Ajax Chemical Laboratories $10,000 prize for synthetising Drammitone, the new wonder drug for rheumatic fever." '

I said, 'You read a lot, don't you?'

She flared up immediately. 'Just because my features match and I don't have pimples, do I have to be a vegetable? So you're "Wisconsin's gift to synthetic chemistry," a successful chemist with the "brightest future in the U.S. field," and not a poet starving in a garret, after all.'

It was my turn to be angry. I said, 'They're a rotten crowd over at *Passage,* jealous and malicious. They can't stand anybody being a literary success. They sent a girl over to interview me about this – at least that's what she said.' I flipped her a copy of the *Asphalt Asphodel,* my book of verse, which was published last year at very little expense to me beyond the cost of printing and binding, and which had already sold 347 copies. 'She asked me a lot of questions which I answered in good faith. It was supposed to be printed under the heading of Poetry. They double-crossed me. They didn't even mention the book.'

She said, 'You lied about yourself to me. The article should have said, "brilliant and successful chemist whose hide-out where he brings his girls is an unsuspected Third Avenue walk-up." ' It almost seemed to give her pleasure to say those things, as though it was a comfort in a way to have her suspicions verified.

I said, 'But Wendy, chemistry is only an avocation with me. I got into it through a clerical error when I signed up for courses in school. Naturally, a man can't exist entirely on writing poetry today, but that's all I care about. And I do live here. I enjoy the noise of the elevated going by. It's like a kind of gigantic metronome. When you're a poet, you don't have to live up to your standard of earnings in outside life. You can live anywhere you please.'

She didn't seem to believe me. She threw me an incredulous glance, then got up and went to the window and looked out on the tracks of the elevated and to the washing strung from the windows of the flat across the street. When she turned back to me, there was an expression of desperation on her face.

She said, 'Well, when do you start making the passes?'

It sounded so hard-boiled and New York, just like so many of the tough kids you meet around. And yet I knew that here was innocence and terror, and something else I didn't understand at all. I waited for the space it took a train to go by.

Then I said, 'What if there aren't going to be any passes, Wendy?'

She came over, sat down by the table again and said, 'In heaven's name, Clip, what is it you want of me then?'

How hard it is to communicate. What a failure are words to try to reproduce heartbeats, longings and hunger. I tried to explain, 'Something I saw in you through the glass door, and that thing was beauty.'

I saw her eyes narrow at the word. I said, 'It is a different kind of beauty, Wendy, for which every man searches endlessly. It is something that lives in him, perhaps as a memory, perhaps only as a longing. It is his dream of the unattainable woman, the sorceress, the angel, the divine human who will combine hell and heaven for him on earth and into eternity.'

I tried to make her understand, 'Sometimes he catches no more than a glimpse of it – the contour of a cheek, the sound of a voice in the night, eyes filled with sudden tears, the weight and smoothness of coiled hair, the warm touch of a hand given in kindness – and never in his life does he come any closer to it. And sometimes it stands revealed in all its wonder, as it did that day on the staircase when something came into your face that was more beautiful than anything I had ever seen or imagined. It was the end of the search.'

'And now,' she said in a hard, flat voice, 'it isn't there any more, and I'm just a brat who let herself be picked up on the street like an alley cat, and taken home.'

'No, Wendy, you're not.'

She sat pulling at her lower lip like a little girl now, for she could change in an instant. Then she said, 'I lied when I said I didn't know what I was thinking of on the stairs that day. I was playing bride. I was pretending I was going to go down the steps to be married to the man I loved. He was kind, understanding, unselfish and honest. I made him up out of my head because I needed him.'

She threw me a swift look, as though to see if she could tell what I was thinking. Then she continued, with a momentary return to her old bitterness, 'Success in New York! The most-photographed face in America! And the men who want only one thing from me, and who never think of offering me a single bit of their hearts in return.'

And she said, 'I could bear that, but I couldn't bear their minds, their dirty minds, so shallow and empty of everything but themselves, their ambitions and their vanities. Business and sex, and nothing else. And even if I had married one, so that he could show me off, it would have been the same. So I made one up. He didn't have much money and wasn't very successful, but I didn't care about that, and neither did he. He cared about me and what I thought about and felt. He thought a lot about things and we talked about them, sometimes through the whole night. He was gentle and considerate and a whole man, strong where others are weak, human and weak where strength is only vanity. To him I was going to give what I have never given to any other, because they all held me so cheap, all those who were so cheap themselves.'

Now she looked at me gravely, and all the bitterness was gone from her face and eyes. She said, 'That's how women dream sometimes. But they can face up to reality too. Take me home, Clip. We have passed each other by, haven't we? Or do you want me to stay? It doesn't seem to matter so terribly to me any more, one way or the other, if it would make you happy. You make the decision for me.'

Now the room was full of the feeling of my wanting her; the walls and the floors trembled with it as when the elevated thundered by, but there was no train passing then. There was no hiding this from such a woman as Wendy, my weakness and my desire, and all this coupled with my silly vanity of playing at poet; there I stood before her, a sham and fake, exposed like all the rest.

And yet I did say, 'I'll take you home, Wendy. Let's go.'

She laughed, but this time it was a kind of deep, satisfied laugh. 'Oh, Clip! You've got guts to turn me out! And you *are* a poet!'

Wendy lived in a brownstone house in the West Eighties. All the way home in the taxi, we did not speak. I did not even try to hold her hand or take her in my arms.

I was thinking, *We will never see each other again, because I have been a fool from beginning to end, and only hurt her. Why didn't I let her stay with me? How close we almost were. Why would she have stayed with me? What made her give up? What had happened to her, to me? What was it I had missed, and where?*

I took her up the steps of the high, old-fashioned stoop to her door. There I said, 'Good-bye, Wendy. I can say good-bye. I can keep from seeing you again. But I can't keep from telling you that I love you, whoever and whatever you are, and always will.'

She reached up to put her arms about my neck and kissed me.

'Clip!' she said. 'Don't you know why I would have stayed with you tonight?'

It was my turn to stare at her, not knowing what to say.

She whispered close to my ear, 'You fool. Don't you know one can look two ways through a glass door. I wove my dreams about you, like a silly girl. I said to myself, 'Perhaps he might even be a poet. He could be, with those strange eyes.' You looked like everything I've ever wanted. Later, when I thought you were just like the rest, I was desperate and didn't care.'

And then she said, 'Come tomorrow, Clip, take me out. Let's learn each other. Let's not rob each other of our courtship. We're just at the beginning. There's so much about each other still to know.'

When I went down the steps, she remained standing for a moment at the door, looking down and watching me. It was not a trick or illusion of the street lamp's light that gave her face the expression of infinite and exquisite tenderness and beauty.

The Awful Secret of
M. Bonneval

The story of THE AWFUL SECRET OF M. BONNEVAL *is more nearly the awful thing that can happen to a well-meaning and innocent author. In this case it was not myself but a friend and respected colleague who was plunged thereby into the most horrible embarrassment which can happen to a writer. But we will come to this harrowing incident in due course.*

If you have ever toured France you will, of course, have done it with the Guide Michelin in your hand and made yourself thoroughly familiar with the style, contents and purpose of this wonderful little volume. Then likewise you can see the fascination this would have for a writer and the temptation to weave a story about the winning of an extra star.

If you are not familiar with this guide book it is sufficient to say that the best restaurants throughout France are designated by one, two or three stars. But there are only ten three-star restaurants, sixty-six with two stars and five hundred and seventy with one. You can imagine then how the one-star chefs yearn for the second and the two-star cooks strive for that rare third star. Whenever you have something for which humans desire and for which they will struggle, you have the basis of a story which your reader can share.

Thus, one day when touring the château country of the Loire, and after a particularly felicitous meal at the one-star Hostellerie Château at Chaumont-sur-Loire, M. Bonneval was born.

He is, of course, not specifically the host of that particular tavern, but you will find him in France wherever you go to a starred restaurant or hostelry, emerging from the kitchen to look things over in his chef's uniform and tall linen hat. He is usually

*stout from the joy of his own food and equally usually a genuine
artist. Likewise you will find Madame, his wife, clad in black,
presiding over the Caisse. This combination is almost obligatory
for a first-class restaurant, for these are the people with tradition
and who really care. Perhaps the most famous, characteristic and
wonderful pair in this category are M. and Madame Dumaine of
the Côte d'Or at Saulieu. M. Dumaine is probably the best chef
in France today and his is one of the ten restaurants with the
coveted three stars.*

*The idea then was born at Chaumont-sur-Loire in the fall of
1952 and I remember working on it in my mind all the rest of
my holiday, driving through Europe, searching for an ending that
suited me. The twist that came to me finally was one of those
fortunate gifts from on high sometimes bestowed upon writers
and for which one can only send aloft a humble 'Thank you.'*

*The story was written at the country home of Geoff and Drue
Parsons at Moigny, outside Paris. Geoff was then editor of the
Paris edition of the 'New York Herald Tribune' before he went on
to bigger jobs.*

*The story was dispatched to agent Ober who promptly sold it
to the 'Saturday Evening Post' who published under the title* THE
SECRET INGREDIENT. *I should remark that while this 'Post' habit of
changing titles is a constant irritant to a writer, the size of the
'Post' cheques tends to salve the wound.*

*The tale duly appeared and happily was a hit, if the quantity
and quality of the fan mail it drew was my criterion, and that
was that. I filed M. Bonneval away in my mind as a character I
would use again if I could come upon an amusing and agreeable
plot. You might imagine that in the meantime M. Bonneval would
have remained decently buried in the 'Post' files. But no. Sometimes by good fortune you endow a character with more life than
intended, with the result that they set off upon adventures of
their own and thereby hangs a strange tale of embarrassment.*

*The victim was one of America's top-flight authors. Some two
years after my story had appeared, this writer and his wife set
off on a tour of Europe. Like many of us who use our profession
to get somebody else to pay for our travels, he signed with a syndicate to send back a story a week in the shape of an essay or an
anecdote or a bit of fiction derived from European sources.*

*Arrived in Paris the writer and his wife were invited to a dinner
party by some friends, but unfortunately the afternoon preceding
the dinner the author became suddenly indisposed, not to any
alarming degree, but sufficiently to make him wish no part of a
large and taxing dinner. He said that he would remain at home*

in his hotel resting, but there was no reason why his wife should not attend, and she did.

During the course of the dinner conversation, apparently the subject of the Guide Michelin, its uses, its integrity, etc., came up and one of the guests said, 'Have you heard of the French chef on the Loire who . . .' etc. etc., and thereupon launched in the tale of M. Bonneval and his adventures in gaining the second star for his hostel. Only he told it not as a story he had read in a magazine, but as a true story which had been recounted to him by a friend who had heard it from a friend who had received it via another friend of a friend who had been there. My paper puppet had made the transition from ink stamped upon wood pulp to flesh and blood. All the details as well as the plot of my story were there, only recounted as true happenings and vouched for.

Now any man who takes on the task of producing a short story or even a short essay, incident or anecdote a week knows what he is up against and everything must needs become grist to his mill. Likewise a good wife will understand her husband's problem and help him by keeping her eyes and ears open. And so did this writer's helpmeet. For she came home to her ailing spouse glowing with her prize which would give him surcease for at least one week, saying, 'I heard the most charming true story about a French chef tonight' and then with great accuracy passed on the story. The writer, not a 'Post' reader, took it as gospel. He wrote it the following week and mailed it off happily to his syndicate, who just as happily shipped it out to their clients and it was duly published not only in various newspapers in the United States but also Europe.

The first I heard of this unfortunate and wholly accidental plagiarism was when I received a desperately unhappy three-page letter with cuttings of the story from the author, with apologies saying that he had received dozens of letters advising him of the identical 'Post' story published two years previous, that he had read it with mounting horror and, of course, had notified his syndicate at once to call in the story where it had not yet appeared. There was nothing to be done about those which had already been published. I never felt so sympathetic towards anyone in my life, for it could have happened to me. I got him on the telephone immediately, commiserated with him, and we agreed that the money he had received for the story should be given to charity. The double existence of M. Bonneval, on paper at least, came to an end. But for all I know he still survives as a real and living person at dinner parties in La Belle France.

THE AWFUL SECRET OF
M. BONNEVAL

Next time you are touring the château country of France and visit the string of airy castles cresting the hilltops along the placid Loire from Blois to Tours, you surely will drop down from the towered and mullioned keep of the Château Loiret, just below Chaumont, to eat a meal and drink the wine of the famous Auberge Château Loiret at the foot of the castle.

There you will unquestionably partake of that superb and unrivalled specialty of the house, *Poularde Surprise Treize Minets* and find your palate enthralled by the indefinable flavour imparted to the fowl by the mysterious ingredient which is the particular secret of Monsieur Armand Bonneval, host and chef of the *auberge*. And like so many, many others before you, you will attempt without success to identify the famous component X which to this day has defied the most educated taste buds in France.

You also will encounter Monsieur Bonneval, stocky, red-faced with short-cut, upstanding, pepper-and-salt hair, youthful-looking because of the energy and kindliness in his face, and Madame Bonneval, a woman of large heart and girth, who, as always in France, will be seated behind the desk in charge of the cash box and the accounts.

And, either perched on the desk next to Madame Bonneval or twining at the feet of her husband as he appears at the dining-room door to check on the effect of his cooking, you will probably observe a small black-and-white cat – not a particularly beautiful specimen, owing to the fact that she is somewhat cross-eyed, but nevertheless the beloved pet and pride and joy of monsieur and madame, your hosts.

As a matter of fact, the famous and succulent recipe is in a way associated with her, Minette being her name. But '*Minet*' in France is also the generic nickname for cats, just as we call them 'puss,' and thus a literal translation of the by-now-world-renowned dish of *Poularde Surprise Treize Minets*, might be 'Chicken-surprise-in-the-style-of-thirteen-cats.'

However, when it comes to inquiring of M. Bonneval how this epicure's delight was named or what it is that makes his *poularde* more tasty, stimulating and unforgettable than any other in the world, and what unknown ingredient is the key to this miraculous gastronomic blend, you will, I know, run up against a stone wall.

320

Guarded blueprints for aeroplanes, battleships and submarines are traded on an international bourse, diplomatic confidences are whispered over cocktails, the secrets of the atom bomb have been freely bandied about; but up to this moment, not one single person in the whole world outside of Monsieur and Madame Bonneval has been privy to the secret of the recipe for this famous delicacy.

Permit me then:

In the days prior to the events I am about to narrate, Armand Bonneval, former assistant chef of the Café de Paris, honourably retired, *Cordon Bleu* member of the Club de Cent, and now sole owner and proprietor of the Auberge Château Loiret, was consumed with a burning ambition.

In the Guide Michelin for 1951, that tourist's and gourmet's bible, which is the automobile traveller's survey of France, the *auberge* was designated by three crossed spoons and forks, denoting a 'very comfortable restaurant.' This was not at all bad, particularly for a restaurant in a village as small as Loiret, where the usual indication was one crossed spoon and fork or none at all. But it did not satisfy the artistic and creative soul of Monsieur Bonneval. In his day he had been a great cook. In his old age he longed for the tangible recognition of his genius. A higher rating would likewise make a considerable financial difference to himself and madame, his partner through fifty years of unremitting toil.

The size and location of his *auberge* precluded his receiving the four or five crossed utensils reserved for the big, de luxe restaurants of Paris, Lyon, Vichy or Cannes. However, the famous Guide Michelin annual has further signs to distinguish the superior cuisines it had tested and listed in villages and towns throughout France – namely, one, two or three stars added to the spoons and forks.

Three stars, denoting one of the best tables in the nation, and worthy of a special journey of many miles, were as beyond the reach and hopes of M. Bonneval as the stars that spangled the firmament above the Loire Valley at night. There were but ten of these awarded in all France.

Nor was there any better chance of achieving two stars, indicating an '. . . excellent cuisine: worth a detour,' of which there were but sixty-one examples in all the thousands of restaurants, *auberges,* hotels and *bistros* throughout the land.

But Monsieur Bonneval did yearn most mightily with his honest heart and Frenchman's pride to be awarded the addition of the single star which would announce to traveller and native alike

L

that he set 'une bonne table dans la localite' and that the visitor to his board would be rewarded with something special.

If his winning of the three crossed spoons and forks had already made him an important man in the district, the star would elevate him to the status of distinguished citizen. If now they just managed to make both ends meet, the added star would enable them to amass a competency towards their final days. Alas, there was nothing specific that Monsieur Bonneval could do to achieve this ambition, for the matter was not in his hands.

As he would explain sadly to Madame Bonneval, when sitting quietly in their apartment above the *auberge* after hours, with his beloved Minette purring in his lap, there were literally hundreds of thousands of eating places throughout France that had to be covered; the inspectors, or official tasters, of the Guide Michelin were only so many; they had but one stomach apiece which would hold only so many cubic centimetres. Worked out mathematically, it might be years before one again appeared to sample the fare at the Auberge Loiret, and perhaps never again in their lifetime.

But if even by some chance one should appear, there was no opportunity for Monsieur Bonneval to prepare the kind of specialty that would be likely to bowl over the taster, for the simple reason that Guide Michelin conducted its tests and listings with scrupulous integrity and fairness. One never knew when the inspector was in one's midst. He came and went in the guise of an ordinary tourist. The Grand Lottery in Paris was not handled with more honesty and care.

'Ah, if one could but know in advance sometime,' he would groan, filled with ambition and desire. 'Who knows but with the star I would be able to take you to Italy on that little trip we planned so long ago.'

And Madame Bonneval would comfort him, 'Never mind, Armand. I am sure you will receive your star somehow, because you deserve it. And besides, it would not be fair if you should know in advance.'

One summer's noon a letter arrived for Monsieur Bonneval that caused him to stare as though he could not believe his eyes, and then call loudly for madame to come and read it to him again, to make sure he had not been deceived. Madame did so, with her circle of additional chins quivering a little. It was short and to the point.

My dear Bonneval: I doubt whether you would remember me, but many years ago you had the occasion to do me a good turn when I was hungry and on my uppers, and I have never forgotten your kindness.

'It so happens that I now find myself in a position to return the favour. Through my connections with the Guide Michelin, upon which I will not elaborate, I am advised that on Friday, the thirteenth of July, an inspector will be passing through Loiret-sur-Loire, and he has been instructed to dine at the *auberge* to check on the quality of your meals. I know that your genius will find the best way to make use of this information. Wishing you the very best of luck, I am an old friend who must sign himself

'XYZ'

There it was – the bolt out of the clearest of skies. Not only was the longed-for visit to take place but Monsieur Bonneval was actually to have notice in advance and time to prepare one of his more superb specialties, such as duck stuffed with chopped truffles, liver paste and *champignons* with orange sauce or his own version of *coq au vin*.

'I will be famous! We will grow rich!' declared Monsieur Bonneval, feasting his eyes again on the page of the wonderful letter. But then he cried in alarm, 'Great heavens! The letter is dated July eighth, but it has been delayed in transit. Friday the thirteenth, when the inspector is to come, is this very day.'

It was true. The calendar on the wall displayed a large red '13.' Suddenly the affair assumed an urgency that was not dispelled by the exclamation of Madame Bonneval, who had glanced out of the window, 'And that must be he, arriving this very minute! He has come for lunch.'

A large and glittery car had poked its expensive snout alongside the *auberge* and discharged one who could only have spent the major portion of his existence sampling the finest foods and wines, for he was as fat as a prize pig stuffed for exhibition. He carried the Guide Michelin in his hand, and entered the front door with a combined expression of truculence and expectancy.

At once he became identified in Bonneval's mind as 'Monsieur Michelin Taster,' friend, enemy, instrument upon which he would play his gastronomic symphony, critic and bearer of the laurel wreath, or rather star, that would eventually be bestowed upon him.

However, one thing was patent. There was not a moment to lose. Already flustered by the unexpected imminence of his trial, Monsieur Bonneval rushed off to the kitchen, crying to madame as he made his exit, 'I shall prepare for him *le Homard dans la Lune!*'

Which was not at all what he had meant either to say or to cook.

'Lobster in the Moon' was the last thing in the world he would have dreamed of making for such an important test, knowing full well that with lobster it can be this way or that way, whereas your ducks, chickens and *gigots* are always safe.

For the recipe is a tricky one, calling for one large lobster, *bien vivant* – in other words, a brisk and lively fellow – to be extracted, cut up, seasoned with salt and pepper, and sautéed in oil and butter, after which the oil is withdrawn and a tablespoon of finely chopped shallots or chives and a whisper of garlic is added. To give this mixture a little authority, a glass of cognac and another of white wine are now introduced, after which three tomatoes are broken into small bits with a half tablespoonful of chopped parsley and a shot of Cayenne pepper, and the whole thing is cooked for twenty minutes in a casserole at a steady heat. The lobster is then removed and stuffed into the 'Moon,' a hollowed-out, crisp brioche. Now comes the delicate moment. The sauce is thickened with a little cream laced with a dash of brandy and the whole thing poured over the hot, crispy, lobster-filled pastry.

A man wants to be in complete command of himself to bring off a dish like that, particularly when it meant as much as it did to Monsieur Bonneval. That he was not, was evidenced when he almost bumped into Minette, the black-and-white cat, as he charged into the kitchen, bellowing loudly for Celeste, the kitchen maid, and Brazon, the man of all work, her lover.

This served only to unnerve him further, for it so happened that Minette had been so fortunate not long before as to encounter a gentleman friend in the park of the château who had been able to overlook the unhappy tendencies of her eyes to cross, and she was now imminently about to be blessed with the fruits of this genuine affection, and a fair packet of them, too, if one could judge from her size.

Nor was it exactly a happy moment in the life of Celeste, who, a few weeks ago, had been seized with the idea of marrying Brazon, and of course had demanded an increase in pay to support this bizarre notion – a request which Monsieur Bonneval, backed by madame, had quite sensibly refused, since one did not say yes to such ideas the first time. As a result, Celeste was red-eyed and snuffly a good deal of the time, and not quite herself.

This was a pity, for she was to Monsieur Bonneval what the deft instrument nurse is to the great surgeon. With paring knife and chopping bowl, a veteran of a hundred routines, she had stood at his side ready to supply in an instant what the master needed in the line of utensils, saucepans, casseroles, chopped onions, shaved carrots, bouquets of herbs and so on.

So there was already a considerable disaster building up in Monsieur Bonneval's kitchen, let alone its being Friday the thirteenth.

The lobster, when produced from the cold room, not only did not answer to the description of a brisk and lively fellow but, on the contrary, was practically in a state of rigor mortis. Cutting him up, hence, was no longer a culinary gesture, but an autopsy. It was Fate giving Monsieur Bonneval one more chance to evade what it had in store for him. Had he been in his right senses he would have dumped the crustacean corpse into the dustbin and started on something else.

But his mind was imprisoned by that inflexibility and rigidity which, in the face of crisis, sometimes affects the best of cooks and housekeepers. Monsieur Bonneval was bent on making Lobster in the Moon, and so he rushed onward headlong to doom.

Almost at once there commenced such a catalogue of kitchen catastrophes as can be appreciated only by the housewife or chef who has battled the extraordinary breed of gremlins that sometimes arrive to interfere, obstruct and frustrate when there is a truly important dinner to be got on to the table.

While Celeste reversed her instruction and scraped a *soupçon* of shallot into a tablespoon of chopped garlic, instead of vice versa, Brazon announced that there appeared to have been a change in the wind, affecting the draught of the huge iron stove, plus a blockage of some sort, and he could seem to put no heat in it, and Odette, the waitress, affected by the mounting tension, upset the soup into the lap of the fat man identified in the mind of Bonneval as Monsieur Michelin Taster. This fetched a bellow of rage from the dining-room, matched only by the sound emerging from the kitchen when Monsieur Bonneval discovered that Celeste, ruminating on the inhumanity of man, had taken his sautéeing pan, which for eighteen years had known no other cleansing than with salt and a piece of bread, and washed it with kitchen soap and water.

Disaster followed upon disaster. The stove, stuffed with newspapers, straw, kindling and coke, emitted clouds of acrid smoke, one whiff of which was sufficient to affect the delicate flavours planned by Monsieur Bonneval. The cream pitcher upset in the icebox, inundating everything therein, and at the critical moment it developed that Brazon had misplaced the key to the wine cellar.

Monsieur Bonneval moved as one in the grip of a hideous

nightmare. Matters went from bad to worse as a tin of fat caught fire, the handle of his best frying pan broke and the lamp upset. Celeste and Brazon went completely haywire, the latter breaking the egg beater and short-circuiting the refrigerator, while the former achieved a new high in destructive confusion by putting salt in the egg whites in place of sugar, and cutting up, on the board reserved for crushing garlic, the almonds destined for the famous *soufflé à la curorange*.

Through all this, red-faced, sweating, the glare as of a wild animal filling his heretofore gentle eyes, struggling to retain his temper and his sanity in the face of trials that would have disjointed a saint, Monsieur Bonneval stolidly attempted to fight his way through the morass of calamities that was engulfing him.

It was a losing battle. Friday the thirteenth was not through with him yet. For just as he was stirring the delicate *sauce vanille* intended to go with the *soufflé* which was browning in the oven, Madame Bonneval, unnerved by the sounds of panic backstage, abandoned her post next to the cash box and invaded the kitchen. Her faith in her husband's culinary powers shaken for the first time, she committed the unpardonable crime of opening the oven door to see how the confection was coming along, just as Brazon unlatched the back entrance, permitting a swirl of cool air to tear through the kitchen and smite the *soufflé* where it would hurt the most.

Purple with outrage, Monsieur Bonneval made a lunge to swing shut the oven door. It was at this precise moment that poor Minette chose to make one of her sagging promenades across the kitchen floor just in time to trip and unbalance Monsieur Bonneval and send the *sauce vanille* splashing on to the top of the range, where it made a most dreadful smell.

Something snapped inside Monsieur Bonneval. Flesh and blood could endure no more. Tortured beyond human endurance, he hauled back his right foot and applied it to the rear end of Minette, who happened to be aimed towards the back door at the moment.

With a terrible scream of outraged indignation, the loaded Minette took off like a blimp released from its moorings, and soaring majestically up into the blue, vanished from sight.

Now Monsieur Bonneval turned upon the humans. '*Vache!*' he shouted at his wife. '*Animal!*' he bawled at Celeste. '*Crétin!*' he nominated Odette, the waitress. '*Cochon!*' he dubbed Brazon.

The reactions were immediate. Brazon resigned; Odette vanished; Celeste threw her apron over her head and had hysterics; while Madame Bonneval swept from the kitchen, went upstairs and locked herself in her room. Bonneval himself carried in the *soufflé* and placed it before Monsieur Michelin Taster, where it gave a soft sigh and collapsed flatter than an old-fashioned opera hat.

The fat man took one nibble at the edge of the thing and then let out a roar that shook the dining-room.

'Criminal! Assassin! Poisoner!' he shouted. 'You call yourself a chef! The lobster tastes of soap, the coffee of paraffin and your *soufflé* is flavoured with garlic! Three spoons and forks they have given you, eh?' and at this point he waved the red-covered volume of the Guide Michelin under Monsieur Bonneval's appalled nose. 'Well, when I am finished with you, you will no longer be able to swindle innocent travellers! Faker!'

And with this he tore the napkin from his collar and stalked from the room. When, a few moments later, the car thundered away from the *auberge*, it carried with it, in addition to the indignant fat man, the hopes, ambitions and large pieces of the broken heart of Monsieur Bonneval.

Bonneval however was of the breed that wastes no time crying over spilt cream, but faces manfully up to the blows of life and recovers quickly therefrom. But he needed the aid and companionship of his wife. Pocketing his badly damaged pride, he hurried to the door of madame's locked room, from which emerged sounds of grief, and spoke through the keyhole:

'Come now, my dear, it is all over. Nothing more can happen. I am punished for my sins. The inspector has departed to make his report, and we shall be poor again. But as long as I have you, I shall not lack the courage to make a start again – somewhere in a place where we are not known, perhaps. Come, old friend, we have been through much together. Do not take a little incident to heart.'

From within, Madame Bonneval cried, 'Little incident! You called me a cow!'

Obviously a special effort was required. Monsieur Bonneval now addressed the door as follows: 'Dear wife, I was wrong to let petty trifles exasperate me into forgetting myself. But look. Even in my anger against Fate, how careful I was in my choice of animals. For is not the cow the sweetest, the gentlest, the kindest and the most beautiful in all the kingdom? Does she not, with lavish generosity and warm heart, play mother with her milk to all mankind? Is not her glance melting, her disposition notable and her character beyond reproach? Does not her soft and expressive face invite caresses?' He ceased when he heard the key turning slowly in the lock.

Thereafter he went downstairs, soothed the waitress, apologised to Brazon and cured Celeste's hysterics with a promise of a raise in salary should the *auberge* not be forced to close.

Notwithstanding the peace declared within his domain, the heart of Monsieur Bonneval was as heavy as a stone, for by late evening Minette had not returned. His conscience was as black as the night because of the kick he had bestowed upon her, and particularly in the light of her delicate condition. He would rather have cut off his right arm than perpetrate an indignity, much less an injury, upon his little friend. He had called and called, but there had been no sign of her.

She had every right to be angry with him – if she was still alive. How, then, to persuade her of his love for her, and his terrible contrition? The hour was past eleven.

He had been calling her since ten. Suddenly an idea smote him. Minette was mad about chicken. He would tempt her with her favourite food.

Purpose now gripped Monsieur Bonneval, and he said to himself, *Little Minette, I shall cook you a Poularde Surprise Royale all for your very own. For you I will cook this as I have never cooked before, for I am very ashamed of having lost my temper and kicked you from the rear.*

He set to work at once, and everything seemed to work like magic, as though Friday the thirteenth had expended its malignancy, and Fate was no longer interested in harassing Monsieur Bonneval. The stove functioned like a charm, Brazon was as sharp as a razor, and Celeste was her old, cool, efficient self, anticipating his every wish. Objects not only behaved themselves but positively co-operated, seeming to leap into his hand when he had need of them.

With a series of deft movements he boned the chicken and then stuffed it with goose-liver pâté, truffles and a stew of giblets and kidneys made in meat stock and laced with a jigger of port wine.

Poor Minette, he thought as he added the ruby-red liquid, *after what she had been through she will be in need of a little stimulant.*

Working now with supreme concentration and passion, the recipe burned into his memory the way a conductor knows every note of a great symphony without the score, he set about making a sauce for the bird, using the bones of the pullet, onions, carrots, leeks, celery and a bouquet, which he fortified with a half bottle of Bollinger '43. *One gives champagne to expectant mothers,* he said to himself as the yellow wine frothed into the brown gravy.

Exquisite odours began to fill the kitchen. It was art for love's sake, and like all true artists and lovers, he became inspired and began to improvise as he went along, making a daring and radical experiment with here a herb, there a spice, a bit of smoked fat, a glass of very old cognac. *For if she is a little drunk she will become mellow and forgive me the more readily,* he reasoned.

And then it was, as he ransacked his cupboard of herbs and spices, looking still further to delight the heart and appetite of Minette, that he found and added an ingredient that never before had been a part of *Poularde Surprise Royale* or any other dish.

When the bird was cooked to a turn, he performed some final rites, garnishing it with truffles and *pâté de foie gras,* poured the magnificent sauce over it, partitioned it, and putting one half on to a plate, went out into the night with this savoury harbinger of everything good and perfect that man has learned to do with food.

'Minette! Minette!' he called, placing himself upwind, so that the evening breeze from the Loire would carry the fragrance to every corner of the courtyard where the missing Minette might be lurking. And still there came no answer.

Some time later, painfully and heartbroken and still bearing the dish, he returned to the kitchen, where, at the late hour just before midnight, he found an unaccustomed activity sparked by Madame Bonneval. Coffee was on the fire, a *soufflé* was in the process of being mixed by Brazon, and the other half of the *Poularde Surprise Royale* was missing.

'Ah, there you are,' madame greeted him. 'What a fortunate thing you decided to cook a *poularde*. Only fifteen minutes ago there arrived a traveller, a poor fellow whose car had broken down. He was starving, and begged for a bit of something cold left over. You can imagine how agreeably surprised he was when I was able to set before him your specialty. He is drinking a bottle of the '47 Loiret Suchez with it.'

Monsieur Bonneval stared at his wife, aghast. 'But, *maman!* It is impossible. I cooked this for poor little Minette, whom I kicked so bru——'

He did not finish, for the door leading from the dining-room opened violently, admitting an excited bespectacled little man with a soup-strainer moustache and wearing a seedy suit, but whose eyes and expression nevertheless appeared to command authority.

He paused for a moment *en tableau,* looking from one to another in the kitchen. Then he rushed to Monsieur Bonneval, threw his arms about him and kissed him violently on both cheeks.

'It is you!' he cried. 'You are the magician who has prepared this delectable, this fabulous, this supreme dish! Chef! Genius! Master! I salute you! Not in thirty-five years have I eaten such a *Poularde Surprise Royale*. And at midnight. A veritable palace of gastronomy, a Sorbonne of cookery. Well, you shall have your reward. A star – no, no, what am I saying? – two stars!' And here he paused, and his look changed slightly to one of cunning. 'Three stars if you will tell me the secret ingredient in the *poularde*, the only one I was not able to recognise.'

Monsieur Bonneval could only gape at him. Could it have been then that the other, that fat one, was not Monsieur Michelin Taster? 'I do not – understand,' he stammered.

'But it is simple, dear master,' the man replied. 'Know then that I am Fernand Dumaire, inspector for the Guide Michelin. I was on my way here to test your cookery when that villain of a vehicle I was driving ceased to function. And then, to arrive at midnight and at once to find set before me this masterpiece. Of two stars you are certain, but as a little deal between us, I will risk the third in exchange for your secret ingredient!'

Sweat suddenly beaded the brow of Monsieur Bonneval. 'The – secret – ingredient?' he repeated.

'But of course. Naturally, I recognised the chervil and the delicate touch of burnet. It took courage to use the basil, and the idea of applying the marjoram to offset the tarragon was capital, while the amount of thyme and sage was perfectly balanced. I should judge the Oporto in the sauce was a trifle more *sec* than is usual – probably a '39 – and the champagne, of course, was Bollinger '43, as anyone with half a palate would notice. But one flavour baffles and escapes me, and I, Fernand Dumaire, must know what it is. For you have changed, improved and glorified *Poularde Surprise Royale*. It has become a new creation and you shall have the honour of naming it. But first tell me the ingredient that has baffled me, in exchange for the third star. Is it a bargain?'

There was a moment of silence. Then Monsieur Bonneval said slowly, 'I cannot tell you, monsieur. I shall be content with the two stars you so generously promised me.'

Madame Bonneval stared at her husband as though he were out of his mind, but the chief taster again fell on his neck and kissed him. 'You are right, my friend, and noble and honest. A great chef must never reveal his secrets. I tempted you and you resisted. Well, two stars will distinguish you so that the world will beat a path to your kitchen.'

At this moment there was an interruption. There came a sweet little call from the outer darkness, and Minette loped into the room, a thin and shapely Minette, though now more cross-eyed with love than ever. She deposited a newborn kitten in the box that had been made ready at the side of the stove. She retired. She came back with another kitten, and another and another. Thirteen times she departed and returned as they watched and counted, fascinated, and the tears of joy flowed from the eyes of Monsieur Bonneval.

When the last one had been deposited and Minette commenced nursing, Monsieur Bonneval declared with deep feeling, 'You said, monsieur, that I might name my *poularde*. Very well. I name it *Poularde Surprise Treize Minets.*'

At this moment Brazon produced the *soufflé curorange* prepared from the recipe of Monsieur Bonneval, a dream, a vision, high, potent, sturdy, uncollapsible, a beige cloud, with the interior construction apparently of reinforced steel. They joined around the table, and with a Moët and Chandon '37 they toasted the two stars of Monsieur Bonneval and the *Poularde Surprise Treize Minets*.

So then, the next time you tour in France and drop in at the Auberge Loiret to partake of Monsieur Bonneval's delectable 'chicken à la the thirteen kittens,' do not, I beg of you, let on that I have given away his secret ingredient and the reason why he could not reveal it even for the honour and accolade of the third star.

It was simple, but a trifle unusual. As you have already suspected, for love of Minette he had seasoned the *poularde* liberally with that herb beloved of all felines, the strongly scented leaves of *Nepeta cataria*, a plant better known to one and all as catnip.

The Hat

THE HAT *is an example of how broadening travel may be and that you never know where the idea for your next story may lurk.*

I was returning from research in Israel via one of those agreeable white motor ships of the Linea Adriatica which make the four-day boat trips from Haifa to Genova, one joyous day of sunshine and adventure after another. These vessels touch at Cyprus and Piraeus giving one a day ashore at each after a heavenly sail through the Greek islands and the Corinth Canal, headed for the toe of the Italian boot.

The trip through the Corinth Canal is unspectacular except, as I remember, for the little brown hawks or falcons which make their nests in holes in the steep sides of this big ditch and sometimes fly alongside the ship whistling or circling the masts. A tug hauls the steamer through this passage; one sits or reclines topside in the sunshine and lets it happen. There are no locks, the ditch simply connects with the sea at both ends.

One does, however, pass beneath a bridge, a high, spidery affair devoted to foot and vehicular traffic. I have made this passage four times and each time as we passed beneath there was a crowd gathered on the bridge. I can understand their gathering, I should have stopped there myself. There is something fascinating about seeing a huge steamer proceeding as it were overland.

Well, during one of these trips some unknown, unidentified Greek overcome apparently by the beauty of the spectacle of our passing beneath him like a toy ship in a bathtub, waved his hat at us so enthusiastically that it slipped from his fingers and, tumbling and turning like a falling leaf, floated down to land upon our sun deck where one of the passengers picked it up, shook it at the gesticulating man who had lost it and who appeared to be roaring with laughter, and then set it upon his own head. It was a brown felt hat, much battered, dirty and worn, and that was that, as far as facts went.

However, I fell to thinking about that hat, the journey on which it had embarked and the man who had originally worn it. I had studied him with my field glasses and he was young, good-looking and obviously a workman for he had workman's tools over his shoulder, a pick and shovel.

Such reflections led me into a consideration of the nature of the old, tried, and well-loved garment. A hat in particular becomes a part of one, and the longer one has had it and the older and dirtier and smellier it gets the more does it become an adjunct with which one is loath to part. In fact man's resistance in giving up an old hat in favour of a new one is a well-known cliché, but one which is founded upon fact. The wife can jeopardise the love of the husband by disposing of an old fishing or camping hat behind the back of her spouse.

And so I began to wonder about this man whose hat had left him to go off on a white ship bound for the West and how he would feel about it.

Now this is one of the joys, I maintain, of being a writer, that once fired the imagination is free to make what it pleases of its contacts with life and people. The man on the bridge probably went home, laughed over the tale of losing his hat and forgot about it. But not my man. He was already beginning to take shape and form in my mind. He was a free and adventurous soul who had only been waiting for that single nudge from fate to break from his cocoon and soar into the blue upon the brightly coloured wings of adventure. MY man was going after his hat.

Thus began this story. As to its developments, who can reflect upon the tale of a poor Greek emigrating to the United States without thinking of the success story of the Skouras Brothers, and this led me to introduce my hatless man into the world of entertainment and the cinema. It was just at this time too that stereoscopic and stereophonic pictures were making their début and the lovely complicating feature of a producing company and an exhibitor being indissolubly united by the mechanics of this new art form stood deliciously to hand.

As to the character of Meyer McManus the Irish Jew who was head of a great motion picture company, I'll confess I went afield for him by way of Dublin which at that time was boasting of a Jewish mayor, an anomaly which was attracting considerable attention. I had never met him but I had read about him. Several years later when I was living in Ireland researching the life of St Patrick I had the pleasure of having a drink with this charming gentleman.

Well there are the ingredients for THE HAT, *a thoroughly inconsequential story which it gave me a great deal of pleasure to write. I have often been damned as a short story writer with the words 'slick' and 'craftsman-like' but the point neglected usually is that to stir up ingredients such as I have indicated were tossed into the mixing bowl of this yarn and come up with a story in which all the parts fit neatly and to my satisfaction is enormous good fun. There is personal enjoyment in every moment of doing this, solving problems, hitting upon little ideas to enhance the affair and producing a finished product in which the joints fit as neatly and tightly as they do in a crossword puzzle.*

The 'Saturday Evening Post' published THE HAT, *and changed the title to* IT HAPPENED IN HOLLYWOOD, *which I must admit is a more lively label than mine. The story went forth and I hope fulfilled its function of entertaining its readers.*

THE HAT

This story begins many years ago on the bridge that spans the Corinth Canal in Greece, that narrow, man-made ditch that makes an island out of the Peloponnese Peninsula and saves a day or so sailing time to and from Piraeus.

Viewed from this bridge, a ship, moving through the towering brown walls of the cut, looks like the vivid toy of a child and the crew and passengers resemble foreshortened dolls with white, upturned, indistinguishable faces.

The smooth progress of a ship proceeding overland, as it were, hauled by its black, insect-like outrider of a tug, has an irresistible attraction for spectators above who wave and shout down unintelligible greetings. The passengers reply in like manner from far below and thus there is established a kind of friendly contact between the voyagers and the stay-at-homes.

This was the emotion felt by George Pavlides, a road worker, as he paused on the bridge on his way home from Souidas, where he worked, to Nikodimou the little village where he lived.

A cheerful, kindly fellow always doing favours for people and known for giving of his best on the job, George had not amounted to very much in life, but this fact did not weigh upon him for there was still plenty of time. He was young, no more than twenty-five, strong and of a generous, happy and carefree disposition, as sunny as the land of his birth.

He had clothes to cover himself, enough to eat and drink and the girls had an eye for him, for he was six feet tall with big brown shoulders, handsome head with dark, curling hair and virile moustache. In all he was well content with life.

The craft now passing in the narrow ditch below was snow white with a single buff funnel to either side of which was affixed a relief in metal of a charging winged lion.

This gallant sight delighted Pavlides as it did many others passing likewise on the bridge. They shouted and waved; handkerchiefs fluttered in the hands of the tiny figures beneath as the passengers on the liner returned the greeting. Pavlides removed his hat and swung it violently back and forth in a gesture of salute and bonhommie towards the strangers gliding by.

He waved it, in fact, so violently and enthusiastically that it suddenly escaped the grip of his fingers and wafted first this way, then that, by the strong air currents in the cut, it sank rapidly to land miraculously on the forward deck of the ship at the feet of a passenger who picked it up, donned it for an instant and then waved it back at its former owner.

At this, George Pavlides shouted with laughter. He yelled, he chuckled, he roared and bellowed. He pounded his sides; he thumped the back of a policeman standing next to him.

'Look look!' he cried – 'My hat has gone off by itself on a voyage. Where do you suppose it is bound?'

The policeman who had recognised the Italian flag and the insignia on the funnel as being the Lion of St Mark replied – 'To Venice, most likely. Was it a good hat?'

'An old friend,' said Pavlides. 'I have had it for years. Oh-ho-ho-ho-ho! Did you ever see anything so amusing?'

In the meantime the ship was gliding on through the cut growing smaller and smaller, soon to vanish in the distance. Still laughing and shaking his curly, hatless head, Pavlides shouldered his tools and continued on his way home.

But that night he found himself for the first time in his life strangely restless and no longer entirely contented. It was true he had had the hat for a long time. Now it had left him unceremoniously and gone off to see the world, leaving him behind. Ought he not to follow it? One does not desert old friends thus. It was not the fault of the hat that this had happened. If Venice was where his headgear had gone then maybe he too ought to journey thither. Soon he felt this overwhelmingly.

The next day, Pavlides quit his job and set out to work his way to Venice where he arrived eventually in good health and full of admiration for this wonderful city.

Unable to speak a word of Italian, he sought out a restaurant where sure enough there were some Greeks who explained to the proprietor that this strong, handsome newcomer had come there from Corinth in pursuit of his hat. This so impressed the owner that he gave Pavlides a job as a dishwasher and later, when he had learned something of the language, a post as a waiter.

One day, wandering the Piazza San Marco, Pavlides passed a shipping office in the window of which was a picture of the very vessel on to which his hat had fallen, or at least one like it. He went in to ask about it.

Ordinarily one who offered in broken Italian such a query as – 'Eight months ago, this beautiful vessel of yours passed beneath our splendid bridge across the Corinth Canal and I dropped my hat. Can you tell me what has become of it?' would have been dismissed as a madman. But Pavlides' smile was so warm and sincere and his brown eyes so trusting that they actually listened to him.

Then, miracle of miracles, a junior clerk sitting at a far desk bethought himself : 'I remember something of the sort. There was a passenger who came in here who spoke of such an incident and that he had retrieved the hat.'

But he could recall nothing else about him. 'I only know that he was on his way to America,' he added.

Pavlides thanked him and went back to the restaurant determined to go to America. 'For,' he explained, 'I have found out that my hat has gone there and if my hat wishes me to go to America, that is where I must go also.'

The Italians thought him mad, but the Greeks, being like Pavlides, free souls, understood him perfectly and directed him to the American Consul where he must apply for permission to emigrate to that country.

This official asked of Pavlides his reason for wishing to go to the New World.

'Because my hat has journeyed there,' he explained through an interpreter, 'and where my hat is I should be likewise,' and he told him the story of the beautiful boat that had passed beneath the bridge and what had transpired.

The Consul – this was before the days of quotas and likewise before the days when U.S. foreign officials had been intimidated – roared with laughter and said to his clerk : 'Of all the cock-eyed reasons I ever heard . . . Give the chap the permit. I like him.'

This was the way it was. Everybody liked George Pavlides. Six months later he left for America and because he had troubled to learn some English he was able to secure a job as a waiter aboard a Greek-American liner on which he made a number of crossings to save himself some money before stepping ashore with his wife on to the then more hospitable Strand of Ellis Island.

Ah yes, the wife he acquired was a tall, beautiful Greek girl with dark hair – a fine woman – by the name of Sophia Karakeno who came from the island of Kythira and was a stewardess.

George loved her for her warmth and good nature as well as her expressive eyes and her full, uncomplicated femininity. During several voyages he wooed her ardently.

'Marry me,' he urged her 'and we will go ashore in America and find my hat together. After all, that is why I have come all this great distance. You will see, it will lead us to fame and fortune.'

Sophia looked in despair at this handsome, apparently irresponsible young man who actually did seem to have travelled this far and for no other reason in pursuit of an old hat he had carelessly dropped from a bridge in far off Corinth.

'What is one to do with one such as you?' she protested. 'I do not wish to get married, but it is obvious that a fellow like you needs someone to look after him. Very well. I will marry you but only on condition that afterwards there is no further nonsense about a hat.'

And with this, George Pavlides was for the time well content for he was convinced that in Sophia he had acquired the most wonderful woman in the world.

The rise of those two giants of the entertainment world, George Pavlides, theatre magnate and Meyer (The Skimmer) McManus, president of Interworld Pictures of Hollywood was almost simultaneous. Although they had never met, the struggle in which they became involved was the result of an intense personal dislike dating from a contretemps which I shall narrate shortly.

Each refused to give in. Newspapers had printed Pavlides' statement: 'If I am ever cotch making business with that skonks I will donate a million dollars colds cash to Grik orphans tsildrens.'

Equally, McManus had been quoted – 'Any time I make a deal with that hyena, sure and I'll donate a million dollars to be divided equally between Hebrew and Irish orphans.' This split was made necessary by the fact that McManus was one of those oddities of nature, an Irish Jew from Dublin, combining the finest features of each. The various orphans hoped for the best but in view of the intensity of the feud there did not seem to be much chance of their collecting.

McManus's nickname, 'The Skimmer' derived from the fact that since he had flashed like a comet upon the moving picture horizon a quarter of a century ago, nobody outside his immediate family and a few intimate friends had ever seen what the top of his head looked like. For he never appeared at a production conference, board meeting, financial agenda, story round-table, or big Interworld premier, uncovered.

There were many rumours abroad as to why he never bared his head in public. One was that he was orthodoxly religious; another that owing to some strange disease suffered in childhood his hair grew only in small green tufts and a third that he had not only no hair at all but the top of his skull was missing and you could see his great brain throbbing underneath his scalp.

Whatever the reason, he was no fool and held the film world in the hollow of his hand. The only figure that matched him in our era was George Pavlides, the one-time Greek immigrant who rose to the ownership of three-quarters of the great moving picture cathedrals in the principal cities of the United States.

For, the Pavlides who came ashore at Ellis Island with his handsome, strapping wife, in the long ago, was already a far different individual from the one who had laid down his pick and shovel in the Peloponnesus to follow in the path of his errant hat.

He was now able to speak Italian, a smattering of French and something that passed for English. He had been around and seen a little of the world and its ways; he had a profession with which he could always earn a living no matter where, since good waiters were scarce. And he was no longer alone.

He retained his cheerful, generous, sunny disposition and his capacity for hard and devoted work. Journeying to San Francisco he secured a job in a restaurant. He had the gift of being able to deposit a plate of noodle soup or an order of Yankee potroast before a customer with the air of one who has the good fortune to be serving a king. Not only that but his example infected others of the help working with him.

In no time at all he was head-waiter, later he was able to purchase an interest and when a grateful partner died and left him his share he became sole owner. His personality, solicitude for his clients and little generosities such as giving away the after-dinner coffee, mints, bonbons and cigarettes, plus his wife's excellent business sense, made it a success and shortly after he opened another and another, extending his chain to New York,

Boston, Chicago, Detroit and Philadelphia. Fifteen years from the time he landed in New York, he was a millionaire.

The hat was all but forgotten or at least never mentioned in the Pavlides mansion atop San Francisco's Nob Hill where he made his home with his stately wife and their three boys and two girls.

In 1939, a fellow Greek who owned a theatre in St Louis found himself in difficulties. With characteristic generosity Pavlides bought the movie house from him at a price far beyond its worth, bailing his friend out but landing himself with a white elephant.

He promptly went to St Louis, threw himself into the theatre business and within a year had evolved the famous Pavlides Palace System in which the patron not only saw the finest feature films and stage show from deep, plush seats uniform over the house, but because of Pavlides' love of people and his desire to share his success with them and make them happy, was the recipient of all kinds of gifts and benefits.

There was a nursery where mothers could leave babies, a television room where father could catch the end of the night baseball game; free lemonade in paper cups was passed down the aisles during intermission, children were gifted with bonbons and bubble gum, skull caps, six-shooters or ray guns whatever the fashion was while their mothers received recipe books, aprons, small, useful household articles; there was always a surprise of some sort. In short, everything that could delight the patron, increase his comfort and enhance enjoyment of the film was freely lavished.

Naturally the result was that the Pavlides Palace in St Louis became a huge success and soon made money hand over fist. Within ten years there were Pavlides Palaces in all of the key cities of the United States and George stood at the top of the entertainment world. At last he had found a field in which he was truly content. He sold out his restaurant chain in order to concentrate upon his theatre empire.

It was at this point he became involved in the battle with Skimmer McManus which shook the nation and eventually threatened both men with ruin.

It came about when Pavlides threw the new McManus picture 'Body of Love,' starring Tanya Tanot, a young ex-sales lady better known for outsized mammary glands than histrionic talent and Ramon Gentile, a Latin scoundrel, out of all the Pavlides Palaces because, as he put it in one of his rare public utterances: 'Is steenky pictsoor. Steenky pictsoor is not good for tsildrens to see, bot it is even worses for mothers. We will not play steenky pictsoors in Pavlides Palaces.'

Naturally, Skimmer McManus took umbrage, particularly since he was known to have occasional lapses of taste and this was definitely one of them. His phenomenal luck which had characterised his entire career did not desert him and the film cleaned up in other houses, but Pavlides' just criticism stung. McManus permitted himself to be quoted to the effect that that Greek ex-strumberry pie hustler wouldn't know a picture if he saw one.

This reference to his earlier days as a knight of the black tie and white apron hit Pavlides where it hurt most, through his children who were now attending fine schools. For the first and only time he lost his temper and referred to McManus as 'Abie's Irish Stinkweed,' and the battle to the death was joined. No Interworld film could get a Pavlides Palace chain booking. No Pavlides Palace could get any Meyer McManus picture.

Each might have been able to survive this and the feud could have run an uninterrupted course but for the sudden advent of 3D. In the scramble to get aboard the bandwagon both men committed a fatal error.

Negotiating swiftly and secretly Pavlides bought the rights to equip his theatres to show Life-o-Scope, the last word in dimensional illusion in which the actors not alone came down off the screen and sat in the laps of the patrons, but practically went home with them after the show.

Operating equally rapidly and sub rosa, McManus bought the rights to cameras, sound and reproducing equipment of Life-o-Scope.

And there they were. When the news broke it rocked the film world. For McManus could not show his films in any but Pavlides Theatres, while the Pavlides equipment would now screen only McManus pictures. Yet each would have remained stubborn, preferring to go bankrupt than meet one another.

But the pressure was irresistible. For they were not only rugged individualists, but heads of commercial empires upon whom thousands of innocent people depended for a living. The news leaked out that Meyer Skimmer McManus and George Pavlides were at last to come face to face across a conference table to try to iron out the tangle into which they had got themselves.

The meeting was held on neutral ground in Santa Barbara, half-way between San Francisco and Hollywood. Reporters and photographers were foiled by elaborate security precautions. Present besides the two principals, by agreement, were an attorney and a secretary for each.

An elaborate protocol and time schedule was set up introducing first the secretaries who appeared carrying pencil, paper and supplies to prepare the arena, then the two lawyers with brief-cases materialised at the same moment and took up their stations.

At precisely the stroke of ten a.m., the two titans appeared simultaneously at opposite doorways leading to the conference table, marched stiffly to the battleground and took their seats, for the purpose of exploring terms and conditions leading to a possible get-together, with each, by further agreement, com-municating with the other only through the medium of their solicitors. Behind the doors waited a further retinue of lawyers, general managers, vice-presidents and press agents.

At exactly one minute past ten, one of these with a shameless eye to a keyhole cried out – 'Great Jehosaphat, they're killing one another!' For it looked as though the two principals were locked across the table in a swaying, clutching, hair-pulling brawl to the death. But so strict were the orders that none dared enter to separate them.

Yet it was not entirely so. And it is my privilege now, by what means I am not at liberty to reveal, to relate for the first time what really happened.

No sooner had the two men seated themselves on opposite sides of the table when Pavlides was seen staring at McManus like a man who is viewing a ghost. However, there was nothing ghost-like about the film producer who, like the Greek, was a big man and well built, with a square head, pinkish eyebrows over shrewd blue eyes. He was dressed in a natty dark suit, with a matching shirt and bow tie and the only thing unusual about him was the fact that he was wearing a . . .

'That hot——!' cried Pavlides, pointing to the somewhat disreputable, stained and crumpled headgear that crowned McManus – 'Where you get that hots?'

McManus, outraged at this incredible demonstration of *lèse-majesté*, since in his orbit no one even mentioned the hat much less asked him where he had got it, started to say——

'None of your gah——' when with an unearthly cry of joy, Pavlides reached across the table and pounced.

'That's my hots what I lose forty years ago.'

The battle was thereupon joined. For a few moments it swayed back and forth across the table to cries of 'Leggo, you idiot' – 'My hots, my hots, my old friend' – 'Take your hands off me or I'll punch your nose' – 'Give me back my hots' – 'Ugh, ye spalpeen, ye'll pay for this——'

Then suddenly Pavlides prevailed. The hat came off and he held it clutched in trembling fingers. The two secretaries and attorneys had eyes only for the top of McManus's head now that his dread secret had been so suddenly and dramatically bared. But there was nothing to be seen there but some quite ordinary strands of pinkish grey hair to match the eyebrows. Could it be that the secret was that there *was* no secret?

Possessed of the hat, Pavlides turned it swiftly, looked into the sweatband and then hugged it to his chest with another cry of joy. 'My hots, my hots. I knew it.' Then he shouted at McManus – 'I know where you got this hots. On a ship sailing through the Corinth Canal when it fells from bridge.'

All the indignation and fight went out of Meyer McManus and he turned deathly pale. 'My God,' he said hoarsely, 'How did you know?'

'Because,' explained Pavlides, waving the hat to and fro in the manner in which he had done so long ago, 'I am the fellows on the bridge who dropsing it!'

'Oh no . . .' McManus moaned and he suddenly looked twenty years older. And then – 'It must be true. There's nobody else in the world would know that.' Then he turned his stricken eyes upon his opponent. 'Don't take the hat,' he pleaded. 'Sell it to me. Sure, and I'll give you anything you ask for it. Just name it.' It was a testimony to his basic honesty that he did not try to lie out of it or even question that the hat belonged to Pavlides and that he, McManus, must give it back.

And it was likewise characteristic of the kind of man George Pavlides was that he did not turn the obvious deep distress of his rival to business uses. On the contrary, his heart was touched. He asked – 'Why you want it? What's thees hots to you?'

For a moment, McManus measured his opponent. Then he reached the decision that frankness was the best policy. There was too much at stake.

'Tis my lucky hat,' he groaned. 'Ever since it came floating down from that damned bridge and I put it on, I've had the breaks. I met the girl that I married on that boat and the guy who financed my first picture. I tried it out. When I didn't wear the hat I made mistakes. When I had the hat on nothing could go wrong.'

He sunk his head in his hands for a moment and then continued in a further burst of candour: 'It ain't me that's made Interworld Pictures – it's the hat. I've always known it. It's the hat always guessed right. Why even that lousy 'Body of Love' was a box office killer even though it was a stinker.'

'Hah!' shouted Pavlides triumphantly, 'you admit thees was steenky pictsoor!'

McManus looked at him bleakly and then at the hat the Greek had crushed to his bosom. His silence was admission.

'Hokay!' said George Pavlides, 'Now I tell you what I do. I *give* you the hots! And I give one million dollars cash to Grik orphans tsildrens.'

Meyer Skimmer McManus looked like one reprieved by the Governor. Slowly his hands crept across the table; his fingers closed about the hat; reverently he lifted it and restored it to his head. Age fell away from him. Youth and confidence returned. He said:

'I take the hat. And I give one million dollars to the Hebrew and Irish orphans of the world.'

'Hokay,' Pavlides repeated, his huge face beaming with happiness. 'Now I tell you whats we both do. We each give one million dollars to the orphans of United States of Americans because this is such wonderful countries allows bums like us become millionaires.'

McManus swallowed and then said – 'It's a deal.'

'So,' concluded Pavlides. 'You been wearing my hots for forty years. Anybody wears my hots forty years is my brothers. I do not fights with brothers. McManus pictsoors plays Pavlides Palaces.'

McManus averred solemnly – 'McManus Interworld Pictures books the Pavlides Palaces.'

'Only,' Pavlides suddenly admonished, 'When I say a pictsoor is steenky – IS steenky!'

Colour came to the McManus countenance, but only for an instant. Then his fingers once more caressed the brim of the battered old hat.

'IS steenky . . .' he assented.

The two men reached across the table and gripped hands with respect and the beginning of a deep affection.

That night when Pavlides arrived home he said to his wife – 'Ho, Sophia! You know whats? Today I find my hots what I dropsings off the bridge at Corinth. You know who is under it? Meyer McManus. He is my brother now. We don't fights any more. This is lucky days for me. What a good thing back there in Nikodimou I make up my mind to go where my hots goes.'

Sophia Pavlides, stately and beautiful with age, who had grown with her position into the sweetest and best-loved matron in San Francisco went over to her huge, friendly-eyed husband who was a man from the top of his grizzled curly head to the tips of his shoes and kissed him.

'What a good thing, foolish man,' she said, 'that I make up my mind to follow where my heart goes.'

The Silver Swans

There is, of course, no end to the diversity of material from which a story can originate – memory, personal experience, frustration, ambitions unadmitted, incidents and happenings in daily life – for that matter there is hardly a waking moment when one is not surrounded by or in contact with story material. THE SILVER SWANS, however, came out of work connected with another story.

To satisfy your curiosity in case you have skipped this preamble and read the story first, Alice Adams the heroine is Miss Dorothy Tutin the brilliant young actress; Richard Ormond Hadley is based upon the professional activities of my one-time fellow Liechtensteinian, Dr Hans Haas the underwater photographer, from whom I also took the liberty of borrowing his beard; and the third character in the story, Dr Fundoby, is rather what I hope I shall be like when I am seventy-five.

In 1955 I was working with the late Henry Cornelius, the moving picture director who made those two enchanting films WHISKY GALORE and GENEVIEVE, in an attempt to get a film script out of a short war-time novel of mine called THE LONELY. That we didn't succeed may be attributed to a number of causes, one of them being you can't photograph what goes on inside a person's head, but at the time the project was a serious one and the picture was scheduled as one of the J. Arthur Rank productions.

At the same time that we struggled with the adaptation we were casting and looking for an actress who could play the heroine, a girl by the name of Patches. She was an A.T.S. officer who became involved in a romance with an American flyer. The American boy was nothing in particular in the story, but the girl somehow had turned out to be something special and we wanted, therefore, someone special to play her, for the success of the story had been based upon her character and personality. When the book was closed and laid down Patches was the one who one remembered and would have wished to know. Corny and I

344

talked to two of the younger British actresses. One was Virginia McKenna and the other Dorothy Tutin.

Miss McKenna had commitments, as I remember. Miss Tutin would have been ideal, she had a flat, round little face with a tiny nose, and, at that time, an attractive gravelly voice which she attributed to the presence of nodules on her vocal chords. She had a warmth and personality of compelling charm. Also she was then already, having hardly reached her majority, a first-class actress and was nightly filling the theatre in a Graham Greene play in the role of a tender young girl in a Catholic household who, having been seduced and abandoned, destroys herself.

Although at the time Miss Tutin was eighteen, she managed to look fifteen and play with the art and assurance of a woman of forty. I remember inviting Miss Tutin out to dinner one Saturday night to discuss the project.

We went to a spot in London called the Club Casanova, one of the places where one could get a decent meal on a Sunday night, in spite of the fact that the proprietor insists upon serving his hors d'œuvres and his sweets from the same trolley.

Miss Tutin, who I think liked the Patches role and the story of THE LONELY, *chose to turn up that night in a little-girl dinner dress, reminiscent of graduation day from Grammar School. This, with her gamine's face, made her look exactly twelve.*

We occupied one of the red plush banquettes, part of the Casanova's décor, amidst glowering looks from the other patrons, which at first I took for jealousy, but later interpreted properly as hostility towards what seemed to be the most blatant example of cradle-snatching of the season.

The Casanova employs a dance band, to divert or annoy the customers, and when I asked Miss Tutin whether she would care to dance she did, and we did, and it was during this pas de deux that I seemed to feel the crystallisation of the sentiments of the other patrons into 'Just look at that dirty, lecherous old man out there with that pure, innocent child, – how revolting!' I got Miss Tutin off the floor and back to our banquette where for the rest of the evening I tried to hide behind the huge silver-branched candelabra on the table. Nobody had recognised the most accomplished actress of the London season.

But that isn't where THE SILVER SWANS *came from, or why. The story derived from the fact that Miss Tutin did live aboard a houseboat named 'Ondine' moored at the foot of Cheyne Walk and everything aboard, including the occupant, was as described in the story. The first time I met Miss Tutin I visited her in her strange and interesting abode and at once thought of this as a background for a short story and someone very much like Miss Tutin as the heroine. In fact I am afraid that during this visit the new story quite overtook the old and drove it out of my mind, so much so, that I became completely fascinated with Miss Tutin's houseboat, her manner of living and her personality, and asked whether she would mind if I put her lock, stock and barrel into a short story. She said she wouldn't.*

Thereafter the story is, of course, pure fiction, but it springs from the kind of character I thought Miss Tutin to be and what she would have done, or might have done, had the circumstances I invented ever presented themselves to her. And this to a great extent is what fiction writing is like. You invent a character or you come against one and learn to know or recognise it as a character, and then to make it stand out and illuminate the page you reveal it against the background and a set of circumstances.

If when you read the story you will accompany me aboard the 'Nerine,' you will see that as I was shown this unusual home or sat out on the stern with Miss Tutin looking across the muddy Thames and watching the un-laundered and cantankerous-looking swans glide by, all the elements of this little tale were there and only needed to be swished around in that kind of mind a bit to come into being. I think that the octopus was my invention as well as the heroine's proficiency upon the theorbo, since I have always been a fascinated admirer of the concerts of the Dolmetsch group. The quasi-Elizabethan poet, author of the lyrics of 'THE SILVER SWANS' which the heroine sings in the story is, I am afraid, myself. I can't think now, five years later, why one should learn to recognise one's true love when the 'Silver Swans come gliding' but it sounded nice to me and seemed like a good idea at the time.

When the story was finished I showed it to Miss Tutin, who approved of it. My agent showed it to 'The Saturday Evening Post,' who bought it. It caused no stir whatsoever when it was published, but the idea of it amuses me and that is why I have included it in this volume.

To round off this narrative the attempt to film THE LONELY was abandoned because I wrote a very bad script and never did solve the problem of showing what my characters were thinking and feeling. Miss Tutin had the nodules removed from her vocal chords and went on to honour the roles of Portia and Cressida with the Old Vic.

I have too one more dampening item to add to the history of this story. I gave it the title THE SILVER SWANS, one that seemed

*o me gentle and gently intriguing and in keeping with the tone
and nature of the tale. 'The Saturday Evening Post' editors, closer
to the public and what they felt would stimulate, excite and compel them to read this item for which they had already shelled out
the price of the magazine, retitled it* WATERFRONT GIRL.

THE SILVER SWANS

I, Dr Horatio Fundoby, one of the assistant Curators at the
British Museum, always take my Sunday afternoon constitutional
along Cheyne Walk on the Chelsea Embankment of the Thames,
where I am frequently mistaken for an artist because of my white
goatee, blackthorn stick and battered hat to which I have clung
for more than forty years.

I am pleased with the sights and sounds of the river, the cries
of the gulls and their exquisite flight, the marine traffic passing
beneath Battersea Bridge, the colourful collection of ancient
houseboats colonised at the moorings of the Chelsea Boat Company and the faint smell of the sea borne by the tidal waters.

On this Sunday of which I am about to tell there was much
of interest to contemplate as I stood on the Embankment near the
entrance to the boat company. There was stationed in mid-stream
a graceful white steam yacht, the *Poseidon* with the curiously
constructed stern which I recognised as belonging to Lord Struve,
the sub-sea explorer. A lovely motor ship from Panama was
anchored near by and a rusty Spanish freighter from Almeria.

My eye was caught likewise by the heterogeneous selection of
colours that had been splashed over the houseboat *Nerine,* appar–
ently since the week before. The boat itself was a weathered
grey, but the companion-way and door had been painted blue,
the hatch a bright vermilion and the chimney yellow.

Indeed, at that moment, the red hatch was pushed halfway
back from within and the head and shoulders of a young girl
appeared in the space striving to thrust it fully open. She did not
succeed and on the contrary it soon became apparent that she
had managed to wedge herself in so that she was able to move
neither forwards or backwards.

Her eye caught mine at this juncture and even from that dis-

tance I was astounded by their extraordinarily luminous quality.
She did not cry out, but her lips silently formed the words – 'I'm
stuck!'

Without further thought I hurried down the steps and across
the gangway as rapidly as my ageing legs – I shall be seventy-five
in November – permitted, past a rusty water pump, a group of
malodorous dustbins and a clowder of contemplative cats. Reaching the *Nerine* which was resting on the likewise malodorous
mudflats, the tide being out, I struggled with the recalcitrant
hatch.

It had stuck through the drying of the paint, but by means of
judicious leverage with the blackthorn I was soon able to move
it and free her. She was very young, I judged, hardly more than
twenty, clad in paint-spattered dungarees and grey T-shirt, not
at all beautiful in the accepted sense, but with a haunting quality
that made itself felt immediately.

She did not break into an effusion of thanks but contemplated
me with serious self-possession, out of enormous grey eyes flecked
with green, the loveliest and most startling feature of her face.
'Do you know who you are besides being a love?' she asked
and then continued – 'You're the Kindly Old Gentleman . . .'

'Out of *'Punch'* whom one encounters in the British Museum . . .'
I concluded.

Her contrition was charming. Her mouth which was wide could
be extraordinarily wry and mobile. 'Oh, I wasn't meaning it to
be rude . . .'

'But I am an old gentleman,' I said, 'I do feel kindly towards
you, my years leaving me no other choice, and it just so happens
that I am with the British Museum – Dr Horatio Fundoby, Assistant Curator in the Department of Medieval Antiquities.'

'Oh,' she said. 'The British Museum.' She fell silent for a
moment, pulling at her lower lip as she contemplated me
solemnly. Then she asked – 'Would you like to see my octopus?'

When I declared myself delighted she led me down the companion-way through a small galley into the main room of the
houseboat, where it was cool and green. I was aware of a bunk,
bookshelves, paintings on the wall, light filtering through green
curtains and two tanks, a small and a large one. The former contained a pair of sea-horses floating smugly, the latter an octopus,
an ugly specimen of *Eledone Cirrosa* at least a foot in diameter.

She was staring at it fascinated. 'Isn't it beautiful?' she said.
'Sometimes I sit and look at it for hours.'

'What do you call it?' I asked.

'Call it?'

'Hasn't it a Christian name?'

She looked at me startled. 'But it isn't a Christian. It would be an impertinence to it to give it a name. I call it Octopus, or sometimes – O, Octopus.'

'And yourself?'

She hesitated a moment before replying: 'My name is Thetis.'

I nodded. 'Thetis was one of the Nereides, the daughters of Nereus and Doris who lived at the bottom of the sea. She was wooed by Neptune but married Peleus and became the mother of Achilles.'

She pulled her lip contemplatively again. 'Actually,' she said, 'my name is Alice. But I took Thetis. I would like terribly to live at the bottom of the ocean.'

To tell the truth, in the little cabin, one had the impression of being under water, the drawn curtains, the illumination of the tanks contributing to the illusion. The paintings on the wall were sub-sea scenes in blues and greens, but the creatures that one saw through the veils of water were weirdly un-fishlike and full of fantasy. I suspected she had painted them herself. And she with her tiny nose, huge eyes and aureole of short cut brown hair might well have been a nymph.

She asked – 'Would you care to have me sing for you?' and when I begged her to do so, pulled from behind a curtain a long-necked, oddly shaped, stringed instrument constructed on the principle of the lute, that made me start. It was a fifteenth-century theorbo.

'My dear, where on earth did you obtain that?'

She looked surprised as though I ought to have known. 'I saved up and bought it – from Arnold Dolmetsch of course. I always wanted one. Please sit down. I am going to sing.'

She closed her eyes and tilted her head back revealing the exquisite line of her chin and throat. Her fingers touched the strings and the theorbo gave forth a deep basso twang. She announced the title of her song – 'The Silver Swans' and then sang in a husky voice that was infinitely moving in its simplicity——

> 'How shall I know my true love?
>   When will my true heart speak to me?
> O, when the silver swans come gliding
>   Then will I know my true love,
>   Then will I with my true love be,
>   For ever with my love abiding——'

There was something inexpressibly touching about her, and some mystery too for behind the dewy youth was something age-

less and wise, yet wholly innocent. But there was yet another
enigma. The verse might have been the work of any of the minor
Elizabethans, but the authentic line of the plaintive sixteenth
century melody eluded me – who should have known.

A sigh escaped me – 'Ah – you have sung it beautifully. But
who, who?' I racked my brains and enumerated 'Dowland?
Weelkes? Thomas Morely? Willbye or Gibbons.'

Thetis opened her eyes. 'Oh no, it is mine. Don't you see, that
was why I needed the theorbo?'

'Do you often compose authentic Elizabethan verse and music?'
I asked.

'Only when it comes into my head.' She leaned forward suddenly and spoke with an odd vehemence – 'How *will* I know my
true love? How shall I tell when I love?'

'How old are you, Thetis? Have you never been in love?'

'Twenty-one. I don't think so. How will I know? Who will
tell me when I am? You are so old and wise. Cannot you help
me?'

It was a cry from a young and anxious heart and deserved reflection. I thought deeply and replied – 'When he is desperately
and unbeautifully ill and you are able to love him. Then you may
be sure . . .'

She mused to herself – 'When he is ill and unbeautiful . . .' and
was lost in thought for a moment. She returned swiftly. 'How
rude and forgetful I am. Won't you have a drink, Dr Fundoby?'

When I replied that I never refused she produced a bottle of
black Jamaica rum and two drinking tumblers and filled them
each two-thirds full. She lifted hers and repeated – 'When he is
ill and unbeautiful. Oh thank you, Dr Fundoby!' smiled bewitch-
ingly and drank it down at one gulp, this astonishing creature,
and never turned a hair, or at any time later showed that she had
had so much as a single drop. It took me a good half-hour to consume mine while we talked.

She had parents who lived somewhere in Bayswater but she
preferred to dwell by herself on the rotting old houseboat
because it was by the water which she loved. She had a job
that kept her nights but did not say what it was. She had been
poor.

Was it the drink, or the craft that had stirred, causing something inside me to react uneasily. Before I could determine, Thetis
proposed that I might like to go out on deck.

Deck at the stern of the craft proved a narrow space perhaps
several feet in depth and four feet wide, just room for us both to
stand. To my surprise, we were afloat, the tide had come in and

we were rocking gently, a motion that threatened to become
formidable as the curling wash from an ascending motor barge
approached.

Past us drifted four of quite the filthiest swans I had ever seen,
their yellow beaks and unfriendly eyes gleaming out of a dark
grey background compounded of oil, grime, coal dust and soot
from the river commerce which twice a year makes it necessary
for them to be collected and taken to a station on the upper
Thames to be laundered.

Thetis regarded them musingly, but I teased her – 'The Silver
Swans,' I said.

'Tarnished silver,' she replied, slightly defiantly. We heard the
thumping of oars in rowlocks and around the corner of a half-
sunken scow there came a sailor in a rowboat. He was a big
fellow, in a blue jersey. He had curly black hair and a spade
beard and eyes of a strangely light colour.

'Oh hello there!' he hailed, white teeth gleaming magnificently
against the dark beard. 'I say, do you suppose I might borrow a
needle and thread for a moment. I've split meself rowing against
this perishing tide.'

'Certainly. If you want to come aboard I'll do it for you,' Thetis
invited.

The sailor grinned. 'Can't. Embarrassing spot . . .'

'Oh!' Thetis went inside, fetched a small sewing basket and
selecting a spool of thread stuck a needle into it and tossed it
into his boat. 'Blue,' she said.

The sailor caught it. 'Bright child,' he remarked. 'Much obliged.
I shan't be long.' He let the tide carry his boat into the scow
where he made it fast, and turning his back, bent to his repairs.

The wash from the petrol barge arrived and the *Nerine* began
to rock alarmingly and a few moments later fatally. I believe
there is no illness with which mankind is afflicted that can com-
pare with the horrors of *mal de mer*. Certainly it is the only one
in the entire category which causes the victim to long for and
cry out to death to come and take him. The motion of the *Nerine*
was one such as I had never endured before.

Just in time, Thetis turned from her interested contemplation of
the blue-clad back of the brawny sailor and noted the colour I
had turned. 'Oh! You poor dear!' she cried, 'I'd forgotten it
sometimes affects people. Come along quickly.'

She took me by the arm and guided me to the bunk inside and
gently helped me to recline, Then she opened a small cabinet,
secured a tablet from a bottle, and popped it into my mouth.
'Trigemine,' she said. 'They discovered it during the war. You'll

be right as a trivet in five minutes. Just lie quietly.' She went out on deck again.

I heard her hail the sailor – 'Ahoy the sewing circle! What's your name?'

'Hadley. Richard Ormond Hadley.' The name rang a bell, but owing to the struggle between the Trigemine and the violently rocking craft I could not tell which.

I heard his return hail – 'Ahoy the nursery! What's yours?'

'Thetis!'

A moment of silence. Then the sailor: 'Oh. You're the girl Neptune jilted because it was prophesied your son would be more famous than his father.'

Thetis said – 'I think that was silly. I should think that a father would be proud if his son turned out greater than he?'

'Yes? Wait until you've been a father. And by the way, speaking of fathers, what's become of yours?'

'He isn't my father. He's a kind old gentleman who was visiting. He got seasick and is lying down inside. I gave him a Trigemine.'

The sailor's snort travelled across the water. 'What? Seasick on that scow? Why it's practically dry land.' Another ship must have gone by, for the *Nerine* rolled even more violently. But the Trigemine was getting in its work. I thought Thetis's reply was surprisingly mild.

'It isn't a scow,' she said – 'It's my home. And she does roll at certain states of the tide. You have to have a frightfully strong stomach.'

'Hoh! I'll wager.'

Thetis said – 'Really, this is quite different. You might get sick yourself.' I realised she was speaking to comfort me.

The sailor roared with laughter. 'Who, me? Listen, infant. I've sailed every sea and ocean there is in all kinds of weather and haven't been sick yet.'

I heard Thetis say – 'There's always a first time. You wouldn't care to try, would you?'

'Let me know some time when it gets really rough.' His boat bumped against the stern. 'I say, you're not really as much of a child as I thought you were. I do apologise for the "infant". Maybe I'll try out your craft some time. Well, thanks for the repairs.'

The Trigemine had triumphed. I felt I might survive. When I went out Thetis was standing on the deck shading her eyes from the descending afternoon sun and looking after the diminishing figure of the sailor rowing in the direction of the fine white yacht.

'Oh,' she said – 'You're better. I knew it. It always works. Wasn't he beastly?'

I commenced to reply – 'We-e-e-ll,' when she continued—
'But wasn't he *beautiful?*'

I did not see my new friend for several weeks. Then on a rainy
Sunday as I walked along the embankment past the boatyard I
heard my name called – 'Dr Fundoby, Dr Fundoby——' Thetis ran
across the gangway and up the steps to the road. There was
anxiety in her bearing. 'Dr Fundoby! What shall I do? My octopus has eaten off one of his arms.'

I said – 'They often do when kept in captivity, no matter how
well you feed them.'

'Oh!' She fell to reflecting, pulling at her lower lip. 'Then I
suppose I'd better call him septopus. Thank you very much.' She
turned and went back to her boat.

Just before she vanished down the companion-way I called after
her – 'Did your sailor ever come back?' She nodded her head
vigorously in assent and then disappeared.

It was shortly afterwards that a friend invited me to see a play,
'THE UNWANTED' at Wyndham's Theatre, featuring Alice Adams, a
rising young English actress and which was due to close soon
after a long run.

Imagine with what astonishment and emotions I sat spellbound
when Alice Adams made her first entrance and proved to be *that*
Alice, the Nereid, Thetis, of the Chelsea Embankment.

In the role of a sensitive girl who is seduced by an older man
and abandoned and who in the end destroys herself she brought
a maturity of interpretation and understanding I would not have
thought possible in one so young and essentially innocent. Her
performance was as moving and haunting as she herself and I
wept unashamedly at the close.

I took the liberty of calling on her the following Sunday. The
already tiny cabin was further cramped by the addition of a new
tank. In it were two pike with saucer eyes and a huge eel. She
had been sitting in front of it watching them. She gave me a
Trigemine at once which I took gratefully even though the *Nerine*
was fairly quiet.

'My dear,' I said. 'Why didn't you tell me who you were? I was
at Wyndham's Theatre last week.'

'I did,' she replied. 'This is who I am here. It's who I really
want to be.'

'You moved me very much in the play. How can you who are
so young and say you have never loved reproduce all the pain
and yearning of love, night after night?'

'Oh,' she replied, thinking a moment. 'That's the other side of
me. I just do it.'

M

She saw me looking at the newest additions to her undersea home, the unblinking pike and the somnolent eel. 'He gave them to me,' she said.

'The sailor? Where did he get them?'

'From the bottom of the river.'

'Indeed. How?'

'He said he went down and looked for them until he found them.'

Now I knew who Richard Ormond Hadley was and wondered whether she did? And whether her heart was to be broken, and her role in the play perhaps even repeated in real life? I took the liberty granted me by my years and asked – 'Is he in love with you?'

Thetis shrugged. 'He's frightfully rude to me. Is that a sign?'

'And you? Are you in love with him?'

She replied – 'I don't know,' and then repeated twice more, each time more intensely – 'I don't know. I don't know! Oh, Dr Fundoby, how terrible it is to be young!' and with that she leaned her head against my shoulder and began to cry, while I comforted her as best I could.

Accustomed to exercise, rain or shine, I came along Cheyne Walk the following week in a violent windstorm. The wash of river traffic added to the already choppy Thames had set the *Nerine* to rocking alarmingly at her moorings and looking down I suddenly feared for the safety of the child, remembering the narrow cabin and the heavy glass tanks though she took the precaution of keeping them but half-filled so that they would not slop over.

Noting that the hatchway was open I hurried across the gangway to the deck and down the companion-way. I had not yet reached the bottom when a deep groan of mortal anguish emerging from the interior caused me to hasten my steps even more.

An astonishing sight met my eyes. Reclining in the bunk of the cabin in apparent extremis was the sailor, Richard Ormond Hadley. Thetis was sitting on the edge, cradling his head in her arms. He was green, was my Lord Struve, the colour of one of Thetis's sub-sea paintings; his brow was clammy, his hair matted, his eyes agonised. For one moment I thought the poor wretch was dying and then as the cabin lurched and a sudden qualm struck me I realised his trouble was that he was not.

'Thetis!' I gasped. 'The Trigemine! Quick! Where is it?'

'Oh-h-h!' groaned the unhappy man on the bunk. 'Won't you all go away and let me die peacefully!'

'I love him!' Thetis cried joyously, cradling the ghastly head closer to her breast. 'Oh now I know I love him. He is awfully ill, isn't he, Dr Fundoby? And I love him even more than when he is well.'

I staggered to the cabinet where I knew the Trigemine was kept. It was locked. A look of guilt combined with stubbornness came over Thetis's features. 'He won't say that he'll marry me,' she said. – 'I don't mind in the least being poor and sleeping in a hammock.'

The miserable man on the bunk who was evidently too weak to arise and escape to land groaned again. 'All right – all right. 'Anything, anything if you'll just go away and let me die. . . .'

I gathered my own failing strength. 'Thetis! For shame! This is medieval torture. Give me the key at once.'

Meekly she produced it from a chain around her neck, and handed it to me. 'He's sailed every sea and ocean in all kinds of weather,' she murmured.

I secured the Trigemine bottle, popped two tablets into my mouth and three into the unhappy orifice of the great sub-sea hunter, diver and marine biologist, Richard Hadley, Lord Struve, and then lay down on the floor to wait for them to take affect.

Thetis looked down at me. 'Will you come to our wedding, Dr Fundoby?' she asked.

The drug within me had not yet made contact. For the first time I was put out with Thetis. 'If he consents to marry a black-mailer, torturer and assassin, I shall be convinced that he is out of his head,' I replied.

The dose had apparently begun its work on Struve for he sud-denly sat up and said – 'I am glad to hear you say that, Dr Fundoby. Promises made under duress . . .'

'But it was your idea to come aboard at this state of tide and weather after I warned you.' Thetis said plaintively.

'Damnitall!' he growled, the colour beginning to return to his face. 'I came to tell you I loved you.'

'Well then,' Thetis asked simply, 'why didn't you?'

His lordship had the grace as well as the ability now to blush. 'Because I was unexpectedly taken severely ill. Look here, Thetis. You'd better know what you're in for if you're going to marry me. Do you know who I am?'

'I don't care who you are, or what you've done,' Thetis replied, 'I love you.' Then half to herself she murmured – 'In sickness and in health . . .'

I was feeling better and sat up. 'What about your stage career?' I asked severely.

Struve looked blank. 'Whose stage career?' he said.

'Good Lord,' I cried, 'are you both blind? This is Alice Adams featured in 'The Unwanted' at Wyndham's Theatre for the last two years.'

Struve stared – 'This child? She is a child, isn't she?'

Thetis nodded absentmindedly. But I said – 'England's most promising young actress. She's all of twenty-one.'

He stood up. 'Great Heavens! I remember readin' something ages ago. I've just come back from the Galapagos and haven't seen a paper for eighteen months.'

Thetis sprang to her feet and went to him. 'Oh please,' she pleaded. 'All my life I've wanted to go to the Galapagos. Are sailors allowed to take their wives with them when they go?'

Struve burst out – 'Hang it all, Thetis. I'm not a sailor. I'm a——' He hesitated since it is somewhat embarrassing to announce yourself as a lord, and then concluded – '—a sort of marine biologist. I do things under water. Your career . . .'

Thetis interrupted – 'Bother my career. I never wanted to be an actress. When I went for a job they said I had talent. I only did it to get money to rent a houseboat and buy myself things like theorbos and octopuses. Do you know what a good octopus costs?'

Struve took her by both arms. 'Thetis – can you be serious for a moment? Do you really mean you'd give up all that for me and come away?'

'Of course. What I really want more than anything in the world is to walk at the bottom of the ocean at the Galapagos – with you, now that——' She hesitated reflecting a moment, 'Now that, thanks to Dr Fundoby, I'm sure I love you.'

For still another moment, Lord Struve held her two arms and looking up to Heaven with an expression of sheer gratitude on his dark countenance mumbled something which I took to be thanks. Then he sheltered her in his own arms with a strangely tender and protective gesture so that her face was buried in his blue jersey and looking at me over her head he said softly – 'You know, Dr Fundoby, God is sometimes just too awesome the way He will pause in His works to answer the need of one single, puny man.'

And thus the prophecy of the silver swans was fulfilled. So too, in this incarnation with myself at the wedding, Neptune married his nymph Thetis, and if the son turns out to be indeed greater than the father, he has only himself to blame.

I still promenade Chelsea Reach, but Cheyne Walk by the Boat Company is no longer the same. Lady Struve, her husband, her theorbo and her quintopus (it having devoured two more arms) have gone off to some tropic isle where they dive and work together in wondrous marine gardens.

A family from Chipping Barnet have taken the *Nerine,* painted her a hideous brown and renamed her *The Nelson.* I see her rocking in the wash, dressed from bow to stern in the international white squares that signal the presence of small, damp fry. And I wonder as I pass whether they too have frightfully strong stomachs, or have likewise discovered the miraculous powers of Trigemine?

The Silent Hostages

Delving into the genesis of a short story often resembles the psychoanalysis of a dream, which appears to consist of two parts. First part is what the psychiatrist will refer to as the 'day residue,' or in others words that happening, or fear or emotion, encounter or fragment of conversation which took place factually some time during the day before and which triggered the dream, and the second part is that which the subconscious desires or needs or fears of the individual make of this original impetus, all the devious twists and turns given it which results in the dream itself.

The resemblance between this and the genesis of a short story is that very often the dream and the day residue thereof have nothing whatsoever to do with one another.

The event that triggered THE SILENT HOSTAGES *was the test of an atomic bomb, exploded by the United States in the spring of 1955 on their Nevada proving grounds. It was called Operation Teapot and was designed to test the effect of an atomic explosion upon ordinary human habitation. At the time of the explosion I found myself in Las Vegas, Nevada, in the course of a 10,000-mile trip around the United States, a kind of rediscovering America assignment for 'Readers' Digest,' a trip which also gave rise to another story included in this volume. Las Vegas was ninety miles from the scene of the test. Yet to my friends and I who stood outside one of the big hotels and gambling casinos at dawn it seemed all too close. At that zero hour we had been promised a cosmic flash that would light up the heavens, followed by the mushroom cloud billowing into the sky, that mid-twentieth century symbol of the ultimate idiocy of mankind.*

These friends were the American writer Adela Rogers St John and the American actor, dancer and musical comedy star Ray Bolger and his wife Gwen. Ray was appearing in one of the shows being given at the hotel to attract people to the Casino and after his last performance we went into the bar which remained open all night with a band to entertain the customers, to wait out the hours until the explosion should take place.

Much of Las Vegas is naïve and innocent, and even mildly entertaining for a few hours, but this bar was a squalid place, filled with amorous drunks too far befuddled to have the sense to go home and enjoy one another instead of the songs being sung to them by the band leader, the latter being a not entirely appetising or endearing specimen of the human race. The songs he sang were suggestive and the movements of his body as he delivered them even more so. Nothing grows quite as tiresome and disgusting as reiterated pornography in any form. The whole smoky, noisy room seemed to be concentrated about one great dirty leer.

And one knew that less than a hundred miles away foolish men were preparing to tamper once more with one of the deadlier secrets of the Universe. Small wonder then that thoughts of Sodom and Gomorrah passed through our heads, or that one almost considered that if one of those things went wrong and set up a chain reaction it might mean wiping human life, all life in fact, from the face of the earth . . . And at that moment we were not at all certain but that perhaps all of us might not have wanted a bit of wiping. We felt crawly and needing a bath. We left the bar and went out into the night of fresh desert air to await that uneasy dawn.

Over a tiny transistor pocket radio we listened to the sands of time running out and the moment of the explosion drawing nearer. The sense of impending catastrophe was increased. The ninety miles intervening between us and what was about to happen seemed suddenly infinitesimal. It appeared that that thing was aimed at us. We reflected, each silently and to ourselves, I am sure, upon our past lives and I suppose made a quick catalogue of major sins. One had tried to live life according to some rules or concepts of ethics and morality and one realised that one had not always succeeded. One realised that one was not in a position to peg any rocks at the poor clowns still besotted in the bar. If the time was really at hand when the Creator was to tire of His puppets, nobody would be excused.

These were morbid thoughts but it was also a morbid moment and we were writers and professional people.

When the final count-down started we went outside where dawn had begun to overtake the night and looked towards the north. A great glare lit up the horizon. We heard no thunder for the wind must have blown the noise in another direction, but shortly after, the horrid cloud appeared.

We looked at one another with a kind of sheepish relief; we were still there. We kissed one another good night with more than usual tenderness and went off to our respective hotels. I remember feeling a little sick as I drove back. Looking over my shoulder the mushroom cloud seemed to be coming nearer.

The next day Adela and I drove to Los Angeles and, crossing the desert, flat and endless with only an occasional building of adobe or a distant water tower to break the monotony, I thought of the idea for THE SILENT HOSTAGES and told it to her. Two professional writers in a car and on the spot so to speak, and the story didn't take long to build and complete itself, though the final twist I only thought of after I returned to Liechtenstein and sat down to write it.

This then was the trigger and the story that resulted has, I am sure, nothing to do with the personal contacts of that evening or the emotions I felt. It is a story based upon a single and unique situation which had never before taken place and in all probability will never take place again.

The situation and the event upon which the story is based made violence necessary to the plot as you will see, or at least so it seemed to me, and perhaps this is where the analogy to the subconscious dream element which is so different from the day residue comes in and is valid. You or another plotting a story around the same event might have used an entirely different idea. My idea turned to violence. Who can tell what dark recesses of my being were probed at this moment, what vengeances I was taking, what catharsis I was needing?

To write of violence is, to a certain extent, to experience violence. Many of us murder our wives, friends and neighbours a dozen times a day in fantasy and thus liberate ourselves from the necessity of physical killing. I think that fictional killing must be something like that too. There are writers who fill their pages with slaughter and blood baths. More often than not there is a reason for this other than the commercial.

I ought to point out quickly at this stage that THE SILENT HOSTAGES is nothing more than a short, short story, a thriller written for the amusement and entertainment of the reader and really hardly worth the fuss and introspection of this introduction. Yet in this instance this is how this story was born.

THE SILENT HOSTAGES

The car carrying the two escaped killers, Wylie Rickman and Art Hoser, nosed carefully into the unidentified desert town, its headlights burning blindingly. It was that darkest hour before dawn of a moonless, starlit night.

Rickman driving, small, dapper with cold, saurian eyes and bloodless mouth, judged it to be Parumph in lower Nevada. Somehow they had missed the Fairbank Ranch in the dark.

Ever since they had murdered their three hostages, the woman and her twins and shot their way out of Beatty, north-west of Yucca Flat, they had been attempting to find their way south-west towards the Mexican border, twisting and turning, driving without lights on back roads and wagon trails, avoiding the glow of towns, fighting the panic of the hunted.

A few hours back they had listened to a news broadcast that caused them to change their plans and begin searching for a settlement where the alarm might not yet have reached. They desperately needed fresh hostages.

Now they approached carefully a brief main street between the small cluster of buildings that mushroomed abruptly out of the desert. They were jumpy, nervous, half drugged by fatigue and deadly dangerous.

Fat Art Hoser who had needlessly killed the policeman the day after they had escaped from the penitentiary at Carson City had turned into a vengeful jelly of cowardice, for he knew what the police did to cop killers. Rickman was more vicious, for he murdered in cold blood and was perpared to sacrifice a human life for every extended hour of his own if necessary. He was aware that if daylight found them without a shield of living flesh they where finished.

The town was apparently an early riser for many of the buildings were blazing with lights. But this was not surprising. Life in desert communities frequently began before sun-up.

Caught in their headlights the tall saguaris cacti, which with the stunted greasewood shrubs and sagebrush grew right to the edge of the town, pointed aloft like warning fingers. But as yet there seemed to be no one abroad in the street.

They passed the usual filling station on the outskirts. Rickman drove cautiously, his Magnum .38 on the seat at his left side. Two rifles and a sub-machine gun were between his partner and himself. Hoser had a double-barrelled shotgun resting on his lap crossing his fat legs and beer belly.

A sedan with its engine running was standing by the pumps. Inside they spotted the white-overalled attendant with another man, apparently making change. It reminded Hoser of the gas station jockey, no more than a kid, they had killed and robbed near Tonopah. Rickman thought only of the hostage he wanted. A woman, preferably with another kid or kids.

As they moved by, Rickman sought to assess the buildings of the town. There seemed to be a two-storey brick hotel, a general store, some shops, a livery stable, several frame dwellings, a café, the usual adobe buildings and at the end of town a small power station with what appeared to be a tall radio mast next it.

A lounger was apparently asleep on the porch of the hotel, chair leaned back, shovel-shaped Stetson tilted over his eyes. A ranch wagon was parked in front of it and a rancher sat at the wheel.

Hoser nervously moved the shotgun. Rickman picked up his gun and said savagely, 'You shoot again before I tell you to and you'll get this across the bridge of your nose.'

They drove quickly by. The rancher did not even bother to turn his head. It was Hoser's nervous and wanton shooting of the policeman after they had escaped from the prison that had started the hue and cry at their heels prematurely.

Glimpsed through a grimy window the café appeared to be filled, with the counterman at his griddle and the waitress serving coffee across the bar. A juke box bawled from the restaurant. An asphalt-carrying tank truck and a big freighter with trailer were drawn up in front, their drivers apparently breakfasting inside.

As they drove on, voices emerged from several of the houses where radios had been turned on by early risers. In a near-by house a telephone was ringing and there was a thumping noise of some kind of pump or gasoline engine. A window a few houses down showed a family seated at early breakfast. It seemed as though only the first rays of the sun were wanted to send the inhabitants of the town spilling out on to the street and about their business.

They passed a frame house with a big sedan parked in front and the blinds up, revealing the occupants. A man in trousers and shirt with braces hanging down was shaving himself in front of a cabinet mirror. In the kitchen, a woman in an apron was bending over a mixing bowl. There was no one in the living-room from which the radio was playing loudly, but in an adjoining bedroom they snatched a view of a cot with a girl of five or six asleep on it and a crib in which there was a baby.

Rickman's thin mouth curled with satisfaction. This was a prize he had not expected. With the baby they might even reach the border. And there were keys, he noted, in the ignition switch of the sedan. The two-tone maroon and cream car they had taken from the salesman they had kidnapped and shot between Tonopah and Goldfield was marked.

Hours before they had sat in the vehicle, lights and motor shut off and concealed by a fold in the foothills miles from anywhere, listened to a news round-up from Las Vegas, which was largely devoted to the harrowing story of the murder trail of the two escaped convicts.

Without emotion, coldly and clinically, Rickman had listened to the list of their killings, the guard at the penitentiary, the policeman at Wilson's Gulch, the boy in the gas station at Tonopah, the salesman at Goldfield, and finally the woman and two children at Beatty where they had snatched them.

And a mile away, a man sitting in a shack by a gate in barbed wire fence, sick and clammy, listened to the same broadcast over a portable radio, the beads of sweat running from his cheeks and temples as the announcer detailed:

'As the chase spread out down the highway from Beatty, with the bandits firing from their car, police did not dare to shoot for fear of hitting Mrs Nellie Bassett and her twins, Tina and Joey, aged seven, kidnapped as hostages an hour earlier by the fleeing pair.

'Apparently when police braving the fire attempted to force the fleeing car off the road, Rickman, Hoser or both shot the mother and two children, threw the bodies from the car and escaped as the horrified pursuit ground to a halt. The children were dead, but Nellie Bassett was still alive and was rushed to the hospital in critical condition. . . .'

The man in the shack fought and lost his battle between duty and instinct, switched off his portable, entered his car and drove off to the north. The sound of his motor and the glow of his headlights caused the two killers to finger their weapons apprehensively, until the noise and the beams of the headlight faded in the distance. Then they had listened to the details of the tri-state police dragnet set for them.

'We gotta get us another hostage. The Fairbank Ranch ought to be where that car came from. There'd be women there.'

Driving blacked out, they crept to the spot from whence the vanished car appeared to have come. The rutty road continued the other side of the wire fence which to Rickman denoted the ranch he sought. The gate was open and they drove through past the shack and large property posting sign. By star glow he was

able to read the big letters 'KEEP OUT!' He did not want to
show the light necessary to read the rest.

Hoser said, 'You sure you know what you're doin'?' and then
added, 'I'm getting sick of all this killing.'

Rickman reached over and hit him on the cheekbone with the
barrel of his .38. The fat man stared down at the blood dripping
on to his hand and said nothing further. He was afraid of Rickman. They had floundered in the darkness for several hours, but
found no ranch. Then, shortly before five the lights on the horizon
had announced the presence of the town in which they now
found themselves.

Rickman drew up behind the parked sedan. 'Shift the stuff into
the car ahead and start her up,' he ordered Hoser. 'When she's
running, come in and grab the kids. I'll take care of the other
two . . .' He slid out from under the wheel with a movement that
was almost obscenely sinuous, shifted the heavy .38 to his right
hand and ran into the frame house.

From the entrance inside the unlocked door he could see both
the man shaving and at the back the woman at her kitchen table.
He threw his gun down on the former saying, 'Don't anybody
move. This is a snatch. Stay where you are. Do as I say and nobody's going to get hurt.' Then he called to the woman, 'You in
the kitchen; if you open your yap I let your husband have it.'

The man in the bathroom froze obediently, motionless, his
razor at the side of his cheek. The gunman could see his own face
reflected over his victim's shoulder in the mirror. The woman,
apparently terrorised, did not stir or utter a sound.

In the next room the radio blatted loudly. Rickman did not
listen to it but was satisfied it provided cover. Seconds ticked by.
Hoser should have had the rifles, guns, ammunition and their
small stock of food transferred to the other car by now. The gunman heard the starter whir, then the sound of the engine catching and turning over with a steady beat. He waited until he heard
Hoser's footstep on the threshold and then pulled the trigger
shooting the man through the back on the left side.

Hoser rushed in howling, 'For God's sake, you crazy fool! Are
you killing again? You'll have the whole town on us . . .'

For once Rickman did not turn on his partner, but stood with
the already recocked pistol, staring blankly at the round hole that
had appeared in the back of the man's shirt in the region of the
heart. The fabric of the garment was smoking slightly but the
man, oblivious to the shock of the bullet or the fact that he should
be dead, remained standing.

Rickman bawled at Hoser, 'Grab the two kids in the bed-

room!' Then he raised the heavy gun, aimed it at the back of the
man's head, fired twice and endured the shock of seeing his own
pale and deadly vision vanish as the cabinet shaving mirror shattered under the impact of the slugs.

With two holes through his head, the man, the razor still gro-
tesquely held at the side of his cheek, yet refused to fall and die
like the others had.

With a cry of rage Rickman leaped forward and brought the
gun barrel down on the fellow's skull which split like a melon
into a hundred pieces just as Hoser came in from the bedroom
calling, 'Hey! These ain't no kids. These are dolls. What's going
on here?' In one hand he held the baby made of bisque, its blue
china eyes open and staring innocently. By the other, he dragged
the department store window-dressing wax mannequin of a five-
year-old girl with dark chestnut curls.

Rickman's nerve broke. He yelled, 'What the hell is this, a
trap?' Berserk he pulled over the body of the headless dummy
by the broken mirror, kicked it, then knocked down the lifelike
wax figure of the woman in the kitchen, swearing incoherently.
Then ignoring the shaking Hoser he dashed through the door
pulling a heavy automatic from a shoulder holster as he did so.

But there was no police patrol car, or posse of armed citizens
converging upon the house. The streets were still empty. It was
beginning to grow light. From the house across the street the
telephone kept ringing.

Down the block at the filling station the customer and the attendant were still immobile at the cash register. The lounger slept
on undisturbed tipped back in his chair on the hotel porch. None
of the figures in the Café and Eatery had stirred. In the near-by
station-wagon the rancher remained unmoved at the wheel.

Rickman, his guns held before him, ran over, yanked the door
open and pulled at the rancher's arm. The wax figure obediently
slipped out from under the wheel and fell to the ground.

The gunman suddenly became appallingly aware that for all
the noise that filled the village street there was not the sound
of any human voice that did not come from a radio, or a single
living thing to be seen or heard. Somehow they had blundered
into a settlement populated solely by department store dummies.
And still the whole truth did not dawn.

He went back to the charnel house of the murdered waxworks
where he came upon Art Hoser kneeling in the living-room before the radio, his whole person quivering abjectly from his but-
tocks to his belly, chin and lips, the sweat pouring off him in
rivulets.

He did not even look up as Rickman came in but stared transfixed at the instrument which he seemed to be praying to as a kind of animate responsible being, mumbling, 'No no! Please! You got to wait!'

Rickman, clutching his two guns which had decided so much for him but would not ever conclude anything again, now focused his attention to the radio as the announcer was saying tensely:

'Everything is in readiness now, the tanks are in position three miles from ground zero; the Civil Defence Workers are in their places on Media Hill. And in just exactly one minute from now, Survival City, or Doomtown as the newspapermen have called it, the guinea-pig village peopled solely with dummies distributed throughout in human attitudes of daily life will be subjected to the disintegrative force of an Atom blast twice that which levelled Hiroshima. . . . Now I will pick up the time signals to zero hour – Twenty seconds – nineteen – eighteen – seventeen – '

Rickman ran screaming into the empty street where in the house across the way the telephone bell was still ringing. 'No no!' he bawled. 'Hey! Wait a minute! Do you hear me? You can't! We're here. For God's sake, wait!'

The last thing he saw was the steel skeleton of what he had thought was a radio mast. But now, outlined against the dawn a dark, torpedo-shaped package hung from the 500-foot tower top. And the last thing he heard was the unison chant from all the live radios in all the dead, dummy-filled houses – 'Five seconds – four – three – two – one. . . .'

Some little while later, the guard who that same morning had deserted his post at the No. 3 Desert Gate of the Restricted Area between Beatty and Mercury, returned alone, a half-hour before his relief was due.

His name was Joseph Bassett and he was the husband of Nellie Bassett and father of the twins, Tina and Joey. He had managed to reach the bedside of his wife and hold her in his arms a scant twenty minutes before she died. Dazed by the completion of the tragedy he had returned to his duty from force of habit.

Still in state of shock he could not cope with the ominous mystery of the tyre tracks, west to east that crossed his post and entering through the open gate went straight as an arrow eastwards towards where the brown mushroom cloud of the recent explosion had begun to lose its shape and drift with the wind.

He stood staring down uneasily at the tracks, wondering who it had been, what had happened to them and what it might portend for him – if ever it came out that someone had gone through there during his absence.

Shut Up Little Dog

In 1955, as noted, at the behest of Readers' Digest, I packed myself and my car off to the United States and drove 10,000 miles around and through America on a tour of rediscovery, for it had been almost twenty years since I had travelled extensively through my own country and the changes brought about by two decades would thus stand out. One of these changes, I noted, was concerned with the American cuisine.

When I was young, let us say in the first quarter of the twentieth century, good food considered from the point of view of the gourmet was confined to two or three restaurants in New York, one in San Francisco and another oasis in the deep South, the famous Antoine's in New Orleans. All the rest was a desert consisting of Yankee pot roast, beef the colour and consistency of shoe leather covered with a sludge of glutinous brown gravy and served with a side dish of grey mashed potatoes. Yet only twenty years later there were more than two dozen cities scattered about the United States where one could get a superb meal, beautifully cooked and served in the American style and containing American meats, shell fish, fish, fowl, fruits and vegetables instead of the interminable apeing of the European.

By and large American small town food remained abominable, but then as you will have discovered for yourselves small town French food is equally abominable, which of course is why the Frenchman carries his Guide Michelin as a travelling bible as well as the tourist. There must be a reason why the Guide indicates a certain restaurant as worthy of a detour of fifty miles and that, I should say, was it. The tourist in France, caught outside a starred Michelin zone and forced to stop at one of those spoon and fork bistros for a meal, confines himself to an omelette and a piece of local cheese. The traveller in America, sentenced to the roadside café or the inevitable hotel 'Coffee Shoppee' knows enough to stick to ham and eggs or wheat cakes with little pork sausages.

But even these over the years have improved in America and some of the specialities of the short order cook, waffles with honey, flapjacks, buckwheat cakes, etc., particularly those catering to the lorry drivers, are most delectable. Somewhere, somehow, pride in purely American cookery has been awakened and interesting meals are now available in the most unsuspected places if upon arriving in a small town or hamlet you will take the trouble to inquire. I should say that one of the last strongholds of really inedible food was the deep South, and yet even here time and local pride had co-operated to elevate a number of dishes to where they might be considered worthy of attention and even notable. One of these was the hush-puppy, a crunchy finger-shaped cake made of corn meal, minced onion, egg and milk and fried crispy brown in deep fat in which fish has been cooked.

My itinerary took me through the capital of the elongated State of Florida where signs informed me that I was now in the home of the famous Tallahasse Hush-Puppy – Try One! I did and became practically an addict during the Southern portion of my tour.

What the Americans have learned is to concentrate on local specialities, fish, oysters, shrimps, lobster, clams, etc., sweet corn, sweet potatoes, pumpkins and prepare them in a manner indigenous to the American Continent and cooking traditions of an earlier age. The results are some towering gastronomic experiences. Some of these dishes you will encounter in the ensuing story, SHUT UP LITTLE DOG.

For quite naturally in my delight at discovering the great strides made in American culinary art my thoughts turned to the eternal hoo-ha made of French cookery and all the palaver and chi-chi that goes with it, and it seemed to me that a good many American dishes I was sampling must receive full marks from any honest French chef and more than a few of the restaurants in which I dined in such cities as Dallas, Houston, New Orleans, Phœnix, San Francisco, Portland, Seattle, and believe it or not Fort Wayne, might find themselves two and even three starred by the Guide Michelin.

And from there, quite naturally, one's thoughts would turn to my friend M. Armand Bonneval whom you have encountered previously in this volume, and who is a compendium of a number of French chefs and maîtres de cuisine I have encountered during my travels in France along the Michelin trail. What would happen if somehow M. Bonneval could be introduced to some of the more exciting American dishes, and thereafter attempted to reproduce them, say for some famous French club of gourmets?

You can, I am sure, visualise the immediate challenge and the pleasure with which I tackled the problem.

Fictional stew is almost like culinary ragout. It isn't only the ingredients you use, but how you mix and apply them. But basically the cooking of it is standard. So in this story is the formula used, which is the one in which you plunge your hero deeper and deeper into difficulties until it seems that he will never be able to extricate himself, at which point some honest or noble trait of character unsuspected within himself, and which on the face of it would appear to bring about the final catastrophe proves to be the unexpected turning point.

To the would-be story writer I can only say, if you will permit me for a moment to change my metaphors, that this is mental chess and you play it until you win, moving your pieces about, people and situations, until you finally score the unbeatable combination. In doing so you call upon all of your resources, travel, experiences, the characters of friends or acquaintances and everything you have ever read or done, and you hope as well for assistance from the subconscious.

Here in SHUT UP LITTLE DOG *is an instance of how this kind of manœuvring operates. I had managed to get myself and my hero M. Bonneval, into such a pickle that I was having unusual trouble in extricating both of us. One final ingredient was missing to make this story come off. The panicked mind began to lash out in all directions in search of it.*

I was intending this story for the 'Saturday Evening Post,' one of whose editors was Mr Stuart Rose, who in private life is a Pennsylvania gentleman farmer and a devoted follower of the hounds, probably the only American editor whose sport is fox hunting. Mr Rose's hobby had already provided me with the plot for one of the débutante stories and now thinking of him it came to my rescue again. Rose – hunt – hounds – hush puppies, and there was the final ingredient no longer missing, and I could now give myself the pleasure of setting down on paper the manner in which M. Armand Bonneval, of whom by this time I was more than a little fond, was able to win the coveted rosette of the Légion d'Honneur.

SHUT UP LITTLE DOG

If there is one thing longed for by the average honest middle-class Frenchman even more than a competence for his old age, it is to wear the rosettes of the Legion of Honour.

By virtue of his diligence and superb mastery of his art plus the caution and thrift of Madame, his faithful partner through life, M. Armand Bonneval, Chef of the *Cordon Bleu* and Honorary Member of the *Académie Culinaire* de France, retired, and now owner of the Auberge Château Loiret, was reasonably well secured for his declining years.

The supreme decoration of France, however, had eluded him. Nor was his position in such a modest village as Loiret on the placid Loire, even though it was on the trail of the tourists visiting the Châteaux in the summer, likely to bring him the prominence that might result in such a coveted reward.

But one could always hope and each time the stout and greying little chef read of the cross and rosette having been bestowed upon some scientist or man of letters, he would sigh, not with envy, but longing.

And Madame Bonneval, as rotund as he, clad in honest cashier's black, seated at her accounts in her tiny office off the foyer of the Auberge would comfort him with – 'It is you who deserves it if anyone does.'

'It is for your sake even more than mine,' Bonneval once said, glancing down at his immaculate white chef's jacket almost as though the Rosette were already looming in his buttonhole. 'When we went for a promenade and the decoration was admired, everyone would look to see this paragon of a wife who had assisted her husband to such eminence.

'Ah, Armand. I do not need any ribbon to convince me of your worth!'

Yet the yearning remained, even after the extraordinary piece of good fortune of their holiday trip to the United States. This was the gift of an impetuous Texas oil millionaire steered to the Auberge by the famous Guide Michelin's rating of three crossed spoons and forks and two stars. After a delicious dinner he fell into conversation with the little chef, saying——

'Man, that was sure a tasty meal, I don't mind telling you. But we got some mighty fine cookin' back home too. You ever eat barbecued spare ribs?'

Bonneval indicated politely that he had not.

'What? Don't tell me you never had a real southern fish fry

370

with hush-puppies, or hot jowl with collard greens and pot likker?'

Baffled, Bonneval shook his head.

'Why Monsoor,' cried the Texan, 'You jes ain't never lived. You and Madame gotta come over and be my guests. We got the finest cookin' in the world in the U.S.A.'

Have you ever encountered a Texas oil millionaire suffering from an aggravated fit of hospitality? They have not only the necessary persuasiveness, but also the cash. The result was that when Monsieur and Madame Bonneval closed the Auberge as they always did from January to April, they embarked at the expense of the millionaire upon a coast to coast gastronomic tour of the United States.

And the interesting part was that M. Bonneval discovered that the Texan was quite right. For the chef was too great an artist himself with the skillet and saucepan to be a chauvinist. He greeted and acknowledged perfection where he encountered it. And he was enthralled by some of the recipes and dishes he discovered in America.

However, upon their return, life resumed its normal tenor and his ambition to achieve the final honour to crown his career remained strong.

Now there is this about an Auberge, honestly conducted, and starred by Michelin, namely that you serve many hundreds of people in a month; they arrive; they order; they consume; they call for the bill and depart, and you do not know whom you have entertained, satisfied or even charmed.

One day a letter arrived at the Auberge out of the blue that sent Bonneval and Madame into an absolute hysteria of excitement and happiness.

It was on the stationery of the *Cercle Intime des Grands Gourmets de France,* in other words, that sacrosanct inner circle of all the gastronomic organisations of the country, those supreme knights of the oesophagus and the gizzard, formed of the most sensitive and exclusive over-eaters of a nation devoted to defying indigestion on many fronts.

The missive read in part – 'As you may know, this Club tenders an annual banquet to His Excellency the President of France and for which each year a French Chef of outstanding accomplishment is selected to compose the menu and cook the dinner.

'Not long ago, the Duc de C. happened to dine at your Auberge while en route. A member of this club, he has professed himself an admirer of your art, he has forwarded such an unstinted and glowing report of your accomplishments, and such is his influence in our club that you have been unanimously nominated for the post of Chef du Cercle for this year's dinner.

'Write us that you accept, cher Maître Bonneval, and send us at once your menu and choice of dishes so that it may be printed and given to the press in advance of the banquet which is next month. You are of course aware that the entire responsibility for the dinner will be yours, and once you have made your choice there is none can interfere or alter your decisions.'

M. and Mme Bonneval read and reread this eloquent letter with tears streaming down their faces and then embraced one another. For the selection as Chef to the Cercle Intimes for the annual banquet tendered to the President and a few members of the *Corps Diplomatique* almost automatically carried with it the coveted award of the Cross of the Legion of Honour.

'My dear husband, I am so happy for you,' wept Mme Bonneval. 'Now at last your true genius has been recognised.'

'Oh would that I were indeed worthy,' cried Bonneval in a seizure of becoming modesty, 'and could somehow give something extra in return for this great honour that has come to me.'

And then, as a lightning from the sky, compounded in part from his deep sense of gratitude and the memory of his recent visit to the vast and fruitful land across the sea, M. Bonneval was riven by an idea. The idea embraced how he might be the instrument to perform a good work, earn his decoration and at the same time indicate his gratitude to the generous host from Dallas who had made it possible for him to learn the culinary secrets of the Texans with their chilis and enchiladas, the Alabamans with their *fritures,* the New Englanders with their soups and dumplings, the Idahoians who produced a fabulous *pomme de terre,* the Californians who roasted meat in a charcoal pit.

'Maman!' he shouted to his spouse who was already seeing the receipts in the black japanned cash box doubled once her husband wore the red rosette – 'Do you know what I shall do? I will combine all that I have learned on our recent trip and cook a United States dinner for the President of France, thus proving my skill and originality as well as cementing Franco-American relations. Will this not constitute a sensation?'

'Perhaps it might be wiser . . .' began Mme Bonneval but then concluded – 'Prepared by you, I am sure that it will be a most wonderful repast.' Had the Chef not been so gripped by excitement and pleased with his marvellous notion, he would have seen that her reply was slightly less than enthusiastic. Often women have a fatal intuition. . . .

Shortly after, M. Bonneval, having accepted the invitation, forwarded to the Cercle his menu, consisting of ten courses and demi-courses spreading from New England to the Mexican border, bounded on the east by the Atlantic and the west by the Pacific oceans.

A secretary acknowledged receipt of this novel and interesting bill-of-fare and confirmed June 15th as the date at the Ritz in Paris. He advised also that although this was likewise the occasion of the annual dinner at the same hotel of the Chantilly Hunt Club, an organisation devoted to the chase supported by wealthy British and American sportsmen currently residing in the charming area of Chantilly, there would be no interference. The Ritz would provide M. Bonneval with his own kitchen and all the assistance he required.

And in due course, also, there appeared at the Auberge Château Loiret, a scruffy-looking reporter from a Paris paper, with dirty cuffs and even dirtier finger-nails. In France it is not unusual for representatives of the press to appear in less than immaculate condition. Hence, M. Bonneval was neither on his guard, nor in his innocence of the world, aware that this specimen was filled with the gall, wormwood and general overflow of malevolence characteristic of his affiliations.

The fellow named his paper which meant nothing to M. Bonneval whose reading was confined chiefly to a sheet giving intimate details of the love and home life of bicycle race riders. The reporter then said – 'I have seen the menu you have presented for the annual capitalistic orgy of . . . that is to say, the *Fêtes des Gourmets* of the Cercle, and wish an interview.'

'But of course, *mon vieux*,' replied the unsuspecting Bonneval, 'Ask me what you wish to know and all shall be made clear.'

'This idea of presenting North American dishes . . .'

'Ah yes. An American millionaire from the famous State of Fort Dallas, in the country of Texas, invited me there. In gratitude to him and this great nation that is aiding us so nobly in combatting the evils of Communism, I shall cook United States.'

The reporter coughed, produced a crumpled cigarette from a soiled packet, extracted a frayed vesta and lit it. Then, consulting Bonneval's menu from a mimeographed sheet he asked – 'This strange item here in the middle of the repast called the "Hush-puppy," – what is that?'

'Oh oh! The Hush-puppy! This is a most famous and extraordinary food of the inhabitants of the city of Florida in Tallahassee where I have visited.'

'Indeed. How, for instance would you translate this dish?'

M. Bonneval reflected. 'To be exact,' he replied, 'It would be called "*Tais toi, petit chien.*" Is not that adorable?'

'Quite,' agreed the reporter. 'But what is it and how did it come by this astonishing name?'

'Ah ah!' said the delighted Bonneval, 'Well may you ask. It is the most touching of stories. It is a dough comprised of white maize flour, baking powder, salt, milk, water and a large chopped onion and fried in the fat devoted to a *friture* of native fishes . . .'

'Yes yes, but the origin of the name,' pressed the reporter.

'I was arriving at this,' said M. Bonneval. 'It is the custom in the southland after the hunt or the fishing to gather about the camp-fire for a fish fry. There the hunters relate exaggerated tales to themselves and their faithful Negro retainers with their dogs of the hound variety who sit around the outer edge of the firelit circle of the camp where the evening meal is cooking.

'The odour of the food frequently excites the younger animals in charge of the darkies, causing them to make the disturbance with barks and whines. Then one of the hunters detaches a piece of this marvellous maize and onion cake fried in the fish fat and hurls it to the animal, saying softly – 'Hush, puppy. Be quiet, little one!' The satisfaction of this food, it is said, is miraculous and once a beast has engulfed a portion of it, no further sound emerges from him and thus the evening's entertainment may proceed without further interruption. Is this not a beautiful custom?'

'Very,' said the reporter and having pumped M. Bonneval a little more permitted the friendly little chef to treat him to a meal and a bottle of wine and then departed for Paris.

The storm broke three days later.

It began of course in the Communist paper with a story headlined – 'U.S. INSULT TO FRANCE! Gesture of Contempt! Native Chef Bribed to give French President mixture fed to dogs of Negro slaves in Florida Concentration Camp!'

The Radical Socialists, fearful that the Communists had latched on to something this time, took it up, as did the parties of the Centre and the Right.

The menu composed by M. Bonneval for the Cercle and which had previously been ignored by the press was now published in every newspaper with stinging comment and editorials reflecting all political and cultural shades and opinions.

'FRENCH CHIEF OF STATE TO DINE ON DOG-BISCUITS' trumpeted one. 'Dishes of the Savage Indians of the Mountains of Texas for France's President' headlined another. 'HAS BONNEVAL BEEN BOUGHT?' asked a third. 'Can it then indeed be true,' inquired a fourth 'that it is seriously proposed at the annual banquet of the sacrosanct Cercle to compel the elected head of the French Nation to consume a drugged cake used to calm hysterical hounds belonging to the uncivilised inhabitants of a still barbarous portion of the United States?'

The Gaullists took the nationalistic line and demanded to know since when the classic French cuisine had not been good enough for Frenchmen. The Socialists wrote of further evidence of expanding American Imperialism and interference with the internal affairs of France.

Bonneval was denounced as a traitor in the Assembly, the first time the members of that body apparently agreed on anything; there were repercussions at the Quai d'Orsay and the ripples eventually reached the State Department in Washington causing a query to be cabled to the American Ambassador in Paris.

Poor Bonneval found himself plunged into a sheer hell of notoriety. He was badgered by the press. Hordes of reporters descended upon peaceful Loiret. He was the recipient of petitions and blackguarding mail and was subjected to abuse and pressure of every kind.

The Cercle itself, consisting for the most part of aristocrats and professional people disinterested in politics took a strong line and issued a statement to the effect that the Banquet was traditional and once the Chef was selected, the entire responsibility for the menu remained with him. The Club would under no circumstances interfere.

But this left Bonneval alone to weather the tempest, buffeted hither and thither. He was no reed, however, but a man of courage and considerable stubbornness. He knew himself and his intentions to have been honourable, the dishes superb; he was a Frenchman and independent and he refused to budge.

And of course as the pressure and fury redoubled, all hope of his Legion of Honour faded, since the President would not dare award it under the circumstances. Indeed, the police claimed to have discovered a plot to bomb the hotel.

The harassed Chef had one silent rooter in the person of the American Ambassador, a cultured and patient man already fed to the teeth with the dangerous antics of French politicians in international affairs and who diplomatically refrained from taking any part in this controversy. But privately he remarked to his wife – 'By George, the little fellow has courage. If he serves that dinner I'll see that he gets a decoration from the U.S.A. if it's the last thing I do.'

But the unhappy affair was taking its toll. With all the con-

centrated venom of the America-haters turned against him, the
unfortunate chef began to lose some of his comfortable rotundity.
Lack of sleep and worry drained the cheerful stove-side red from
his face.

But the dignity of M. Bonneval under these attacks was something splendid to see as he stood firm on his decision to present
the best dishes of France's old friend and ally from across the
sea. His physical as well as moral courage was an example, so
much so that a few more daring souls even began to speak up in
defence of his rights.

And then, suddenly and inexplicably M. Bonneval yielded.

At first the news was received with astonishment and scepticism
until it proved to be true, confirmed by the Cercle. The pressures
had apparently been too much for Bonneval to bear and giving
in, he had presented a substitute menu in honest French for the
President's banquet.

Most saddened by this news was the American Ambassador, so
much so that he almost cancelled his acceptance to the invitation
to the dinner, but on second thought and the persuasion of his
wife, reconsidered.

The Communists crowed; the Gaullists exulted; the Socialists
pointed with pride. And only two people really knew what final
straw had proven too much for the back of this stout little
culinary camel. It had been none other than Madame Bonneval.

Unable any longer to bear the spectacle of her gallant husband
withering away before her eyes she had said to him a week before
the date of the affair – 'Armand, I beg of you. Do what they wish.
You cannot hold out against all of France.'

'Never! No one may dictate what I, Armand Bonneval shall
cook!'

'Armand, my husband, do this for me. I cannot bear these
attacks any longer. I shall have a breakdown.'

Bonneval regarded his wife long and fondly. 'There is no
power on earth could make me give in but you,' he said finally.

'Oh Armand! Do you promise?' Madame was deeply touched
for she knew that never had a greater compliment been paid her.

'Very well then. I promise.'

'Ah! I am so happy. See, I did it only for you. Now you will
receive your Legion of Honour. In the end you would have
regretted having lost it, besides making yourself ill.'

'Wretched woman, what have you done?' cried Bonneval. 'I
should never have yielded for myself. Give my back my promise.'

But this Madame refused to do, insisting it was true that the
strain was too much for her and in the end Bonneval went into

the little office and mused upon the devious ways of women.
Then, suddenly, with a curiously intense expression on his
countenance, and removing his chef's toque and napkin for
greater freedom of thought, he penned the substitute menu and
sent it off to Paris. I have a copy of it before me and reproduce
it as it appeared in all the French newspapers:

'Bouillabaisse des Palourdes de Normandie à la Creme
Saumon de Loire Diable sous Cendre, Sauce d'Enfer
Entrailles de Jeune Porc à la Bama
Feuilles de Navets au Lard,
Quenelles de Maïs Blanc au Pays Fleuri

Poulet de Bresse, Terre Marie
Pommes de Terre du Senegal douce sucré
Soufflé Indienne

Salade Rouge d'Avocado
Gâteau de Courges'

You have no doubt read in your news magazines of the tremendous success of the banquet of the Cercle and the cheers that
echoed for the great chef who cooked it. But you will not know
about the strange affair of the disturbance next door, plus the
astonishing behaviour of the American Ambassador.

The matter of the interference from the adjoining banquet hall
will remain your secret and mine when I have revealed it, but
there were several in the vicinity of the American Ambassador
when he seemed to be in the grip of an unfortunate seizure of
near apoplexy who declared that his difficulty appeared to be, as
the dinner progressed, to keep from laughing himself to death.

But first we should glance backstage to the special kitchen of
the Ritz where guest-chef Armand Bonneval, like Toscanini,
conducting without a score created his fabulous banquet wholly
from memory and without referring to any text.

Refusing all assistance provided in the form of fryers, sauce-
makers and junior cooks, he buzzed about the kitchen, a veritable
dynamo of energy, whipping salt pork, minced clams, potatoes,
onions and cream into the wonderful Bouillabaisse, with his own
hands preparing the hot sauce containing onion, ketchup, vinegar,
Worcestershire sauce, various peppers, paprika and chili powder
for the charcoal grilled salmon and crisping the long, sausage-
shaped quenelles in the fat wherein frizzled the fascinating dish
of swine's intestines flavoured with cloves and chopped red
peppers.

With deft touch and loving care he golden browned the tender

Bresse chicken sections, creating the thick cream gravy to pour over them. To the tubers imported from French Africa he added honey, orange juice and brown sugar; he took particular care with the vegetable pudding and the avocado salad and lavished attention upon the dessert browning in the oven.

Marvellous odours, rich and spicy filled the kitchen and were wafted out to the two banqueting rooms beyond, the one where the Cercle waited hungrily and next door where the Chantilly Hunt Club was likewise dining in great state, formal red coats and all.

Reports tell how the members of the Cercle were enthralled by the very first dish, the wonderful soup concocted by their guest-chef; they began to applaud with the appearance of the fish course with its new and marvellous sauce and their enthusiasm knew no bounds with the arrival of the pork dish accompanied by the quenelles the like of which, for flavour, they had never tasted before.

Tears were shed over the chicken course with its accessories of fabulous potatoes and extraordinary soufflé. Excitement mounted to a fever pitch with the unusual salad, and when the fragrant, mahogany brown, spicy *Gâteau de Courges* appeared, the dignified members of the Cercle, stuffed to the eyebrows were prepared to carry M. Bonneval in triumph upon their shoulders.

However, this had to wait upon the address of the President of the nation and the summoning of the guest-chef to the banquet room to receive the plaudits of the members and France's highest decoration.

It was at this moment, just as the Toastmaster announced – '*Messieurs, le Président de la République*' that the disturbance next door broke out precipitating a crisis such as not even the oldest member of the Cercle could recall.

For as the Chief of State rose to his feet, several dozen hounds collected in the hall without, gave tongue simultaneously in shrill whines, barkings, yappings, yelps and shrieks. It was the famous Chantilly Pack being brought to the banquet for the annual ceremony of being blessed by the Bishop of Chantilly.

Held in leash outside the banquet hall in the foyer, they yelled vociferously in both French and English, while the President of France stood on his feet, unable to hear himself think, much less speak and the Chairman and members of the Cercle turned crimson with embarrassment. No one knew what to do. Indeed there seemed to be nothing to be done to save the situation.

But attend! Likewise outside the door up to his knees in bay-

ing beagles there waited one who was also in possession of a
tremendous secret. It was none other than M. Armand Bonneval
ready to be called inside to take his bow. He saw the impasse.
He realised the solution. For him to see and to know were to act.

'Vite! Vite!' he called to an assistant near by. 'Bring the
quenelles! Run! Fetch the remaining quenelles at once!'

The assistant ran. He returned with a huge dish heaped high
with crispy, fragrant, brown, sausage-shaped cakes. Bonneval
seized them and flung them by handfuls to the screaming
Chantilly pack. 'Taisez-vous, mechants chiens!' he cried.

The animals flung themselves upon the succulent offerings.
They gobbled. And a moment later, nothing but silence, golden
silence broken only by almost inaudible canine snufflings of joy
filled the foyers and banqueting rooms. The President commenced
to speak; ten minutes later M. Bonneval made his entrance to be
greeted with a standing ovation and ringing cheers as the distinguished new member of France's Legion d'Honneur.

And outside in the hall, a baffled Negro kennel boy in the
employ of an American film man, owner of the Chantilly Pack,
fingered one of the golden-brown, sausage-length cakes and
shaking his head said – 'He called 'em quenelles, but dey looks
like, dey smells like, dey tastes like and dey sure enough *acts*
like good, old-fashioned Tallahassee Hush-puppies . . .'

Ah yes. By now you will have guessed what that wicked M.
Bonneval had done to revenge himself upon his tormentors, evade
the promise extracted by his wife and maintain the dignity of a
Chef of the Grand Cordon Bleu, retired, to whom nobody tells
anything about what he shall or shall not cook, or how.

But if not, you will only have to imagine yourself a mouse at
a quiet and almost secret investiture in the American Embassy,
where M. Armand Bonneval was decorated with the U.S. medal
of the Legion of Merit, the citation reading in part – 'For courage
in the face of great adversity and an unexampled demonstration
of supreme friendship for the United States of America.'

For, being the only American present at this exclusive feast of
the Cercle, none but the Ambassador who had been born in
Alabama, educated in the mid-west, attended Harvard Law
School and practised law on the Pacific Coast was aware of
the true nature of the French-sounding repast prepared by M.
Bonneval.

Picture the diplomat's joy, for instance, when the Bouillabaisse
arrived and he found himself eating the finest Boston Clam
Chowder to be had outside of Gallagher's Fish House on South
Market Street. Imagine his delight at next being presented with

Barbecued Salmon with Round-Up Barbecue Sauce, as it is prepared in the Columbia River section of the Northwest, where the big sockeyes run, followed by Alabama hog chit'lins with turnip greens, pot likker and genuine Florida-style Hush-puppies.

His enchantment, amusement and affection for the little chef grew with the appearance of Maryland fried chicken with cream sauce, candied yams and old-fashioned southern style corn pudding, was augmented by the good red Gaucamole the way they used to make it in Monterey and climaxed by the appearance of the famous *Gâteau de Courges*, which any French dictionary and a little imagination and skill translates into good old New England pumpkin pie.

None of the above, of course, appeared in the citation; the Ambassador never mentioned it to anyone, nor did Bonneval ever breathe a word, not even after his red rosette was securely implanted in his buttonhole.

Neverthless, the facts have somehow managed to leak out and appear in this space, unfortunately or fortunately as you may care to look at it, considering that great delicacy, the Tallahassee Hush-puppy has probably made its last appearance in la belle France.

Love is a Gimmick

Sometimes the work researching one story will suggest another as one is taken far afield into strange and interesting realms. The idea for LOVE IS A GIMMICK was born while researching TOO MANY GHOSTS.

TOO MANY GHOSTS is a mystery novel, a thriller which appeared in serial form in the 'Saturday Evening Post' in the United States and in 'John Bull' in Great Britain before its publication in book form. It introduced what I hoped was a new kind of detective, a ghost breaker and de-haunter of haunted houses.

To gain the necessary information and knowledge to write this book required a library of more than a hundred diverse volumes dealing with every form of spiritism, charlatism, psychical research and the subject of ghosts, poltergeists and things that go bump in the night. The research took eighteen months and led me through psychical research, legerdemain, photography, chemistry, psychiatry, spiritualism, stage illusions, poltergeist phenomena, etc.

A part of this reading was a study of the life and work of the late Harry Houdini the illusionist and escape artist and certainly one of the greatest showmen and magicians of all time.

There was still a third facet to this fascinating man, namely his implacable enmity to the fake spiritualist, ghost message writers, clairvoyants, trumpet mediums and all the rest of that kind of trash which flourished during his heyday. Houdini called them all cheats and liars and challenged them to produce a manifestation that he could not duplicate. None ever did so successfully. The man himself was a wonderful character because he actually wanted to believe in another world. He was sentimental about his mother and after her death would have welcomed a genuine communication from her. He was shocked and dismayed by the drivel poured forth by the mediums and the infantile mechanical methods employed to gain their effects.

It was inevitable after Houdini's death that a book should be *written revealing how he accomplished his almost incredible escapes, and through these and coupled with general study of the subject one learned that supernormal phenomena were far from established and when tricks were performed upon the stage in the form of illusions or escapes which appeared to be impossible they actually were that – plain and simply impossible. They were done either with the aid of an accomplice or a gimmick, gimmick being a carnival word to cover a multitude of tampering.*

But what glowed through it all, the stories and revelations, was the strength and the courage of Houdini, and while he was extraordinarily powerful in his wrists and fingers it was his courage which attracted me. Even if your escape is planned, rehearsed and the gimmick familiar and fool-proof to you, it takes more than ordinary human nerve to permit oneself to be handcuffed or straitjacketed, padlocked into a mail sack, nailed into a wooden coffin and dumped into an icy river in the middle of January.

Courage, particularly the kind of courage that I myself lack, has always fired me and therefrom originated the basic idea for this story.

Houdini faced many kinds of challenges during his career and in one way or another beat them all. Some of the means he used to beat them are revealed in this story. But even when he was dead and gone (and incidentally no so-called medium ever established contact with him though Houdini had promised to try to communicate if he found there was a life after death) the challenge remained. Could Houdini have been defeated? This problem I carried about in the back of my head for a year.

And then one day I was walking along the famous Bahnhofstrasse in Zürich, the street which corresponds to Bond Street in London and Fifth Avenue in New York, and looked into the window of a toy shop which had a display of magic equipment and boxes of tricks for young people. Amongst them I noticed a gadget I hadn't seen since I was a child at the turn of the century with my own magic box. This was a straw-plaited finger-grip.

You slipped one on to your forefinger, or preferably that of an uninitiated companion, and the harder he tugged the more impossible it was to get it off, for the interwoven plaits of straw simply gripped more tightly under pressure of pulling. This principle has been used even commercially for lifting certain articles by crane. The way to get it off, of course, is to push against the grip instead of pulling. The plaited straw then enlarges and the finger is easily freed. But as long as the strands of straw used in the plait are intact it is impossible to pull them off the finger. The skin will come off first.

I went inside, bought five of them, took them home and experimented for an evening and knew that I had my gimmick. Now the short story based upon Harry Houdini could be written.

Houdini's method of escape from the normal strait or restraining jacket was based on muscle control, agility and strength. No one was ever able to put one on him without Houdini's gaining sufficient slack for him to begin to manœuvre his arms over his head and in a position to manipulate the buckles of the jacket. Then using his extraordinarily muscular fingers he would open the buckles through the canvas.

But supposing someone could devise a way to deny Houdini, or my Houdini character in the story, the use of these powerful fingers? And this is where the straw-plaited, child's magic, finger-stalls came in as used by my unsavoury villain in LOVE IS A GIMMICK. That villain, incidentally, is a composite of several unappetising officers of the law I encountered during my days as a reporter.

This was the means used to deny my escape artist the use of his fingers for when they were inserted into those straw traps he was as good as dead. The harder he pulled to free himself the more tightly they would cling. It was a horrible gaff and thinking of it at night sometimes gave me the cold sweats until I had the story written and out of my system.

I might add that I do not doubt but what if Houdini had suddenly found himself faced with the deadly gimmick I had devised he or his assistant would have found some way of circumventing it in time, for they were both brilliant originators and certainly at all times far more shrewd than the police who tried to trap them. Since Houdini's escapes tended to cast ridicule upon police or gaolers they often tried to devise tests which on the face of them appeared to be beyond human solution. They also sometimes tried to double-cross him by putting sand in the locks or otherwise cheating. Houdini and his helpers had to be doubly alert, for if successful any one of these could have cost the magician his life.

If it would amuse you to have any kind of clue to the solution of this story, I refer you respectfully to my title.

LOVE IS A GIMMICK

I went back today and looked at a diary I wrote thirty years ago and put away in the bottom of an old theatrical trunk. It was the account of the end of The Great Armando. And I got out something else, too, and looked at it again for the first time since it had come into my hands so long ago. It was a canvas straitjacket with leather straps, the metal buckles rusted from contact with the waters of the Detroit River.

Still sewn into the sleeves was the gimmick, that simple and devilish device of a mean and murderous man which, as I wrote in my diary back in 1925, destroyed The Great Armando as surely as a bullet in the brain or a knife stuck in his heart. Only we never found his body afterwards.

The Great Armando was a farm boy from Perrysville, Ohio, whose real name was Joe Ferris. I was his partner for five years and loved him like a brother. He was a queer, brave, moody fellow whose father was American and his mother Polish. He was the strongest man I ever knew, particularly in his fingers, hands and wrists.

He wasn't even a big guy, being no more than five foot ten and stocky, with shoulders and chest like a barrel. And I guess the most important thing in the world to him was the legend we'd built up about his escapes. He boasted that there wasn't a prison cell, manacle, lock or restraint that could hold him.

And it was true, in a way. He was the greatest showman I ever knew, with piercing black eyes and a big shock of black hair. When in public he talked with some kind of spick accent he'd picked up from a Mexican knife thrower during his carny days. But in private with me, he was as American as chewing gum, cornflakes and batting averages.

When he was a kid, a carnival came through Perrysville and he ran away with it from his old man's farm. He picked up everything good and bad a kid can learn around a carnival, but when he met an Australian who taught him to escape from rope ties, he found his life's work. Thereafter he concentrated on escapes and worked up a fair living with an act devoted to getting out of rope ties, straitjackets, handcuffs, and so on.

But he didn't become The Great Armando and hit the big money until I joined up with him in 1920, after the war. If that's blowing my own horn, Joe Ferris would have been the first to acknowledge it. It just happened I had what he needed to take him out of the class of the mediocre performers barnstorming

384

the country with cheap carnivals and put him in the ranks of the world's great illusionists whose names will never be forgotten, like Robert Houdin, Maskelyne, Herrmann the Great, Thurston, Harry Kellar and Harry Houdini.

My name is Carl Hegemeyer, master mechanic and locksmith. My father came over from Germany in 1888. He taught me the accumulated knowledge of eight generations of locksmiths, which could also be summed up in the sentence – anything that can be locked can likewise be opened, provided you have the right key or instrument.

But I had another accomplishment that made me indispensable to the myth of The Great Armando. I could look at a key and several hours later duplicate it from memory. When we travelled around, I had the finest little portable, power-driven metal lathe and key cutter with me. I could plug it into any hotel-room outlet or in emergencies run it off the battery in our car.

An hour or so after a preliminary conference on any escape challenge at which I saw the key used to lock the device, Armando would have a duplicate. Slipping it to him or concealing it was no problem for a man with his training in sleight of hand.

There's no such thing as magic. You know that. You've seen a lot of magic shows from out front where the magician performs the apparently impossible. Well, it not only seems impossible; it is. There's a gaff to everything.

Gaff is the carnival word for gimmick, the trick, the concealed device, the common-sense explanation of how it is done. And usually the gaff is something so simple you don't want to believe it. You'd see The Great Armando buried handcuffed in a stone sarcophagus, and three minutes later he'd be out of it, taking his bow. Common sense would tell you he couldn't do it unless he had superhuman powers or assistance. But the kind of showmanship he'd give you would make you want to believe in the superhuman powers. That's what you paid your money for.

Yet, in nine cases out of ten, he had assistance. I provided it. With my help, he escaped from a sealed subway caisson, a time vault in the National Bank, a 4,000-year-old Greek stone coffin, the punishment cell at Alcatraz, and countless types of manacles and restraining jackets.

But don't forget, he had moxie along with it. Even if you know the gimmicks, it takes guts to let them lace you into a straitjacket, stuff you into a Government mailbag and padlock it, nail you into a packing case bound with rope and drop you into an icy river in midwinter.

N

The only one to come near The Great Armando was Houdini, and everything Houdini did, Armando did better. Houdini did the river-escape trick, only he used handcuffs that he could get out of in ten seconds. Nobody but Armando dared to do it with the straitjacket and letting an expert truss him up.

Yet, as I wrote in my diary, the straitjacket finished him; least ways, the gimmick in it. And a woman put it there; the only woman he ever loved.

He was a queer duck, was Joe Ferris. Nobody ever knew him or got close to him, not even I, and I was his trusted partner. I suppose that was the Polish in him. Often he was moody and suspicious. He kept his money stashed away in cash in safe-deposit boxes under different names that I never even knew. He thought only of his reputation and the myth of The Great Armando. He said to me, 'Remember this: whatever happens, The Great Armando never fails.'

Yet he was no fool either, and knew the risks he was running. He once told me, 'The first time I get a real bad scare, I'll quit and nobody'll ever hear of The Great Armando again. But up to now, I haven't seen anything we can't beat.'

But that was before we met up with Sheriff Jules Massin, of Ossowo County, in the tough River Rouge section of Detroit, where we were doing the water escape as preliminary publicity to Armando's being booked into the Michigan Palace Theatre in Detroit. The sheriff had taken up our challenge to lace Armando into a straitjacket from which he could not escape.

On the face of it, it was routine. There was no straitjacket made that Armando couldn't get out of in less than a minute. But we never took chances. Armando would not guarantee to get out of any restraining device unless he could inspect it first. The padlock on the mail sack had to be closed and opened in our presence. This gave me the necessary gander at the key. And the packing case had to go on exhibition in the lobby of the theatre before and after the stunt. That's when we gaffed it. We thought we had every angle covered. Only we never figured to come against a man with murder in his heart.

There was a crowd in the sheriff's office the day we went there to inspect the restraints and set up the stunt – deputies, detectives, police, reporters and photographers. The sheriff's wife was there too. His office was on the ground floor of his home. At first I didn't notice her. She had a scarf bound around her head, European style. She had pale cheeks and prominent eyes, that seemed absolutely devoid of expression.

They did not even flicker when the sheriff, noticing her in the forefront of those crowding around his desk, snarled, 'What the hell you doin' here, Tina? Can't you see I'm busy?'

She was submissive to his abuse; every line of her body proclaimed her to be cowed and hopeless. Yet she did not go, and soon other matters claimed the sheriff's attention.

The sheriff was a mean man. Mean, dirty and dangerous. He wasn't a copper for nothing; he liked it. We meet all kinds in our racket, from plain smart alecks who think it is fun to make a monkey out of a performer, to cops and jailers who don't like to see you make a monkey out of them. But we'd never run up against a guy nursing murder in his heart because it was for free. Armando always signed a release.

That was the sheriff. I knew him for a killer – a killer inside the law – from the moment I walked into his office. He was over six feet tall, fat, burly and dirty. His clothes were dirty, his skin, his finger-nails and his teeth. His breath was bad. He wore a fancy gun in a belt holster. You could see he loved the power it gave him.

Massin threw a straitjacket on to the desk and sneered, 'Anything wrong with that?'

It was an ordinary violence-restraint jacket with straps and buckles, the easiest type for Armando, for the canvas was not unusually thick. No matter how strong the manipulator, Armando, by swelling his muscles, could always reserve enough slack to get his arms over his head. Then he opened the buckles through the canvas. I told you he had the most powerful fingers in the world. In that department he was superhuman. That's why he was called great.

I picked up the jacket to show Armando. But he wasn't looking. Something strange had happened. He was staring instead at Tina Massin, and on his face was an expression such as I had never seen there before.

I had to catch my breath. Her headcloth had fallen back upon her neck, revealing her blonde hair and the perfect oval of her face. She looked like the pale, imprisoned princess in the book of Grimm's fairy tales I had when I was a kid. The impression she made upon me at that moment was one I would never forget.

Have you ever known it to happen where you see someone for the first time and in that moment you know that person's life story almost as though you had read it in a book? She was of foreign extraction, maybe Polish or Finnish. I guessed she had been taken from an institution or orphanage into the sheriff's establishment as household drudge. She had no doubt first been abused, and later married because it was more convenient to own a wife than a servant. There are some women who become the hopeless, submissive captives of the most appalling men. Such a one was Tina Massin.

They were caught up in each other's eyes, these two utterly different and contrasting strangers, the showman with the long black hair and piercing glance, the pale girl with the thick silken hair, and eyes that were for the first time alive and filled with a kind of pleading. Any moment it would become obvious that two people had found each other, had fallen in love and were attempting to communicate.

I created a diversion by tossing the jacket back on to the desk. 'That's O.K.,' I said.

The sheriff sniggered unpleasantly. 'It's the way I strap 'em into it,' he said. I was satisfied to let Armando deal with that. The post-office inspector produced the mailbag. I bent over to examine the thickness, fittings and padlock. I had a dozen keys that would open it. Armando would have two of them concealed on his person, attached to a fine wire. Once out of the straitjacket – a matter of sixty seconds – he would push out the key and manipulate it, again through the material of the sack.

It was O.K. Nevertheless, I made them open and shut the lock several times to make sure it hadn't been gaffed with shot or sand. Mrs Massin dropped her handkerchief. Armando stooped to pick it up, as did she. Their fingers touched for an instant. I was still bent over, examining the mailbag.

I heard her whisper to him, 'For heaven's sake, don't do it.'

The time set was ten the next morning at the Western and Lakes Railroad pier where there was a big travelling crane. The document releasing the sheriff's office and Detroit police from all responsibility was produced and the photographers jostled for position. Somebody handed Armando a pen. Mrs Massin made a slight gesture with her hand. Their eyes met once more. She licked dry lips and, imperceptibly almost, shook her head. The sheriff missed the byplay, but sniggered again.

'Going to welsh?' he asked, and then, addressing everyone in general, said, 'I say all greasers are yellow.'

Joe Ferris flourished the pen dramatically. 'Armando he nevaire welsh,' he said, and signed.

The light in Tina Massin's eyes was extinguished. All the life went from her. She was hopeless, despairing, submissive. She turned and went out of the room.

I went to see Harry Hopp, an old-time reporter friend on the Free Press. I told you we never left anything to chance. I didn't like the set-up for two cents.

I asked, 'What's the background on your fragrant sheriff of Ossowo County?'

Hopp said, 'Can't tell you anything good about him. And as long as you're asking, he hates carnivals and the carny crowd. They can't get the time of day in his county. You better watch out for that baby.'

'Yeah,' I said, 'I got that. But why?'

'Shakedown,' he replied. 'There was a carnival through here five or six years ago really loaded with grift. They shelled out plenty to the sheriff to operate, but when he came back again for a second handout, they beat him up and threw him out. Maybe your boy friend even was with the carny and saw it happen. Massin's death on anything connected with travelling shows or midways.'

That night I said to Armando, 'Listen, Joe. Were you ever with a grift show that beat up a sheriff around here before you started in with me?'

He reflected and then said slowly, 'So that's where I know him from. When he tried to shake me down, I poked him, and that started it.'

I said, 'I don't like it. He's got it in for you. Let's call it off. We can do it in Cleveland next week.'

He looked at me as if I were out of my mind, and asked, 'Have we got all the angles covered?'

I went back over things in my mind. There was nothing that could happen that we hadn't thought of. 'Yes,' I said.

'O.K.,' he said, 'we go. We can't afford to back out.'

But I was wrong. There was something I hadn't thought of – something so simple and elementary as a means of destroying Armando that it never dawned on me until it was too late.

The day of the test was damp, cold and sunless. There were chunks of ice floating in the river. In spite of the raw, blustery weather, the pier and several adjoining piers were black with people. We'd had a big press in advance of the attempt.

The stunt was routine and we'd done it a dozen times before. The gaff was this: as soon as they started to nail the cover on to the box, Armando would begin working his way out of the strait-jacket and the mailbag, while I'd stall, suggesting putting in more nails or tying the rope tighter, until I got a signal from Armando that he was free of the restraints. The crate had been gimmicked by us the night before with a concealed sliding panel in one side. Fifteen seconds after the box disappeared beneath the surface, he'd be out of it.

It was that simple, like all stage or escape illusions, except it was the way Armando did it that made it look so good. It is a part of the showmanship in that kind of act that when you really think a guy is in danger he's as safe as he'd be at home in bed. The real deadly stuff doesn't show. Like staying under, holding your breath for more than two minutes in freezing water, and then coming up amidst ice floes or risking being carried away under the ice by the current. He had a right to call himself The Great Armando and to be proud of his rep.

When Armando and I arrived, there was a big bunch of reporters, including Harry Hopp and several sob sisters and a horde of photographers, and newsreel-movie men. Capt. Harry Stevens, of the river police, was giving directions to a police launch that was to pick Armando up if and when he appeared. He was not too pleased at being used for a publicity stunt and greeted us sourly.

He said, 'O.K., O.K. Let's get going and get out of here. You fellows signed a release, didn't you?'

Sheriff Massin, wearing a big sheepskin-lined coat, said, 'Yup. Got it right here.'

Armando slipped out of his cloak. Underneath, he was wearing trousers and sweatshirt of light, warm wool, and sneakers. The sheriff stepped over with the straitjacket, a nasty, self-satisfied smile on his face. Tina Massin was there in the front row. She wasn't pretty any more. Her face was tear-stained and filled with fear. Her eyes were fixed upon the jacket.

I spotted something about the sleeves that had not been there the day before. My stomach started to sink. I said, 'Here, wait a minute. Let me see that jacket. It's been gimmicked.'

The sheriff said, 'They're stalling,' but handed it over.

I turned out the sleeves. Inside, to the canvas lining, had been sewn ten finger grips of plaited strips of coloured straw. You've seen them in any magic or trick store or child's magic set. Once they are slipped over a finger, the harder you pull the more tightly they grip. A device also used commercially for hoisting, there is no possible way of tearing loose from it. The secret of escape is to push against the grips. The plaits then contract and enlarge so that the finger can be removed. But fastened inside the long, narrow sleeve of the jacket, there was no leverage to push. And deprived of the use of his fingers, The Great Armando was as good as dead.

I saw Armando's eyes narrow when he saw the fatal trap, and the sweat beads form on his upper lip and under his eyes. It was the first time I ever saw Joe Ferris afraid.

I said, 'What the hell is this? Those things weren't in there yesterday when we inspected the jacket.'

Massin said, 'Well, they're in there now.'

Tina Massin seemed about to faint. I had a picture of her sitting up all night, with the sheriff standing over her, sewing in those terrible devices designed to kill a man for free.

Captain Stevens came over, took the straitjacket and looked at it and the innocent-looking toy finger grips plaited in reds, yellows, greens and purples.

'What's the idea, sheriff?' he asked.

Massin bustled truculently and replied loudly, so that all the press could hear. 'This greaser says he can get out of anything, don't he? I had a feller once I hadda take to the loony house. Killed three guys. He got out of the jacket. He had hands like a gorilla. I fixed him up like this. He didn't get out. O.K., so let this greaseball put up or shut up. They seen them kind of grips a dozen times before in their racket.'

Captain Stevens looked doubtful, but I could sense that he was secretly pleased, in a way, that a performer who had put them to a lot of needless trouble was going to be shown up.

He said to us, 'What about it, boys? You don't have to go through with it if you don't want to, but make up your minds and let's get out of here.'

Harry Hopp, the Free Press reporter, said, 'Don't let him do it, Carl. It's sheer murder. I'll see that he doesn't get the worst of it in the papers.'

Massin laughed his loud, dirty laugh. 'I knew the fourflusher would welsh.'

'Welsh nothing!' I shouted. 'Our contract clearly stated——'

'Quiet, everyone!' It was Armando. And even in that crisis he didn't forget the phony Mexican accent. 'Shut up, Carl.'

But he wasn't looking at me. He was looking straight at Tina Massin and she at him. There was no mistake. They were in love all right. They had found and lost each other in the same moment. They were saying good-bye, for there was no hope for them. She was the wife of a brute who would never let her go. And he was faced with an insoluble dilemma. Because if he went through with the stunt he was a dead man. And if he backed out he might as well be dead, because he would never again be The Great Armando.

He said, 'All right, sheriff; I am ready.'

The sheriff stepped forward, laughing. 'So long, sucker. You asked for it.' Things moved fast then as he went about his for-free murder, forcing each finger of Armando's hands deep into the plaits of the straw finger-grips; then pushing his knee into Armando's back in order to haul the straps tighter.

And all the time Joe Ferris continued to look only on the white face of this girl he had come to love in such a strange manner, and who had been forced to become his executioner. Her eyes were lost in his. Her lips moved, though no sound came, but I would have sworn they were communicating for the last time.

When four men lifted the mail sack, with Armando inside it, into the packing case and the electric crane travelled over and lowered the lid on to the top, Tina Massin gave a soft cry and crumpled to the pier in a dead faint.

The sheriff laughed, saying, 'Now what the hell's the matter with her?'

A newsreel cameraman shouted, 'Hey, sheriff, will ya look out? You're in the way of the shot!' I felt as if it were I who was going to die.

I jumped on to the box to stall as long as I could, and give him a chance, even though I knew it was hopeless. There was no signal from him as usual, to let me know he was out of the jacket and sack, waiting for the plunge with his finger on the gaffed panel that would slide open and free him as soon as he sank beneath the surface.

Then he hadn't got out. The child's toy had defeated him. The legend of The Great Armando was a thing of the past. But I was determined to save the life of Joe Ferris.

The sheriff cried, 'Lower away!' and there was a cheer from the crowd as the steel cable payed out. The weighted crate went in with a splash and began to settle as the water poured in through the interstices.

I had a sickening vision of Armando trussed up like a mummy in the horrid canvas jacket, his fingers helplessly trapped in the straw grips, the icy water pouring into the case, the mail sack filling up, his last gasp for oxygen; then the hopeless last-minute struggle, tugging against the inexorable grips, and the final bubble bursting from the tortured lungs. And after that, silence.

Air was rushing up in a dirty surface swirl as the case sank with its burden. When my stop watch showed two minutes and there was no sign of an arm or dark head breaking the grey river surface, I bawled in panic, 'Haul away! Get him out of there! Something's gone wrong! Get him up, do you hear!'

There was some confused shouting and I could see the police captain shouting futilely at the man in the operator's hanging booth of the crane. But there was no rattle of machinery or running of steel cable over the wheel. Something had happened to the crane or the power, for I could see the operator wrestling with his levers.

I went over the side of the pier into the water. Men and women were screaming. I had a crazy idea I could swim down, work the panel and get him out of there, sack and all, and up to the surface. I fought the cable and my bursting lungs. Then the police launch came and fished me out. After ten minutes, the power came on again and the crate was raised. But there was not a chance in the world that The Great Armando was still alive. The sheriff had won.

Workmen attacked the case with axes and crowbars. Interns from an ambulance, their white trousers showing beneath their dark overcoats, stood by with their equipment. With a splintering and wrenching, the side of the case broke away, revealing the locked mail sack.

And I was the first one to see that it wasn't full enough! With a yell, I broke away from Harry Hopp, seized the key from the postal inspector and opened the padlock.

It was empty! No, not quite empty. Inside buckled as though it had never been unfastened, the terrible finger grips still in place, was the straitjacket, neatly folded. But of The Great Armando there was no sign. He had accomplished his greatest escape!

It was his last, too, for he was never seen again. The police dredged, grappled and dived for three days, but his body was never recovered. He had defeated the vicious finger grips, the jacket, the mail sack, and the case, and got out, and then, perhaps at the last moment, exhausted from the struggle, his strength gone, he had drowned and been swept downriver or under a pier.

I went to a hospital myself with pneumonia. They said in my delirium I swore I'd kill Sheriff Massin for murdering my friend and partner. It turned out that it wasn't necessary. Six months after the disappearance of The Great Armando I read in a newspaper that Jules Massin was shot to death in a saloon by the saloonkeeper he had attempted to shake down. I never heard what became of Mrs Massin after that.

A couple of months after I got out of the hospital, Captain Stevens, of the river police, sent me the straitjacket, complete with the sheriff's deadly gaff, as a souvenir. I couldn't bear to look at it, and put it away, with my diary of how it all happened, in the bottom of my trunk. Then I went back into the locksmith business.

All that was thirty years ago. Now I am holding the jacket in my fingers again. For two days ago I saw Joe Ferris, The Great

Armando! And with him was Tina Massin! I'll swear it! I couldn't have been mistaken, even though his hair was white and his features changed. She looked almost the same, except happy. It happened when I was coming out of a movie house in Athens, Georgia.

I said, 'Joe! Joe Ferris! And Tina Massin!'

They denied it. They stopped politely, but their expressions remained blank.

The man said, 'You must be mistaking us for someone else. My name is Vernon Howard, and this is Mrs Howard here. I'm in the grain-and-feed business. Anyone in Athens knows me. And now, if you'll excuse Mrs Howard and me——'

Vernon Howard's Grain and Feed Store was at the corner of the Boulevard and Pecan Street. When I instituted inquiries as to how long it had been there, the invariable answer was, 'Oh, 'bout as long as I kin remember.' But when I got down to cases, no one seemed to remember them back for thirty years or longer.

When I returned to New York, I dug out the straitjacket of Sheriff Massin. I hadn't touched it since the day I thought it had killed The Great Armando. The colour on the finger-grips of plaited straw had run, but otherwise they were exactly as they had been on that fatal day. I examined them. Then I took a magnifying glass. I tried them out by putting my fingers in and yanking. They pulled loose. And after that I knew the secret of how The Great Armando had escaped from the inescapable trap laid for him by vindictive Sheriff Massin. The finger-stalls had been subtly gaffed by his wife. The straw plaits had been cut with scissors in such a way as to defy casual inspection, but in every case destroying the tension of the plaits, so that they no longer pulled against one another.

I remember the look between them, the money he had stashed away in safe-deposit boxes, and his remark, 'If I ever get a real scare, I'll quit and nobody'll ever hear of The Great Armando again.' And how easily he could have swum ashore under cover of the excitement, and vanished, to return when he read Sheriff Massin was dead.

Yeah, we'd thought of everything, except one thing. And in the end it was Joe Ferris, The Great Armando, who had the guts to put his faith in love as a gimmick.

The Lost Hour

*Did you ever wonder what happened to the hour that is lost
each day on the West-bound voyage of the 'Queen Elizabeth,'
the 'Queen Mary' or any of the big five-day express liners, when
at midnight the clock is stopped for one hour and time stands
still? I did, and hence this long short story, or novelette.*

*One of man's favourite fantasies is speculation upon the
mystery of the flow of time. The present is already the past. The
future rushes in upon us with the speed of jet propulsion. Down
through the ages writers have experimented with finding cracks
in time, or formulas for slipping through the layers of speeding
seconds, minutes and hours in the hope of finding themselves
transported into the past or permitted to peer into the future.*

*All of these, of course, resulted in fantasy tales of one kind or
another, and so has mine.*

*Essentially the basic theme of this story is as old as man's
imagination. It is that of the mouse who turns into a lion, the
timid man who in crisis finds his courage. There has been reiterated all too often that there is no such thing as a new plot,
and indeed this is so. There is only an occasional new twist to an
old one.*

*I can remember how it began. It was during one of my cross-
ings to the United States aboard the 'Queen Elizabeth,' and I can
still see myself sitting in the smokeroom with a gay party as the
smokeroom steward prepared the auction pool on the ship's run.
And I remember looking up at the clock, the hands of which had
stopped at midnight and no longer moved. All about me was
laughter and chatter of conversation and the clink of glasses;
dance music penetrated from the near-by lounge and no one was
noticing or caring that the inevitably moving finger of time had
been stilled. The huge liner with its passengers and crew of
almost two thousand, two thousand different souls were steaming*

*through the sea between time as it were. Man had learned even
how to make the sun stand still, for I remembered a flight I once
made on the Comet from Rome to London. We took off at sunrise
with the sun poised like an orange on a table upon the rim of the
horizon, and there it remained for as long as we flew due Westward, unable to gain upon us. To what use had man put these
latter-day miracles? Was there any magic inherent in these timeless hours?*

*The thought of magic fired my imagination, for through all of
my life my private yearning has been to be a magician — not the
kind that does card tricks or pulls rabbits out of hats, but a
genuine working wizard like Merlin. I am sure this is one of
man's oldest dreams, to be able to blast, to transform, to levitate
and to perform outside the laws of nature. But only to writers is
it given to realise this exquisite fantasy.*

*Magic it was to be then, at least for myself in my incarnation
as Edwin Reith-Jones the timid character who had been sent out
into the world to perform an impossible task. For us the sixty
minutes when the clock was stopped was pregnant with magic.
During that non-hour we could slough off our faults and fears
and become heroes. For what kind of a man would it be who
would most need to make use of this magic but one who lacked
the courage or the presence to make use of seconds, minutes,
hours and days that were timeful? Thus for one hour each midnight, for five nights aboard this great express liner, Edwin Reith-
Jones and I were able to elude the lifelong enemy of our own
true persons.*

*The rest of the cast of the story soon fell into place or were
invented to do their work. Some stories begin with characters
and then take over and often go their own headlong and head-
strong way. But for a story of this kind you create or engage
symbols to carry out your designs almost as you would engage
actors, where the director 'phones Central Casting and asks for
such and such types. You may then say, 'But then these are not
real life characters.' But then this is not a real life story either. I
warned you at the beginning that this was a fairy tale in which
the author himself escapes from that sometimes too grim and
unhappy thing known as real life.*

*In reading a story and condemning it as 'escape' fiction one is
prone to forget that it is more than a pastiche designed to dope
the reader and enable him or her to escape momentarily from
the complications of life. It is the writer himself who is frequently
the fugitive. Writing stories is often more relaxing and revealing,
and certainly cheaper than the psychiatrist's couch. I can think*

*of many stories I have written which have performed just this
service for me. In fact they have played a dual role in my life,
simultaneously affording me psychic satisfaction or release from
frustration, and earning me a living as well. I do not know for
which I am the most grateful.*

THE LOST HOUR

Edwin Reith-Jones, painfully shy and, as always, suffering from
lack of self-confidence, sat by himself at the far end of the
deserted Veranda Bar of the R.M.S. *Gigantic*, westbound, and
contemplated the ship's electric clock over the doorway, the
hands of which had stopped at midnight. It had been some ten
minutes since they had been in that position.

Clad in a dinner jacket with red carnation, the uniform aboard
the *Gigantic* after six p.m., he regarded the stalled timepiece and
the sign above it, which read WESTBOUND ALL CLOCKS WILL BE
STOPPED ONE HOUR AT MIDNIGHT, through a haze in part compounded from Scotch whiskies he had consumed in his loneliness
and in part from the fears and worrisome thoughts that dogged him.

They should never have sent him on this trip. He simply wasn't
the man for it. Indeed, he remembered painfully the conversation
overheard outside the chairman's door in the office before he was
admitted:

'Reith-Jones? Good heavens, you can't! The man's an absolute
rabbit when it comes to dealing with people! He'll never put it
over!'

And the reply, 'At least he's honest. It's wretched luck, but I
don't see that there is any choice.'

Nor had there been. A concatenation of circumstances, including an illness and an accident, made Edwin Reith-Jones,
chief accountant for the Manchester cotton firm of Selwyn &
Havas, the only responsible member available for the important
mission of journeying westward aboard the *Gigantic* and contac-
ting Sir Malcolm Gordien, the London financier.

Sir Malcolm was on his way to the United States to seek American aid for the cotton industry and to offer in return a kind of
cartelisation which, in the event of war, would mobilise British
production with American. The small but growing firm of Selwyn

& Havas wished to be a part of the scheme and share the aid. It was a job requiring the ability to meet and impress people as well as knowledge of the business.

Edwin's unobtrusiveness was so marked as to be almost obtrusive, for his hair was so fair as to be nearly white, as were his eyebrows. He was forty-five, but with his pale blue eyes, pink skin and plain, innocent features, he looked half that. Only a slight truculence about the chin seemed oddly out of harmony with his other, negative qualities. Sitting alone at the bar – most of the passengers having congregated for the dancing in the lounge – he gave the impression that he wasn't there.

His thoughts turned to Lisa Lisbon, the Hollywood film star. He had seen her descending from the Veranda Grill, trailing perfume, the rustle of expensive clothes and men behind her.

She would be in the lounge now, dancing with any one of the group of powerful and notable men rumoured to be in love with her – Victor Vaughn Craig, the explorer and writer; Sen. Austin Gregg, of the Foreign Relations Committee; or the Earl of Morveigh.

And then in his mind's eye he himself held her in his arms and she was dancing with him. She was a wondrously beautiful woman with roan-coloured hair, exquisite brown eyes and most delicately chiselled features. She was so beautiful it made the heart ache to regard her. He remembered that she was dressed in a gown of copper sequins that exactly matched her hair. She was a more famous actress than even Greta Garbo had been.

He dismissed his dreams. As much chance of realising them as bearding Sir Malcolm Gordien and persuading him to include Selwyn & Havas in his combine. He did not even know Sir Malcolm by sight. And furthermore, he could not dance – at least not any known intelligible step. He could only sit, a nervous, socially timid, useless fellow, alone at a bar, absorbing Scotch whisky.

He said to the bartender, 'May I have another or is it time?' referring to the British closing laws.

'Ain't no time at sea, sir,' the bartender replied, setting up a new glass and pouring. Then, with a nod towards the halted clock, he added, 'Ain't no time at all now. We're between time.'

Was it the whisky or the words which had the most curious effect upon Edwin Reith-Jones? Surely not the former, for he held his liquor like a gentleman. No! The phrases ran through his mind and blood like fire. He felt suddenly different – strong, brave, gregarious, powerful. The barkeep had said it. Time was standing still.

Between Time! There was a difference of five hours between
Great Britain and the United States. For an hour each night then,
at midnight, they were adrift not only upon a trackless ocean
but in a boundless universe where no time was kept.

Suddenly it came to him that with Time standing still, everything during that hour was unreal and taking place in a vacuum.
Nothing really counted – not the Scotch he was downing, the
glasses the bartender was polishing, the miles the ship's vibrating
screws put behind her, nor words spoken, actions done, contracts
signed, beliefs expressed.

Slipping thus in between Time, a man could escape at last from
the straightjacket of his nature. During that non-existent hour he
could be anything, do anything, including – the idea came to him
almost as an inspiration and a command – invite the most beautiful film star in the world to dance and proudly whirl her in his
arms before the envious and admiring eyes of all. Forty-five
minutes of the precious lost hour remained.

Outside Time, Edwin Reith-Jones discovered when he reached
the lounge, was a peculiar clarity, a sharp awareness of people,
of tensions, but particularly of himself and his own powers, that
he had never experienced before.

Lisa Lisbon was not dancing. She sat, looking neither bored nor
entertained, with Craig, a handsome giant; Senator Gregg, a grey-
haired man with a beautifully sensitive face; and the lean, red-
headed Earl of Morveigh. Near by were two other suitors – Saul
Wiener, president of American Pictures, and a pink-faced, boyish-
looking man, playing canasta at a small side table.

There was yet another member of the group, a gaunt fellow
with snapping dark eyes, high cheekbones and a long, humorous
nose. He had big hands, which were at the end of arms too long
for his sleeves. A man of forty-odd, with grizzled dark hair, brush-
cut, he was smoking a black cigar and watching everything with
amusement. This was Cy Hammer, Lisa Lisbon's agent.

There was another party adjacent that impressed itself upon
Reith-Jones. It consisted of a typically well-to-do American family
– a father and mother with two girls in the awkward thirteen-to-
fifteen age bracket. But the girls were not sisters. On the contrary,
they could not have been more different. The one was a wide-
eyed, innocent-looking child, blonde and breathless, who resembled her sweet-faced, well-mannered mother. The other, taller,
pale, self-possessed, with Italian-cut black hair in the latest style,
looked sophisticated and hard. Yet there was about her, Edwin
felt, a curious yearning quality of desperation that did not seem
to match her artificially brittle voice and laugh and the shocking

fact that, though she was obviously still a leggy, undeveloped child, she wore lipstick, mascara and eye shadow and her fingernails were painted bright red. Although she was chattering animatedly, she never took her eyes off Lisa Lisbon.

Secure within the confines of the hour that did not exist, Edwin Reith-Jones marched up to the movie star, bowed and asked, 'May I have the pleasure of this dance, Miss Lisbon?'

The group looked up in surprise at the intrusion, Saul Wiener pausing in the discard of a queen to remark, 'So who is this guy?'

Victor Vaughn Craig's cold eyes appraised the newcomer. He said stiffly, 'You must excuse Miss Lisbon. She does not care to dance.'

In Time, Edwin would have blushed to death on the spot. Outside the clock's iron jurisdiction, he said evenly, 'Why don't you let Miss Lisbon answer for herself?'

Lisa's rich, warm laughter rang out. 'Why, it's the Boiled Turnip!' she cried, but with such immediate and engaging friendliness that Edwin could only take it as the dearest of compliments. 'Oh, that's dreadful of me, but I always name everyone. Of course, I'll dance with you.'

Craig said sharply, 'Lisa!' and the Earl of Morveigh raised an eyebrow. But the star was looking across to Cy Hammer, who removed his cigar, winked at her and merely said, 'Have fun, kid.'

Lisa Lisbon arose and cast her magnificent glance over her assembled swains. 'Why shouldn't I dance with him?' she inquired. 'You boys have been boring the garter belt off me for the past hour.'

Edwin was suddenly caught up in two near-by dark eyes staring into his for a moment, and felt that a message of deepest despair was being sent forth to him. But what it was, or why, he could not fathom. The eyes belonged to the strange, tall child with the make-up. Then Lisa Lisbon gave herself into his arms. The band was playing a foxtrot.

At that moment the ship lurched, as it had been doing for some time, due to the fact that the *Gigantic* had passed Land's End and an angry following sea snapped at her from the Channel. She rolled all of the dancers, adept and tyro, including Edwin and Lisa Lisbon, the width of the dance floor, shrieking and laughing.

With a surprisingly deft movement, Edwin swung Lisa around at the end of the slide, so that it was he and not she who crashed into a pillar.

'Nice going, Turnip,' Miss Lisbon chuckled in her sweet, deep contralto. 'Hang on, kid. Here we go again,' as the reverse roll started them sailing back. They made two more trips before the band leader ended the set and Edwin brought a breathless Lisa Lisbon back to her party.

'Oo-oo-of!' she said. 'Haven't had so much fun since I used to slide on the ice as a kid in Milwaukee.'

The men all arose stiffly to receive her, their faces trying to register disapproval of this odd albino Englishman who had crashed their midst.

'Thank you very much,' Edwin said. Then he added, 'I say, would you perhaps care for a turn up on the top deck with me, Miss Lisbon? It's jolly nice up there.'

Victor Vaughn Craig loomed a menacing six feet four. He said, 'Miss Lisbon would not care for a turn on deck. You've had your dance. Now how about making yourself scarce?' Implied was : 'while you've got your health.'

The Timeless Edwin Reith-Jones said succinctly, 'Why don't you go soak your head, old boy?'

Cy Hammer was grinning like a gargoyle. Lisa's laugh temporarily postponed the crisis. 'That's telling him, Turnip . . . Victor, when I have my dialogue written for me, it will be by a script writer . . . O.K., Turnip. We'll go topside and look at the moon. I think I like you.'

She took Edwin's arm and marched out of the lounge with him, followed by the stares of some two hundred or so passengers and the adoring gaze of the queer, made-up child.

When she reappeared alone, the orchestra had packed up for the night and the entourage and most of the other passengers had gone from the lounge. Cy Hammer still remained there, waiting.

He stared in astonishment as the star came in. The immaculate axis of Lisa's gown no longer bisected her exactly. One false eyelash was gone, her lipstick displaced and an appreciable amount of the magnificent roan-coloured hair was disordered. Her cheeks were pink and there was a shining in her eyes.

Hammer regarded her quizzically and said, 'A limey did this?'

Lisa fell into one of the overstuffed lounge chairs next to him. 'Wow, what a man!' she said. 'That was close. Two more minutes and it would have been all up with little Lisa.' She felt the air with her fingers where the missing eyelash should have been, and then hastily stripped off the remaining one.

Hammer smoked tactfully for a moment, and then, since he was devoted to Lisa and her business and there were no secrets between them, he inquired, 'What broke it up?'

Lisa replied, 'I don't know,' and then, 'Yes I do. We were up forward. The ship's bell struck. He looked at his watch, said, like a bad actor, "Great heavens, what have I done? Can you forgive me, Miss Lisbon?" and bolted before I could say a word.'

She sat there a moment with a reminiscent and girlish smile about her mouth. Then she said, 'The sweetness of him, the tenderness, the sweetness of the things he said to me. Nobody is ever sweet to me, Cy. He made me feel like a woman again, instead of like a doll or a prize animal.'

The agent regarded her with astonishment. Then, without speaking, he reached over and patted her hand. Lisa turned her warm smile upon him. 'Take me down to my cabin, Cy,' she said. 'I want to dream.'

The tall, dark-haired child with the sophisticated make-up and manner was Melanie Holcombe, the unhappy shuttlecock of the notorious Chicago Holcombe divorce case of a decade ago. She was returning alone to her father in Chicago from Paris, where she had been living with her mother in the European whirl that meant Cannes in the winter, London in the season, autumn for the racing, at St Moritz for New Year's.

She had been befriended on the boat by the Chamberses and their daughter, Florrie. They had taken the unhappy child under their wing, sat with her at the table, taken her to the movies and provided a kind of base for her.

All this, Edwin Reith-Jones had found out by accident, when he had gone to the purser's desk to make inquiries about Sir Malcolm Gordien, and, finding the chief purser in conversation with the ship's doctor, had been too shy to intrude.

'It's a rotten shame,' the purser concluded. 'The old girl's just taken a new lover – one of the de Neuilly boys. Melanie was in the way, so she's sent her packing back to her father.'

The doctor asked, 'Won't that be better for her? Girls usually love their fathers.'

'True, but old Holcombe won't have any use for her. He's just married again – some young television actress. I saw pictures of them, taken at Sun Valley. She looks a real featherbrain. I feel sorry for the kid.'

Reith-Jones felt sad and depressed. He knew now the reason for the unhappy expression in the girl's eyes. It was the same look of seeking and longing found in the eyes of a stray dog searching every passer-by for the one who will eventually take him home and give him love and shelter. He forgot about Sir Malcolm Gordien and went away. He wished somehow he might talk to the child.

That evening Edwin emerged from the moving-picture theatre through the smoking-room, which was crowded in anticipation of the big auction pool on the ship's run.

Lisa Lisbon, in blue-and-silver lamé, surrounded by her entourage, saw him pass and called to him, 'Hi, Turnip! Come over here and sit with us!'

Crimson with embarrassment, he could do no more than go over as he had been bidden, and face the hostile or indifferent glances of the important people with her. It was Cy Hammer who made place for him and ordered him a double Scotch, which he downed quickly to give him courage, and another on top of that.

The ship was sorting itself out and Edwin was learning names and faces through listening. The pink-faced man engaged in the eternal canasta game with Saul Wiener was Hamlin Mason, another suitor, head of National Motors, of Detroit. And the man a few tables away with the too-large head and perpetually sneering expression on his face was Frank Patch, the left-of-left British Socialist M.P., labour leader and good friend of the communists.

Edwin wanted to ask which one was Sir Malcolm Gordien, but did not wish to parade his ignorance before the others. He searched the room for one who might possibly be he, and felt the tension of expectation as the time for the bidding neared. The gambling lust already lay thick over the room, like the layers of blue smoke from the rich cigars. Syndicates and combines were forming to bid for the favoured high numbers.

He watched the smoking-room steward searching for a volunteer auctioneer among the passengers. A famous comedian turned it down with 'No, thanks. I'm on vacation.' A well-known journalist took one look about him at the assembled money power and, with a quiet shudder, asked to be excused.

The steward finally went to his desk, rang a bell and pleaded, 'Ladies and gentlemen, we know everyone is anxious for the auction to begin, but we have not yet been able to secure an auctioneer. Won't some gentleman kindly come forward?'

A buzzing hum followed as people at various tables urged others to go up and sacrifice themselves.

Edwin Reith-Jones' pale eyes found their way to the smoking-room clock, the hands of which were fixed at midnight. Time was suspended again. He rose to his feet.

Lisa Lisbon laid a quick detaining hand upon his arm. 'Turnip, sit down,' she said. 'They'll eat you alive.'

But Edwin Reith-Jones, the famous wit, entertainer and auctioneer, walking confidently to the desk across a planet that had ceased to revolve through space, seized the gavel and said, 'Ladies and gentlemen, and fellow cut-throats——'

In the gasp that followed, Victor Vaughn Craig said, 'What an egregious little bounder.'

But Lisa's anxious expression cleared as she breathed, 'I think he's going to get away with it.'

'There's one rule to this auction,' Edwin was saying. 'When the hammer falls, it's final. Any opening bid of less than fifty pounds from this aggregation of captains of industry, financiers, millionaires and plain, unassuming second-story men will be treated with the contempt it deserves.'

There was a titter. Saul Wiener said, 'What did he call us?' and then added, 'What's with his face? I never saw a feller without any eyebrows like that before.'

Lisa said, 'He has them, only they don't show.'

Cy grinned at her. 'You find out everything, don't you, Snooks?'

The steward drew the first number from the bowl. Edwin went to work. He was fast, funny, accurate and hypnotic as he drew bids from all quarters of the room. The pool grew to record proportions.

Low Field came up. The sea was smooth, the big ship racing through the night. Nobody bid for it. Edwin cupped the number in his hands and then cradled it. 'Poor little orphan,' he said, 'nobody wants him.'

'Oh,' cried Lisa, touched, 'Cy, you buy it!' But Hammer's call of fifty pounds was immediately jumped and spirited bidding resulted, with Edwin finally knocking it down to him for two hundred and fifty pounds.

'What happened?' Hammer said. 'He put the whammy on me. I need this number like a hole in the mind.'

'That's my li'l ol' Turnip,' Lisa purred; and then soothed, 'Never mind, Cy. Something may bust during the night and slow us down.'

'And now, ladies and gentlemen,' Edwin cried, 'the number you have all been waiting for, Number Five Hundred and Seventy, the captain's choice.' One number in the pool was always supposed to be the captain's estimate of what the run might be.

A pre-battle hush fell over the throng in the smoking-room as Edwin's washed-out eyes wandered over them, weighing them. By now he knew all the big combines and syndicates, as well as the wealthy individuals, and for all he had mental names. The Wolves were on the starboard side, the Tigers to port, and the Hyenas dead centre. Then there was Madame Vulture, Mr Snake Eyes and Old Veins-in-the-Nose.

The Tigers opened the bidding at one hundred pounds, the Wolves raised it to two hundred, and the Hyenas said three hundred.

'Right,' Edwin called cheerfully. 'Now let's separate the men from the boys. Who'll say five hundred?'

Veins-in-the-Nose did. He was a florid, portly man with a great shock of white hair and possessive eyes. Madame Vulture raised it to five fifty; Snake Eyes said six hundred; and to the surprise of everyone, Victor Vaughn Craig bid six fifty. It was a fantastic sum, but the record amount in the pool made it a good gamble.

Too rich for their blood, the syndicates dropped out. Veins-in-the-Nose growled six seventy-five. Pale as a zombie, Madame Vulture, a Parisian *couturière*, whispered seven hundred. Craig took her off the hook with a call of seven twenty-five, drawing an admiring look from Lisa. Her big guy might not have a sense of humour, but he knew how to fight.

Edwin now had them in his net, and swept them along by twenty-fives, until to a hushed room he said, 'Nine hundred and twenty-five pounds am I bid by Mr Craig.' He pointed his hammer at the florid gentleman. 'It's against you, sir. Would you care to continue? I'll take ten pounds.'

Veins-in-the-Nose stared heavily before him, but remained silent.

'Going, then, at nine hundred and twenty-five pounds . . . going –' Edwin brought the hammer down with a smart crack on the desk top.

'Nine thirty-five,' said Veins-in-the-Nose.

'Sold to Mr Victor Vaughn Craig at nine hundred and twenty-five pounds, and congratulations, sir!' Edwin called.

The florid gentleman was on his feet. 'I said nine thirty-five, Mr Auctioneer.'

Edwin said, 'I beg your pardon, sir, but you were too late. The hammer had fallen.'

'Sir, I say the hammer had not fallen! My bid was in time! I demand that you accept it!'

At once the room was divided into two camps shouting, 'Yes, yes!' or 'No! Stick to your guns, auctioneer!'

Edwin declared firmly, 'I repeat that your bid was too late. I stated the rules clearly at the beginning. The number goes to Mr Craig, and that is final.'

Lisa Lisbon breathed, 'Oh, Turnip, Turnip, I love you,' and Craig muttered, 'The little guy's got guts,' causing Lisa to remark, 'Oh, hadn't you noticed that?'

But the old gentleman with the veins in his nose was shouting

o

in uncontrolled temper now. 'Sir, you are impertinent! I tell you my bid was in time and insist that the bidding be reopened! I guess you do not know who I am!'

A harassed-looking assistant purser arose. 'Just a moment, Sir Malcolm. I'm sure this can be straightened out . . . Mr Auctioneer, in view of the strong protest made by Sir Malcolm Gordien, do you not think it might be advisable to reopen the——'

The name 'Sir Malcolm Gordien' rattled about in Timeless space and bounced off the incorruptible hide of Edwin Reith-Jones, who interrupted with, 'I think nothing of the kind.'

There was laughter, which angered the purser, who said, 'I am afraid, sir, I am going to have to ask you to alter your decision and reopen the——'

'You mean you are ordering me?' Edwin stared at him incredulously.

The assistant was in a bad spot. Sir Malcolm was a V.I.P. traveller. 'As an officer of this ship, I am. Sir Malcolm is entitled to——'

Edwin laid down the gravel quietly. 'Very well. You may damn well go to hell and run your auction under any rules you jolly well please. I'm through with it. My decision stands. You can do as you like. You, Sir Malcolm, are, in my opinion, a cheat and a bully. And now permit me to——'

He paused midway in this dramatic farewell. His eyes had caught the smoking-room clock. The hands stood at eight minutes past twelve, and, as he watched, twitched to nine after. Time was on the move again.

He turned as white as his hair. His countenance seemed to be a void pierced only by two pale, terrified eyes.

'Oh, dear,' he murmered, 'what have I done? What have I done?' He looked up at the clock again and once more repeated, 'Oh, dear,' and Lisa Lisbon, her heart riven for him, expected at any moment he would add, 'Oh, my fur and whiskers! I shall be late! What will the duchess say?' exactly like the White Rabbit in *Alice in Wonderland.*

Instead he put down the gavel and incontinently fled the room up to the sun-deck railing, where he was sick. Then, limp and weak, he went to his cabin, thus missing the final act of the little drama in the smoking-room.

The assistant purser, having taken over the gavel, said, 'Mr Craig, do you consent to the reopening of the bidding at nine hundred and twenty-five pounds?'

The big man said, 'Your question comes a trifle late. However, I do.' There was a murmur of applause and approval.

Sir Malcolm cleared his throat. 'Nine thirty-five.'

'Victor,' Lisa Lisbon said, 'shut up. I have a hunch.'

Craig reflected a moment, studying the beautiful girl and liking the sincerity of the expression about her eyes. 'Have you now, kitten?' he said softly. 'That's good enough for me.' To the purser he said, 'Thank you. That will be all.'

The number was knocked down to Sir Malcolm Gordien for nine hundred thirty-five pounds, something over twenty-six hundred dollars.

A little later a fourth engineer appeared at the door, whispered to the smoking-room steward and went away.

The steward pounded the gavel once and said, 'Ladies and gentlemen, the engines will be stopped for a half-hour or so at one o'clock for a minor adjustment. We are advising you so that you need feel no alarm when we lose way.'

A rebel yell issued from Cy Hammer. Then he cried, 'Lisa, you witch! You called it! I love you!' and he reached over and kissed her. The delay would drop the twenty-four-hour run covered by the pool well into the figures of the Low Field.

Lisa Lisbon had arrived at her eminence in her profession as well as her emergence as a woman through hard work, brains and the devotion and prescience of Cy Hammer. He had picked her a little over eleven years ago, when she had been an almost un-known M-G-M starlet, one of a dozen on the roster, used mostly for cheesecake and publicity stills. At that time, too, she had been crushed by the loss of her husband, Mark Lisbon, a script writer whom she had married when she was twenty. He had enlisted in the marines and was killed at Iwo Jima.

Hammer had penetrated the exterior of what seemed to be a brittle and unhappy girl to the talent beneath and had offered her work, self-sacrifice and stardom. Once she had accepted, she had never wavered, and they had formed an extraordinarily suc-cessful business partnership. Hammer had never made a mistake in choice of vehicles and directors in her slow, steady climb to the pinnacle. She had never let him down.

Theirs was an unusual relationship in that he was likewise the repository of all her thoughts and secrets. She kept nothing back from him and consulted him about everything, including her dressmaker, hairdresser and love affairs. When one broke up badly or she was hurt, she came to him and he was there to pick up the pieces. And because they were united in a business part-nership, there was nothing that could not be discussed between them – no shock, no outrage and, above all, no censure. Each deeply respected the other as a grown-up, with no personal axe to grind.

The next day, on her way to the lounge, Lisa encountered Sir Malcolm Gordien in the main-deck passageway, and he acknowledged her presence with a slight bow, though they had not been formally introduced.

Walking alongside him, Lisa said, 'You know, you were a rotten sport last night. You ought to be ashamed of yourself.'

Sir Malcolm replied with icy indignation, 'I did not ask for your opinion, Miss Lisbon. You realise that you are being extraordinarily impertinent.'

Lisa stopped and, perforce, Sir Malcolm had to do likewise. She turned the full shock of her beauty and smile upon the financier and looked him levelly in the eye. 'When your face makes up the way mine does, Sir Malcolm, you can get away with it.'

For a moment they duelled wordlessly and she triumphed, for she had reminded him that his success in making millions of pounds was no more than hers in enslaving as many people who flocked to see her pictures.

Sir Malcolm suddenly melted and laid aside the dignity which he had acquired overnight with his title. 'I suppose you can,' he said, smiling, 'particularly with an old man.'

'You know you didn't make your bid before the hammer fell.'

'Of course I didn't. But the silly twerp irritated me.'

'Don't you think you ought to apologise to the Turnip?'

'The who? Oh, the Reith-Jones fellow.' Sir Malcolm looked at her with the sheepish air of the delinquent, and asked in the tone of voice used by a small boy ordered to do something unpleasant, 'Must I?'

'Yes, you must.'

'Very well, then. I will.'

Lisa reached up, kissed one corner of his moustache, and for an instant leaned her velvet cheek against his. 'Oh,' she cried, 'I like men!'

Sir Malcolm said, 'I'll look him up. Come, let us drink a glass of champagne. I haven't felt so good in years.' They continued on, arm in arm.

There were two further incidents that third evening, and both occurred during that hour when midnight stood still. In one of them, a mild and unobtrusive Englishman with pale eyes and albino hair, seemingly reading a book near by, turned upon Frank Patch, smug, bitter Left-Wing Member of Parliament, who had been sounding off to a group within earshot of Senator Gregg, to the effect that Britain would no longer support American imperialistic warmongering policies.

Edwin Reith-Jones, secure once again, unhampered by Time or consequences, laid his book down sharply and said, 'You are a liar, sir. You sit with the Socialists, but you speak for the communists. Englishmen will never abandon their friends or knuckle under to yours.'

In the startled silence that followed this outburst, Sir Malcolm Gordien said, 'Hear, hear! Well said, sir,' and Senator Gregg looked up sharply and asked, 'For whom do you speak?' This had been a voice he had not heard in recent days in Great Britain.

Edwin answered almost irritably, 'For every Englishman who has a roof over his head and isn't a Nazi slave and doesn't wish to be a communist one. We are myriad.' He turned upon Patch again and cried, 'You are base and traitorous, sir! You belong to Russia and have the vicious ingratitude of the runny-nosed little boy who flings mud at his benefactor! You have no sense of brotherhood or honest blood in your veins! Brother answered brother and blood stood with blood in 1917 and 1941! You are no Englishman, sir, but a communist, and we will never support you!'

The incident ended when Patch, flushed and angry, arose and stalked out. History might have received an infinitesimal nudge. Sir Malcolm's plan might now fall upon slightly more receptive ears. But the second incident was perhaps the more important one, for a human soul was saved.

It began innocently enough with a good night kiss. Near by where Melanie Holcombe sat with her friends, Florrie Chambers got up and said, 'Good night, Daddy. Good night, Mother.' She put her arms about her father's neck and kissed him, and then did the same with her mother.

Mrs Chambers held her tightly as she said, 'Good night, darling. Sleep well.' For yet another moment the two lingered in embrace, gazing at each other with love and intimacy.

But Edwin Reith-Jones had been watching the expression in the eyes and on the painted face of the other girl. Only that day he had talked with her for an hour on deck, and gauged something of her loneliness. Now he experienced a thrill of horror.

Florrie said, 'Coming, Melanie?'

'No.' Florrie went. A minute later Melanie arose stiffly and said, 'Good night, Mr and Mrs Chambers. Thank you very much for all your kindness,' and walked away, but with ever-increasing pace, so that by the time she had reached the far door of the lounge, she was running, and Edwin Reith-Jones after her.

For, from those who have succeeded in escaping the confines of Time, there are no secrets, and to him, the expression on the face of Melanie during the simple, tender good night scene had been that of one already dead.

Lisa Lisbon arose impulsively. Cy Hammer lazily stretched and put a hand on her arm. 'What's up, Snooks?'

She said, 'Let me go, Cy. I feel that something dreadful is about to happen. Didn't you see? He felt it too . . . No. No. Let me go alone.' The glances of all the men who were in love with her followed her to the door.

At the boat-deck starboard rail, Edwin reached Melanie in time. But she had one thin leg over and was poised to plunge into the roiling, black, phosphorescence-coated eternity below.

'No, no, Melanie!'

He pulled her back from the rail and sheltered her in his arms, where she collapsed, sobbing. He let her cry herself out; then commenced to talk to her in the darkness, quietly, soothingly, about herself and the life that animated her.

He said, 'Listen to me, old girl. Look at yourself. Feel your body. Hear the beating of your heart. This is a wonderful thing. You must not destroy it. You are alive to see, hear, think and know. Some people are born to be loved, others to give it. To give is good, too, Melanie. There are so many in this world who need it.'

And he said further, 'Melanie, you are old beyond your years and will understand. Do you wish to kill the body in which sleep the unborn children to whom you will be able to give the love that has been denied to you? Some day they will be awakened and will cry out and reach for you. And between you and them will pass just such a look as you saw tonight betwixt mother and daughter, because it will be yours to give.'

And he said finally, 'Have courage, youngster. Take care of this which is so perfectly made, against the day when you will surely know the happiness of receiving as well as giving love.'

Lisa moved out of the darkness. A ship's light fixed the tears on her cheek and made them shine like the jewels at her ears and throat. She said softly, 'Melanie,' and then, 'Edwin. My dear, good Edwin.'

At the masthead a bell chimed. Simultaneously all over the racing vessel electric impulse surged through the clocks again.

'Take her,' Edwin said hoarsely, and gently shifted the child from his arms to those of Lisa. 'Take her and keep her. Her father will make no objections. She worships you. You can make her into a fine a woman as you are. But first you must help her to be a child again. Let her stay with you.'

He was gone. Lisa remained with her arms about the girl, her cheek resting on the small head with the too glossy hair.

'You may come with me if you like, Melanie,' Lisa said to the child, who was crying softly again. Then, gently, with her handkerchief, she wiped the ravages of the mascara from the cheeks of the too-soon woman who was to have her girlhood restored to her.

It was the following night, troubled, that Lisa searched the ship for Edwin. Half of that hour during which the moving finger wrote not was gone by the time she found him standing at the stern rail below the Veranda Grill, looking out across the white wake and into the stars, dreaming she could not guess what dreams, except that they were bounded neither by Space nor Time.

She stood beside him, taking his arm and leaning against his shoulder in silence. She said, 'It's the enchanted hour, isn't it, Turnip?'

He looked at her. 'You know?'

'I guessed. It wasn't difficult. This is that hour between Time when one may be wise and brave and all-knowing. I came to you because I need help, Edwin.'

'Yes, Lisa.'

'Whom shall I marry?' He did not reply at once and she continued: 'I want to marry again. I am living a lonely, selfish life.' She counted her suitors off on her fingers: 'Shall I be Mrs Victor Vaughn Craig, keeper of a literary lion; or Mrs Saul Wiener, queen of Hollywood; or Mrs Hamlin Mason, ruler of motor society; the Countess of Morveigh, with a castle; or Mrs Austin Gregg? Gregg is being talked of for the presidency.'

'Which one do you love?'

'In each one there is something that I can love and respect.'

'Who will make you happy?'

Lisa reflected. 'I despair of that. Besides, that wasn't what I asked.'

Edwin, staring out after the broad white track their ship painted on the dark surface of the ocean, replied, 'Take the one who is kind. Kindness outlasts everything else.'

Lisa nodded gravely and remained lost in thought.

Edwin turned to her and for a moment seemed to look her through and through.

'Lisa.'

'Edwin.'

And thus they remained, recognising, knowing and loving each other. They loved beyond words, beyond even the taking of each other, for in the sharing of this magic hour they were for one shattering moment too deeply moved by what they experienced.

Here was that perfection of which each had dreamed and sought at some time through life; that understanding, tenderness and unawakened passion, that blending of heaven and earth that men and women look for in each other and so rarely find.

At that instant they were one. They could have lived together into all eternity; they could have died together with equal happiness. They did not even kiss, but remained lost in each other, enveloped in such sweetness as neither had ever dared to hope for in mortal life.

And yet both knew in that moment that they were also lost to each other, for it was the enchanted hour, and as unreal and illusory as a dream. But, unlike a dream, neither of them would ever forget what they had seen in each other and what they had felt, the heights of human affection they had scaled in that moment of halted Time they had shared, the exquisite surge of love that filled their eyes with tears and their hearts with pain.

With the striking of the ship's bell reality would return.

Lisa said gently, 'You're married, aren't you, Edwin?'

'Yes. For twenty years.'

'Happily? Is she kind to you?'

'No.'

'Why not, Edwin?'

'It is my fault. I never had confidence in myself. When I married her she was sweet and lovely. I didn't turn out the way she hoped. I'm nothing more than a clerk. It made her bitter.'

'And is there no escape?'

'No. She needs me. I am that cherished daily reminder to her of her wasted life. I am all she has.'

Lisa said, 'Not to believe in oneself is a sin. We are punished for our sins.'

Edwin replied, 'Yes, I know,' and looked at her again, but differently, for this was their final parting, his acknowledgment of the weakness that would for ever send them different ways – two who had so nearly gained paradise.

He glanced at his watch. 'Lisa,' he said, 'there is one minute left!' He put his hands on her arms, holding her away from him, looking into her eyes. 'Close your mind and open your heart.'

For the first time she appeared confused and unable to meet his glance. She asked, 'What do you mean, Edwin?'

He held her for an instant longer to emphasise his words. 'Look close to home, Lisa!' Then he let her go.

From for'ard, borne on the wind of the ship's thrust, came the sound of the striking of the bell. Lisa shuddered quietly, turned and walked away into the darkness.

For the fifth and last time on that strange voyage, the motionless hands of the clock marked the enchanted hour. Lisa Lisbon and Cy Hammer stood at the rail beneath the Veranda Grill, from which came the gleam of pink table lamps and the sound of music.

They were in the shadows, almost where she and Edwin had stood the night before. The deck beneath their feet was shuddering with the turning of the twin screws as the giant vessel raced through the night to keep her rendezvous with the tide in the early morning in New York.

Lisa was silent, for she was thinking that there were many kinds of enchantment, if one believed in them, but only one from which there was no escape in the end, no matter what the hour. And yet, in a sense, this queer, magic Timelessness that the shy little Englishman had evoked helped now to give her the courage to face what must be faced with this man at her side, and which might spell an end to all enchantment for evermore.

Hammer, who had been looking out at the wake as Edwin had the previous night, turned to her with his friendly, quizzical glance and asked, 'What's the matter, Snooks? That little Britisher get under your skin?'

For the first time, Lisa wished to deny it, but she could not. One spoke only the truth when all clocks stood still. She replied, 'Yes, in a way he did – unforgettably.'

Hammer nodded. 'It's funny where you find it, isn't it? I think perhaps he was the best of them all. But it won't work, will it?'

'No,' Lisa replied.

'Badly hurt this time, kid?'

'No,' Lisa replied again.

Hammer said, 'That's good,' without surprise, and Lisa was aware that he was not curious as to why, or when, or what had happened, but was only expressing deep relief that she was not in trouble.

Beneath their feet the deck quivered. All about her, non-Time quivered too. This had been Edwin's gift to her.

'Cy,' she said, in a voice so filled with timidity that she hardly recognised it as her own, 'will you answer me a question truthfully?'

'Sure, Snooks. What's on your mind?'

'How long have you been in love with me?'

Hammer glanced at his watch, and Lisa's heart seemed to stand still. What if he replied, 'And what makes you think I am?'

The gesture with the watch reminded her of that of the Englishman twenty-four hours ago. And she thought how much like Hammer he was in kindness, gentleness, goodness and steadfastness. How quickly he had understood and approved of her decision to take the miserable, difficult, abandoned girl, Melanie, to live with her. And yet she now knew there was something further that Hammer had. He was strong. When the ship's bell chimed, he would still be there. He would always be there.

Hammer had finished his calculations. He replied quietly, 'Eleven years, seven months, two weeks, three days, fifty-eight minutes and eighteen – no, sorry, nineteen – seconds, twenty now.'

'Why didn't I ever know? How could I have been so blind?'

Hammer's warm, slow smile spread over his face, crinkling his eyes, which were full of tenderness. 'Agents aren't supposed to have hearts.'

'Or actresses either, if it comes to that,' Lisa said almost bitterly in self-reproach. Then, 'Cy, will you marry me?'

'If you ask me prettily,' he replied lightly, but she saw that he was deeply moved, as indeed she was at having found her love at last, and with a sense of home-coming.

She leaned her forehead against his shoulder to press and feel the dear, comforting boniness of it. The ship's bell struck the end of the enchanted hour.

'Please marry me, Cy,' Lisa Lisbon asked humbly. 'I have been in love with you for a long time, I know now. Everything else is and was an illusion.'

He took her hand in his and held it firmly and tightly clasped, and they remained standing there for a long time, shoulder to shoulder, looking out over the star-illuminated waters and thinking of the joy and comfort they would bring to each other in the days to come.

Lisa Lisbon and Edwin Reith-Jones encountered each other for the last time on the crowded, noisy pier the following morning. Lisa and Hammer had been eased through customs quickly, and they had collected Melanie. There had been no one at the pier to meet the child, though there was a telegram instructing her to proceed to Chicago. They were on their way out when Lisa saw the Englishman. He was standing, with his sparse luggage, by a window, gazing out forlornly over the mid-town skyscrapers.

She pressed Hammer's arm, and then went over to Edwin, and

it was characteristic of Hammer that he only nodded understand-ingly and then went on with Melanie to await her at the exit.

Lisa said, 'Good-bye, Turnip.'

Edwin blushed crimson, reached for his hat, found he was not wearing it, and finally managed to take the hand she extended. 'Good-bye, Miss Lisbon – Lisa.'

She said, 'You're unhappy. You shouldn't be. You've got Sir Malcolm Gordien eating out of your hand.'

He replied bleakly, 'It was expected of me. It's what I was sent for.'

Lisa continued, 'You saved a life and a soul; you've spoken up for your country before important people and done it a service; you have helped me to find a happiness that might have passed me by. Cy Hammer and I are going to be married.'

'Oh, splendid!' Edwin said, and then repeated, 'Splendid.' Yet the bleakness did not leave his countenance, and beneath Lisa's questioning gaze he said finally, 'What will happen to me? I've stolen five hours and done things in them I've never done before.'

'What did you do with the final hour?' Lisa asked.

'I prayed,' Edwin Reith-Jones replied, and the girl nodded almost as though this was what she had expected him to say.

She said, 'It is true. You lived between Time on five borrowed hours. You will have to give them back.'

'Yes, but how?'

Lisa smiled. 'On the return journey. They'll be taken from you again, willy-nilly. There's never anything for free. You pay or give back.'

'But what will I be like afterwards?'

'The same good, sweet, gallant, great-hearted gentleman you have always been. But you will probably never make love to another girl or beard another lion.'

'And is that all that will remain?'

'No,' Lisa said gently. 'There will be dear and tender memories. This is all we ever really steal from Time. God bless you, Edwin.'

She reached over and kissed him; then turned and walked away to where Cy Hammer, Melanie and reality were waiting for her.

Edwin Reith-Jones remained standing there and watched her go, but the expression in his pale eyes and on his unobtrusive countenance was no longer either bleak or forlorn.

Orchestration for Twelfth Night

This story has probably the most curious history of inception of any that I have written. It was not written to make money or to sell: it was not written on speculation. Instead it was conceived partially as a kind of Christmas gift to a magazine of which I was very fond and to its late publisher who while he was alive was for many years my friend and highly amusing companion, the late David Smart, founder and publisher of 'Esquire' Magazine.

David was a curious man, tough, cynical, experienced in life and disillusioned by same, and all this leavened by an inner soft-ness and sentimentality, coupled with a most engaging sense of humour. He was one of the few millionaire publishing tycoons who could laugh at himself. I had enormous affection for Dave Smart. There are certain editors and publishers one enjoys being associated with and David was one of them.

I worked for him as a columnist, writing a monthly piece called THIS MAN'S WORLD *for 'Esquire' for many years. We had times of violent and raucous disagreement when I would resign or he would fire me, but before too long* THIS MAN'S WORLD *would be back in the magazine again.*

I thoroughly enjoyed writing this column for in it I could give vent to the most outrageous ideas or notions and write them as I pleased. I was happy to be able to get gripes off my chest monthly and the preparation of copy for 'Esquire' was always a joy.

David was an odd man with a curiously blind spot for writers and writing, and in particular writers of fiction. He simply had no concept how we or our minds worked. He also found it diffi-cult to pay writers. He had been brought up in the clothing business where you get tangible materials for your money. He never quite mastered the idea of such an abstraction as writing being likewise a commercial commodity. I had encountered this frame of mind before in the days when I worked on the 'Daily

416

News,' and as editor of the Sports Department found myself involved with the business department. You could get them to shell out for presses, drinking fountains, lavatory fixtures, paper clips, but what did you have when you spent money for writing?

Dave also could not understand why if one had the ability to write a successful story or book, one could not repeat it immediately. If a cutter could cut a suit of clothes which sold he could do it again and again. I remember there was one story of mine which was a favourite of David's which later appeared as a book called THE SMALL MIRACLE, and as a film NEVER TAKE NO FOR AN ANSWER. It all seemed so simple and easy on the face of it, and he would be at me to ask why I didn't keep on doing this. I had the formula, hadn't I? Why not turn out a whole series of such tales and grow rich?

I remember arguing with him about this one Thanksgiving when I was a guest at his home outside Chicago. He wanted a Christmas story and why couldn't I put one together the way I had put together THE SMALL MIRACLE? So I said all right, we would take a rainy afternoon and try to synthesise a Christmas story which would be popular. We would do it together.

At the end of a four-hour session we were exhausted; we had no story, but David had learned something. I had let him flounder with me through a morass of story making, the plot twist that won't stay bent, the characters who insist upon going their own way, the forbidden use of the long arm of coincidence, the problems of cause and effect, and the difficulties of producing the effect of a piece of life in a small compass of space. In working up the proper, valid and water-tight plot one thinks up a hundred ideas which are self-defeating. The professional writer doesn't get discouraged by this because he knows that the hundred and first or the hundred and fifty-first idea may lead to a solution. He can if need be turn his story inside-out or up-side-down, or look at it both ways from the middle and each time get a new slant and possibly new ways of solving the problems. The layman merely sees insuperable obstacles and unsolvable dilemmas. What is that reiterated cry I hear from the frustrated or would-be writers? It is 'I know I could write but I can't think up any plots.'

I think if I did nothing else for my fellow craftsmen I did in David Smart's lifetime somewhat increase his respect for them and certainly elevated the prices he paid them. His sudden death left me forlorn. I missed him greatly, I still do. Some years later I went back to writing my column for 'Esquire' again for Arnold

Gringrich, his one-time editor and after his death the new publisher of 'Esquire.'

This is a long way of getting around to the ORCHESTRATION FOR TWELFTH NIGHT, *but in my own heart it was a Christmas present to the memory of David Smart; it was that Christmas story which he and I failed to work out that rainy day on his estate in a suburb of Chicago and which didn't jell because we were trying too hard and anyway that isn't the way good stories are written.*

For technical reasons my 'Esquire' copy had to be in between four and five months in advance and even further in advance for the huge Christmas issue of the magazine, and I used to write of snow and ice and the jingle of sleigh bells and the glitter of Christmas-tree ornaments in the heat and greenery of July.

Over the years that I wrote this column I had rung almost all of the changes on Christmas I could think of – sentimental, nostalgic, and the particular July that still another column for Christmas was due I somehow couldn't face going through all this again, or finding some new variation to the old Santa Claus themes. And so I fell to thinking about what I would really like to do and about the magazine which had been good to me for a long time, and in particular about David who thought that one could simply sit down and knock together a Christmas story, and I decided that this is what I would try to do for that Christmas issue. Instead of writing my usual column, I would write a fiction story and it would be a kind of a present to David.

There was no trouble with this one for all of the elements must have been simmering in my subconscious for a long time, for that is really where stories come from.

The ingredients are familiar, the three kings from the East bearing gifts to the child in the manger, but the setting has been altered, and the kings are three odd people, all of whom I have encountered and all of whom I like for their own integrity.

It was a treat for me to write this story. Since it was going to replace my regular column it didn't have to compete for the editor's eye or for space or a big fiction cheque. I could just write it as my Christmas contribution, send it along and it would appear.

I cannot say whether David Smart would have liked it, but I have included it in this book in the hope that it will appeal to you.

ORCHESTRATION FOR TWELFTH NIGHT

The three men struggling from different directions against the gale-lashed rain that drenched the dark Eastchapel Street hard by the bend in the River Thames, converged upon the light that gleamed out of the pitch darkness of the miserable, stormy Twelfth Night that engulfed London. Each hoped to find temporary shelter from the cold and the soaking storm.

The light shining from the covered loading shed of the deserted brewery and refracted by the downpour beckoned like a star. It was past midnight. The morning of January sixth, twelve days past Christmas, had been born. Shivering and huddled to themselves, the three men hurried their footsteps and arrived almost simultaneously beneath the shelter of the roof of the loading platform where it was at least dry, and where their welcome was pronounced by the pair who had arrived there before them.

The woman who lay on a pile of sacking only moaned and whimpered and then cursed softly, but the man kneeling beside her in the shadows said bitterly: 'Gor! It's got to be a nigger, a Jew and a bloody drunk.'

The three, startled by the voice, brushing and shaking the rain from their clothing, looked at one another for the first time and saw that the man had spoken truly.

The Negro was young and dapper in a tan raincoat. His head was as round as a leaden musket bullet. He was hatless and the drops of rain glistened beneath the light as though his kinky hair was shot through with diamonds. He wore gold-rimmed spectacles and his skin was ebon-dark. The whites of his eyes were creamy and the eyes themselves were of extraordinary luminosity.

The Jew wore the long, square-cut beard of orthodoxy and it was mottled with grey. He was clad in what once had been a Chesterfield overcoat and a bowler hat and his back was bent beneath his pack from the straps of which he now eased himself. In his eyes was the melancholy of his race and lot, but the lines of his face were set to reflect good nature and cheerfulness.

The drunk was an apple-cheeked cockney with a red nose, gnarled chin, a gaping mouth with stained and missing teeth, and naughty, piggy little eyes. He wore no coat and his checked jacket and trousers were rain-sodden as were his traditional neck-cloth and peaked cap. But he was so half seas over from beer that he did not mind, and he stood in the circle of the light, grinning boozily and occasionally shaking himself like a terrier.

The kneeling man, a big bruiser in rough clothes whose heavy, lumpy features were stormy with anger and self-pity repeated – 'A Jew, a bloody drunk and a nigger.'

None of the three men thus characterised appeared to take offence. The Jew with his pack divested, poured the water from the rim of his bowler hat ignoring the appellation as one who had grown used to it and no longer even heard it.

The drunk uttered a strange gibberish – 'Be-deet da bedeedle um bum' while at the same time stamping and shuffling his feet and waving his arms in apparently some new way of getting warm, his grin expanding to show his bad teeth, his wicked little eyes twinkling.

The Negro said to the man and the woman in the shadows of the raised loading platform from which in the daytime the beer kegs were rolled on to the drays and hauled away by big grey percherons – 'Are you in any difficulty? I hear the woman moaning. I should like to be of assistance. I am *Mister* William Matumbwe of Nigeria.' His voice was as musical and mellifluous as an organ note. The curious manner in which he emphasised the *Mister* caused the Jew to cease drying his hat, put it back on and glance at him interestedly, but led the rough-looking man to spit and rasp – 'no black is *mister* to me . . .'

The Negro smiled, and the smile brought a curious and comforting kind of beauty to his round face. 'Oh yes,' he said, 'There is one who must be, and that is myself. For I have worked long and very hard to earn the title and it is the greatest title I have ever had and the one of which I am justly proud.'

The man spat again, but Mister Matumbwe continued cheerfully – 'Oh, you are lucky perhaps that I am a highly educated nigger. Bachelor of Science, Christ Church College at Oxford – 'The House,' you know, and degree of Master of Surgery from the University of London where I have just completed my studies. That is why I am entitled to be called Mister. If the woman is ill you could not have a better nigger happen to come by here, I am sure.'

The Jew who had not been paying much attention to what Mister Matumbwe was saying brushed a small puddle of rain from the top of his pack and loosened the cover. 'Could I sell something perhaps to any of you gentlemen, or the lady? I have many interesting articles. It is still not too late to acquire a small gift for someone. Everything is reasonably priced.'

The drunk had subsided against the far side of the loading shed balanced on his heels, bent in the middle with his rear braced against the wall in the attitude of one who is about to sit

down. There was an expression of great concentration upon his
face and his lips and fingers moved rhythmically.

The man with the ailing woman cried – 'Gor, you mean you're
a doctor? Why the hell didn't you say so before? My old woman's
time's come. Bloody National 'Ealth Service. Try and get 'elp
when you need it. I was wanting to get her to the 'orspital when
she got took on the way. Reckon the kid'll be here any minute . . .'

'Ah . . . I thought so perhaps,' Mister Matumbwe said and
moved to climb up on to the loading platform, but the woman
screamed and then shouted – 'No, no! Get away! I don't want
any dirty nigger touching me . . .'

But the Negro completed his climb and talked to her soothingly
as he would to a child. He said – 'Shhhhh. Do not be afraid. I
fear, madam, that you have no longer any choice in the matter.
But you will see, I am very gentle.'

He moved over to her and placed a hand upon her stomach.
His touch was indeed gentle and curiously it quietened her at
once so that she left off cursing and only whimpered a little and
stared at him out of frightened and pain-racked eyes. She was
still handsome in a strong, blowzy way, though no longer young.

Mister Matumbwe nodded his head and said – 'Not just yet.
But soon. Quite soon. I take it this is not a *prime ibs*?'

'Not a wot? Blast yer, talk English.'

'Her first child.'

The man laughed unpleasantly – 'Not bloody likely. She's 'ad
four wot we can't feed decently now. Wot's she want to go and
'ave another for, that's what I'm asking?'

Mister Matumbwe replied – 'Sometimes these matters are determined elsewhere.' He arose and faced the two men below him as
though he were addressing them from the lecture platform :
'Gentlemen, we are about to experience an emergency. Fortunately, I feel myself well qualified to cope with it even though it
will be my first delivery outside the hospital. However, I shall
require some assistance, that is to say we must make do with
what we have.'

He leaped down from the platform and crossed to the drunk
who was still in his almost-sitting position against the wall, and
addressed him respectfully : 'You, sir, who are you, and what is
it you do?'

The little fellow's mischievous eyes looked up at Mister
Matumbwe out of deep crinkles as he asked without rancour –
'Wot's it to you?'

Mister Matumbwe had the most endearing quality of never
being, or appearing to be, offended. He replied – 'Oh, it is only

to ascertain whether you might have any particular skill that could be put to some use at the moment of crisis. . . .'

The cockney stood up, threw his head back and roared with sudden laughter. 'Skill, is it? 'Arry Napes is the name. 'Arry Napes from Eastchapel. King o' the Buskers they call me. I'm a whole bloomin' performance by meself.' Then he sang – 'Be-dee, be-da, bedeet-do-da!' and did a shuffle and kick.

Mister Matumbwe gazed at him in bewilderment for an instant and then his magnificent white teeth appeared framed by his smile. 'Oh, but of course. A busker is one who performs in the streets for pennies to the queues waiting to get into the theatres. And you are their king. . . .'

'Ask any one in Eastchapel about 'Arry Napes. I'm me own bloomin' orchestra as well. Took in moren'a couple o' quid tonight by the Palladium where the Panto is playing. Coo, I'm not 'arf a Panto all by meself. Here's a example——' He sang – 'Hi tiddlyum-ti, bedeep ba boop ah beedley um bum,' and danced a creditable buck and wing.

Mr Matumbwe pressed his hands to his forehead in deep thought and concentration and then dramatically pointed a pink and ebon finger at Napes – 'Oh, excellent. You will be the anaesthetician when I call upon you.'

He turned to the Jew. 'And you, sir, are a pedlar.'

'Moshe Konig, at your service. But I do not understand what is to happen. You spoke just now of an emergency.'

'The woman is about to have a baby. I shall deliver it.'

'Ach, the poor! – On such a night and in such a place. What is there I can do to help her?'

'Have you by any chance some alcohol in your pack?'

Konig shook his head. 'Alcohol I do not carry – but wait. I have some most excellent eau-de-Cologne and bottles of scent, almost as good as French, and very cheap. I always try to procure the best for my clients at low prices. I will give you what I have. There is alcohol and spirits in it.'

Mister Matumbwe's happy smile illuminated his countenance. 'Yes, it will do as disinfectant in the emergency. How kind of you to offer it. Any kitchen utensils?'

'A few. But the knives, I am afraid are not very sharp. With prices what they are, goods are not what they used to be.'

'Oh, no, not knives, but if you have something curved as well as flat in the manner of a . . . Well, a cake lifter for instance . . .'

The pedlar was already delving into his pack and spreading out his wares – 'Oh, excellent, Mr Konig, most excellent. Those will do splendidly. I am sure it will not be a difficult delivery. . . .'

'Hoi,' called the man on the platform, 'Hoi, Mister . . .' He could not bring himself to speak the name tacked on to the Mister and so he finished – 'Mister Doctor, what about getting on with it?'

Mister Matumbwe turned to him. 'Your wife will let us know when she is ready. In the meantime, what is your name and occupation, and your wife's name and age?'

The man looked down in surly fashion upon the young surgeon and finally muttered – 'Sam Boles. Dockworker. The old woman's thirty-two. Name's Anna.'

'Ah, a dockworker. You must be glad the strike's over, what with another baby coming.' He climbed back on to the loading platform.

The word 'strike' acted upon Sam Boles as though he had been touched with a live wire.

'Gor!' he yelled – 'Strike! I've lost three months' wages on their blinking strike, me with a fambly, for a sixpenny rise. It'll take me two year to make back what I've lost by them making me stay out. 'Oo are *they*? That's what I'd like to know. Strike, says they; go back, says they; lost yer seniority, says they; arbi-trate, says they; *they've* raised prices again, they say. All right, you and your bleedin' education. YOU tell me who *they* are.'

Mister Matumbwe reflected deeply for a few seconds, his round chin in one cupped hand. Then he replied somewhat incon-sequently – 'Better perhaps to ask who He is?'

'He? What he? Wotcher talkin' about?'

'*Him*,' said Mister Matumbwe. 'He who is more than all of them and us too, put together. God whose dream it all seems to be. . . .'

'Coo,' commented Harry Napes, who had moved over closer to the loading platform. 'You sound like a ruddy preacher.'

Mister Matumbwe looked pleased. 'Yes, do I? There was once a question in my mind whether I would study for the ministry or medicine. But I am glad I decided . . .'

A cry from Anna Boles interrupted him, but it was one of despair and anger rather than pain: 'I don't want another. I tell you I don't want it. God knows I never wanted another.'

Mister Matumbwe was at her side in an instant, his eyes search-ing her tortured face and figure with anxiety and tenderness, as his fingers gently examined.

'Yes,' he said. 'Now is the time,' and then – 'Madam, if God knows, then He has decided otherwise for His reasons, and you had best take it in good part, for the child is coming now.'

But the woman would not be hushed. She complained: 'What's

anyone get out of anything? Drudge and slave for what? Not so much as a half-crown to go to the flicks once a week.' Her voice rose querulously – 'What's in it, one kid after another, always one a-suckling and pulling the life out o' you?'

Mister Matumbwe looked reflective before he replied earnestly: 'There is a very good formula, National Dried Milk, three level tablespoons, one and one half teaspoons of sugar, mixed with four ounces of boiled water, in a sterilised bottle, five to six feedings a day. And the Infants' Welfare Centre will give you cod liver oil compound and concentrated orange juice. But of course breast feeding is the best for the child if you are able to do it.'

But now another cry burst from the woman, no longer one of self-pity or complaint, but vibrant with animal anguish. Mister Matumbwe turned to Harry Napes: 'Dance, Mr Napes,' he commanded. 'Divert her. You are the anaesthetician, the only one we have. We have nothing to give her to take her away from pain, but you. Give your best performance.'

Just beyond the loading shed the rain was still seething down out of the black, gusty night. Mister Matumbwe ordered the pedlar: 'Collect rain water in your bowler hat, Mr Konig; we shall need it to wash the child.'

The busker had pushed his cap on to the back of his head, and taken up position within sight of the woman in labour where he began slow and comic gyrations to his self-made music – 'Da da da-DEET-da-da, beedle-da-o, beedle-do-o, boompa tum boom.'

'Watch him, madam,' Mister Matumbwe said to the woman, 'and you will see a better show than the Christmas Panto at the Palladium, for he is the King of the Buskers.'

Then he removed his sack coat, rolled up his sleeves, doused his hands well with eau-de-Cologne and turned to the business of ushering a new life into the world.

He did so with humility but also great love in his heart towards this woman, for she was his first patient. To maintain his own courage even in the face of what appeared to be a simple cephalic presentation he muttered Latin medical phrases – 'occipito dextra posterior,' which for all of any of the others might have been incantations.

And yet, through it all, he was also living a dream, and in the dream, the little head that was presenting itself was coal black, for he was back in his native Africa, and this was but one of a steady stream of coal black heads he would deliver with equal skill and tenderness in the hospital he planned to build and the mothers would recover free from infection and the babies would survive, properly fed, cared for and looked after, ignorance and disease would be banished . . .

'Rum-tum-tummy tum hi-de-vo-do . . .' The Busker was dancing and grimacing with his rubbery face and froward eyes now like a hula girl, now executing buck and wing and soft shoe. The rhythms came through to Mister Matumbwe like the beat of the jungle bongo drums that he remembered as a child before he was sent down to the lowlands to the Mission School.

At his elbow was Moshe Konig with his bowler hat full of soft rain-water. Sam Boles stood looking down, his hands working nervously, an expression of anxiety on his lumpy features.

Racked with pain as she was, the woman Anna could not keep her eyes from the jigging, bouncing figure on the floor of the loading shed and the gargantuan shadow cast by the single yellow light that accompanied him.

Mister Matumbwe, Mister Surgeon Matumbwe, applied skill and imagination to help her, but there came a time of desperation when the birth slowed. He dared not trust further the primitive instruments at his command and he did not know what to do.

'Beedeet da CHA!' croaked the Busker, leaping into the air to his left and clicking his heels together, 'Bee doh dee CHA!' He leaped to the right, again cracking his heels – 'HOI!' and he rose straight up into the air in the manner of a ballet dancer attempting an *entrechat*. Coming down, however, he landed in a puddle in the middle of the stone floor, made when the rain had run off their clothes, his feet shot out from under him and he fell on his behind, throwing out spray to all sides from beneath him.

'Blow me!' he cried. 'It's like a bleedin' skating rink!'

The woman Anna gave vent to a great convulsive blast of laughter, for she had never seen anything quite so comic in her whole life, and the child was expelled, giving notice with a thin cry that pierced the laughter.

Mister Matumbwe did what was requisite and then almost like an offering, held the infant aloft for a moment and his beautiful voice filled the cavern of the loading shed.

'Behold,' he cried. 'The miracle!'

The others, looking, saw only a newborn babe, red, wrinkled and incredibly ugly, not knowing that the black man referred to the miracle of the handing on of the flame of life in man's interminable relay race down through the ages and at which he had been privileged to attend.

'The boy better be wrapped in something warm,' Moshe Konig remarked, and delving into his bottomless pack produced a woman's white flannelette nightgown in which he carefully and gently wrapped the child while Mister Matumbwe attended the mother and made her comfortable. Then the pedlar freeing the child's head from the swaddling clothes, laid it squalling in the mother's arms. Searching in his pack further, he found a golden butterfly on a stick which he laid beside it. Or rather it was a butterfly cut out of paper-thin copper with jewelled eyes and spring-like coiled wire feelers that quivered as the mother's breast rose and fell, but beneath the rays of the single yellow light, the toy gleamed like red gold.

Same Boles said – 'Look 'ere now, we carnt pay nothing . . .'

Moshe Konig bent over the two on the sacking, looking down upon them with a grave sweet smile, moving the toy so that it shivered and made a dry rattling sound with its wings. 'Sha, sha,' he said – 'Who is asking?'

But Boles was filled with suspicion. He looked angrily from one to the other and asked – 'Wotcher expect of me?'

Mister Matumbwe looked up at the question and his grave glance behind the gold-rimmed spectacles took in the Busker, who had come over to the loading platform to inspect the baby and was grinning his impudent, broken-toothed smile, and the bent figure of the old pedlar curved over the pair huddled on the sacking, as he rattled the golden toy, and he found himself filled suddenly with an unearthly joy and exaltation.

'Nothing!' he cried, 'nothing at all. Take all that has been given as a gift of the Magi. For, gentlemen, do you not know what night this is?'

They stared at him. The baby stopped crying and outside the shed the storm had suddenly abated. The wind had dropped and the rain fell now only gently.

'It is the night of Epiphany, the Twelfth Night. And do you remember the Gospel according to St Matthew, Chapter II?' His face filled with wonder and his voice vibrating with the sincerity that filled him, Mister Matumbwe began to quote:

'Now when Jesus was born in Bethlehem of Judea in the days of Herod there came wise men from the east to Jerusalem . . .

'And Herod sent them to Bethlehem and said, Go and search diligently for the young child . . .

'When they had heard the king they departed; and lo the star which they saw in the east went before them, till it came and stood over where the young child was. When they saw the star they rejoiced with exceeding great joy.

'And when they were come into the house they saw the young child with Mary, his mother, and fell down and worshipped him;

and when they had opened their treasures, they presented him
with gifts; gold, and frankincense and myrrh . . .'

Moshe Konig turned his sad, wise eyes upon the black man and
asked – 'What is it you are trying to say, Mister surgeon?'

Mister Matumbwe replied ringingly: 'Only that this morning
something very great and wonderful has happened; a babe was
born. For there is not an infant delivered into this world, white,
yellow, brown or black that does not have the breath of Jesus in
him, who does not at the moment of birth in his innocence and
the immediacy of his arrival from the breast of the Creator, share
in the spirit of Jesus.' But he finished on a lower, shyer note – 'So
you see, perhaps it was suitable that we should bring him gifts.
For who shall say that we are not Three Kings come out of the
East, following the star that led us hither?'

The silence was broken by the long, deep sigh of Moshe Konig
in whose head and heart old legends and prophecies were stirring.

'Oh, yes, it might well be, gentlemen,' Mister Matumbwe continued, 'for you, Mr Napes, are a king, the King of the Buskers,
a king out of Eastchapel, are you not? And the very meaning of
your name, Mr Konig, is "King" . . .' His warm, earnest friendly
smile embraced them both.

The face of the Busker parted in his jagged grin. 'And 'oo's the
ruddy third king?' he asked, and then nodding his head in the
direction of the confused and dour Boles – 'Not this bloomin''
'Appiness Boy 'ere?'

'Oh no,' said Mister Matumbwe, simply. 'I am.' And it was as
though there had been a ruffle and a fanfare.

Moshe Konig sighed again – 'Ahhhhhhh. This must be so. Only
kings and Jews possess the dignity never to feel offended.'

'Yes,' Mister Matumbwe repeated – 'I think indeed we are Three
Kings from the East bearing gifts of gold, frankincense and myrrh.'

And here Mister Matumbwe seemed to increase in stature and
beauty as though the majesty was swelling within him as he explained – 'You see, at home in my own country in the Northern
Province of Nigeria, I am King Matumbwe The First, for my
loved and honoured father, King Nkukawa, but recently died
there while I was completing my studies here. But when I return I have decided I shall not be King, but *Mister* Matumbwe,
graduate of the College of Surgeons of London, for of this title
I am most proud of all.'

A strange voice broke in. "Ello, 'ello, what's all this going on in
'ere?' They all turned and saw the constable, his shiny black rubber macintosh and helmet glistening in the yellow overhead light
of the loading shed.

The spell was broken. The sound of the drums and bugles of royalty faded. Mr Matumbwe replied for them in the precise, careful English of the African student – 'There has been an emergency birth here, constable. I am a qualified surgeon and have seen it through successfully with the aid of these kind people. Mother and child are doing excellently, but I recommend they be taken to hospital now. If you will arrange to telephone for an ambulance . . .'

The police constable had finished the voluminous entry in his notebook; the ambulance was on the way. Moshe Konig's pack was closed again; Harry Napes had pulled down the peak of his cap and turned up his coat collar around his neck-cloth. Mister Matumbwe once more had lapsed into the guise of an insignificant, young African in tan raincoat and gold-rimmed spectacles. Sam Boles stared down at them all from the height of the loading platform, still dully suspicious, for he could not believe that he was to get off scot free without payment for what he had received.

Napes gave the 'thumbs up' gesture, nodded cheerily at Mister Matumbwe and said: 'Well, good night, Guv'nor. You're a bit of all right. . . .'

Moshe Konig shouldered himself into the straps of his pack. He said – 'God bless you, Mister Surgeon. You are greater than any king.'

Mister Matumbwe laughed nervously. 'Oh, do you think? How kind of you to say so.' He looked up at the woman with the child and the golden butterfly once more, and counselled: 'You will remember the formula for bottle feeding I told you. It is most efficient. But of course, if you could see your way clear, madam, breast feeding is the *very* best. Well, good night, and good luck. . . .'

The three passed out of the loading shed into the gentle rain and their separate ways.

Some Conclusions for Young and Old

One hopes that you have been entertained. Whether or not the stories in this volume and the preambles too, or discussion thereof will be of any use to the student or would-be story writer is problematical for purposely I have not entered into those somewhat arid areas of techniques and construction. The absolute art of the short story, commercial or otherwise, is felt and practised rather than learned. The technique of the short story has to do with form, construction and as I have indicated here and there, formula. But the writing of one is a study in economy, concentration and suggestion.

If these stories have one thing in common to recommend them to those who would likewise try to write and feel that they have a flair for this kind of narration, it is that they have been commercially successful and have been bought and paid for at high rates and published. With one exception all of them have appeared in America and Great Britain – in highest paying, coated stock, slick paper, illustrated weekly or monthly magazines.

Critically I am given to understand this is contemptible and condemnable and I have been both condemned and contemned for the moral and manner of these tales and their professional execution. Still if one wishes to write saleable and publishable fiction which will see the light of day instead of languishing in trunks or bottom drawers amidst rejection slips, this is one way of doing it.

When I was a young writer the chief criticism levelled at the big slicks, the high-paying magazine market, and that chiefly by unsuccessful writers, was that they insisted upon the 'happy ending,' and that you could not sell them a story that did not make this concession, or which did not conform to popular standards or tested formulas. The magazines have changed over a period of thirty years; they have become broader and more courageous and are encumbered with fewer taboos; but the

*criticism still persists among the uninitiate, would-be fiction
writers, who because they are unable to find a market for their
bad scripts excuse themselves by saying that realism and the
unhappy ending cannot be sold and that the entire magazine
market is in a conspiracy to flatten out life and present it in terms
of sugar-coated falsehood.*

*It is untrue, at least as far as I am concerned. Never at any
time in my career have I had a story rejected because of a so-
called 'unhappy ending,' nor has any editor ever suggested that
a story might be acceptable if I would change the ending and
make everything come out all right.*

*No, it just won't do as an excuse for making the grade you
want to make – and when you hear complaints that the popular
magazines will print nothing but escape stories, you are listening
either to someone parroting a cliché or to a writer who is suspect.*

*It is true that the most of the high-priced popular magazines
feature the formula story with the sugary ending, and many of
these stories are so much junk, but there is no rule against the
realistic or honest story provided it is readable and entertaining,
and if there is a good deal of cheap and shoddy writing in slick
magazines, who is to blame, the writer or the editor? I would be
inclined to blame the writer and the law of supply and demand.
Every big editor I ever knew gives vent to a shout of joy when he
gets his hands on a really good story. Many of them are story
fanatics, genuine worshippers of the art form, and they will make
the fortunes of men and women who can write them. They would
like to see every story in every issue a gem of its kind. There
simply are not enough good writers to go around, and issues must
be filled.*

*Also there is no law that just because a story is bitterly or
misanthropically realistic and has a tragic or frustrating ending,
it automatically becomes a great piece of literature. My recollection of the story-tellers who have withstood the test of time
to become classics is that they maintained about the same ratio
of happy to unhappy endings as do the modern magazines. The
one thing they never neglected was to be entertaining. The
villain who gets his, the poor boy who overcomes obstacles to
become wealthy and famous, or who marries the daughter of the
boss, the two lovers happily united after many vicissitudes, were
not invented by the 'Saturday Evening Post,' 'Cosmopolitan,'
'Collier's,' 'Woman,' 'Woman's Own' or 'John Bull-Today.' The
story in which the inequalities, terrors, and injustices of life yield
to things as they ought to be, in the very best of all possible
worlds, is a very ancient dream and was first expressed in folklore*

and fairy tale. Perhaps such stories are bad for us, but if so many millions of people love them and are diverted by them, then they are a part of the people and their lives and there must be something to them. You tell me what's wrong with romance, and since when.

The popular magazines on their various levels, and with consideration of the audiences they are aimed at, demand that primarily their writers shall be entertaining. You may quarrel with an editor over differences with regard to what he and you consider entertaining, but not with his motive, which is honest in every respect, including that cardinal sin which is known as pandering to public taste. I see nothing particularly wrong with public taste or in pandering to it from the point of view of the editor who is charged with putting together and selling a volume every week or every month. If he fails to meet public taste, circulation falls off and he loses his job.

Magazines of all classifications are no better, or no worse, than their readers want them to be, and the material contained in them is always the best they are able to purchase in the open market. The time test of a story does not depend upon where and by whom it was first published. Nobody today remembers the names of the periodicals that published Charles Dickens, Rudyard Kipling, G. K. Chesterton, Conan Doyle, O. Henry, Mark Twain, Edgar Allan Poe, Bret Harte, and others, but their stories live on because people liked them.

I have no objection to anyone who wishes to look down his nose at popular magazines so long as his criticism is based upon personal reaction to the contents and distaste for it rather than the snobbery that comes from swallowing false clichés or approaching a tale from the standpoint that if it appeared in a popular magazine it can't be good. It is quite true that in many of the popular magazines both in the United States and Great Britain the contents are opiates to drug the senses of the readers, but then nobody is forced ever to become an opium eater and the drug likewise has its medicinal uses. If certain magazines falsify, as indeed they do, so do millions upon millions of people to themselves and to others before they so much as poke their noses inside one of those periodicals. Falsification of life very often is all that makes it bearable. There is no cure for this, one learns to live with it, and make allowances.

And besides it is wise never to lose sight of the functions of the story-teller down through the ages; men and women have turned to him not to be lectured or educated but to be entertained and diverted. They have sat at his feet or turned to his written word at such times as they were weary from the day's work or made unhappy by personal problems or the difficulties of existence and they have relied upon him to move them to tears or to laughter, but above all I think to give them hope. To live vicariously the struggles and misfortunes of others and see them emerge triumph- antly from the same snares set for them by life that enmesh us is an unquestionable catharsis. Whether this is good for one I am not prepared to say. I do know that this is what one seeks in one form or another when one opens the pages of a book or a magazine.

Do cats eat bats, do bats eat cats, do authors need agents? And what is an author's agent and what does he do? It is a queer profession, this middleman who bridges the gap between writer and editor and concerns himself with the peddling of fantasies for rent and groceries money. And who created this gap between writer and editor, does it exist, and is it necessary? And why doesn't the editor pay the agent a percentage for services rendered as well as the author?

The value of a literary agent to the sale of a good story to the right market for the right price varies from nil to seventy per cent. No literary agent I know of has ever sold a bad story to a magazine because of his ability to sell or blarney. If the story is not right and saleable the agent is helpless. An agent rarely, if ever, has been able to persuade an editor to change his mind and buy a story after he has turned it down. The layman is often baffled over the functions of an agent and why he exists at all. This section may help clear the mystery.

To the editor, the purchaser of magazine fiction, the agent represents a certain standard of quality. Since an agent lives off the ten per cent he charges his clients, he is interested in handling only writers who either are successful or have shown definite promise of developing. Under those circumstances he would automatically screen out the same hopeful but inept crew of amateurs and dilettantes who bombard the magazines with bad manuscripts.

The good agent is in effect a kind of pre-editor. For a young writer to acquire a competent and recognised agent is half the battle in the psychology of getting the editor to consider his work in the light of purchasable material. We know that a great story will sell itself, but to get that great story through to the attention of the responsible editor is not always so simple, since members of the editorial staff of a magazine are human beings as fallible in their profession as are writers in theirs. But this we know: when an author's story appears on an editor's desk bound in the distinctive cover used by the agent, it is a guarantee of three things: that the agent has sold the writer's work before and believes him a good business risk, otherwise he would not be handling him; that he has read this particular story; and that he believes the story is right for the style, type and needs of the particular magazine to which it has been sent. The editor, if he trusts the agent, knows that his time will not be wasted in reading the story and he is ready to render an accurate and impartial judgment of the piece strictly on its merits. Sometimes a telephone call from the agent to the editor calling his attention to what he believes is a particularly good piece of work will further prepare the ground for a quick and interested reading. Thereafter the piece is strictly on its own. If it clicks, the editor spares a moment of warmth for the agent who enabled him to acquire this fine piece of property instead of sending it to another. If it flops, a black mark goes against the agent as well as the writer.

How does one acquire an agent? In a number of ways, by personal introduction and recommendation, by submission of material and by accomplishing a sale or two without their services. An agent is a business man who is interested only in handling successful and saleable writers. If you can prove to him that you are successful and saleable as a writer or give tangible promise of becoming one, you can acquire an agent. Mine in the United States took me on after I had sold a number of magazine articles on my own. A friend introduced me, we had a chat, he agreed to take me on and we shook hands. There never was so much as a scrap of paper between us. Until his death a year or so ago Harold Ober was my life-long business manager, salesman, adviser and friend, a function and tradition carried on by his British counterpart and partner, Mr Edmund Cork. Could I get along without an agent now that I am accounted successful? Probably not and I certainly do not intend to try. I know that there is nothing connected with my profession about which I do not consult Edmund Cork and ask his advice and counsel, no story or project that I do not discuss with him.

Among other things, the agent is deemed necessary because it is quite true that the average writer is a poor businessman and does not know how to place a proper value on his work or services. Also the agent remains as a hangover from a period when there was something faintly discreditable about writing for money, and the days when the publishers took shameful advantage of the scribblers. The writer was a poet who was supposed to dwell at least on the side of Olympus if not at the top, and haggling for guineas, shillings, and pence was considered far beneath his dignity.

Today the agent does our haggling for us and protects our tender sensibilities from contact with the vulgar commercial aspects of the business that might have a tendency to stifle the beauty in our souls. He sets the prices, wangles us raises, cushions the shock of rejections, sends out clean copies when the old ones get frayed from too much editorial thumbing, listens to our complaints and gripes, sympathises when editors fail to agree with us on the epic qualities of a story, lends us money when we are broke, gives matrimonial advice, makes appointments with editors, listens to offers that come in and screens out the clucks, crackpots, and cheapjacks, supervises contracts, gets the income tax made out, takes the blame and acts as the fall guy when we pull a boner, and generally makes himself useful as a business manager as well as a steady and loyal friend in time of need. For all this, mine have my love and blessings.